D0941641

FUNDAMENTALS OF
Electricity

BOOKS IN THE ELECTRICAL SERIES

Published by the American Technical Society

AUTOMOTIVE ELECTRICAL SYSTEMS
Frazee-Bedell

DIESEL-ELECTRIC PLANTS
Kates

ELECTRICITY AND ELECTRONICS—BASIC
Steinberg-Ford

ELECTRICITY AND ELECTRONICS AT WORK
Steinberg-Ford

ELECTRIC ARC WELDING
Austin

FUNDAMENTALS OF ELECTRICITY
McDougal-Ranson-Dunlap-Graham

HOW TO READ ELECTRICAL BLUEPRINTS
Heine-Dunlap-Jones

INTERIOR ELECTRIC WIRING AND ESTIMATING—INDUSTRIAL
Graham

INTERIOR ELECTRICAL WIRING AND ESTIMATING—RESIDENTIAL
Uhl-Dunlap-Flynn

PRACTICAL DICTIONARY OF ELECTRICITY AND ELECTRONICS
Oldfield

RADIO-TELEVISION AND BASIC ELECTRONICS
Oldfield

SMALL COMMUTATOR MOTORS
Graham

SMALL NON-COMMUTATOR MOTORS
McDougal-Graham

(Courtesy Westinghouse Electric Corp.)

Large water-driven generators used by the Bureau of Reclamation on the Coulee Dam in the State of Washington.

FUNDAMENTALS OF

Electricity

WYNNE L. McDOUGAL

Formerly Head, Department of Electricity, The Pullman Free School of Manual Training, Chicago; Associate Member, American Institute of Electrical Engineers

RICHARD R. RANSON

Supervisor of the Public Works Division, Engineering Department, Cutler-Hammer, Inc., Milwaukee, Wisconsin; Member, American Institute of Electrical Engineers

CARL H. DUNLAP

Consulting Electrical Engineer; Associate Member, American Institute of Electrical Engineers

Fourth Edition by KENNARD C. GRAHAM

Electrical Engineer; Consultant, Apprenticeship Instruction Material Laboratory, Bureau of Trade and Industry, California State Department of Education

AMERICAN TECHNICAL SOCIETY · CHICAGO · U.S.A.

FIRST EDITION
1st Printing April, 1943
2d Printing May, 1943
3d Printing 1945
4th Printing 1946

SECOND EDITION (REVISED)
5th Printing 1948
6th Printing 1950
7th Printing 1952
8th Printing 1953

THIRD EDITION (REVISED)
9th Printing 1954
10th Printing 1955
11th Printing 1957
12th Printing 1958
13th Printing 1959

FOURTH EDITION (REVISED)
14th Printing 1960
15th Printing 1961

PRINTED IN THE UNITED STATES OF AMERICA

LIBRARY OF CONGRESS CATALOG CARD NUMBER: 60-6659

CONTENTS

CONTENTS

CONTENTS

PREFACE TO THE FOURTH EDITION

To keep pace with the continually expanding frontiers of electrical and electronic knowledge and new applications of familiar principles, a new edition of this text has been prepared. This, the fourth edition, has been completely revised. It presents in a thorough and practical manner the most important principles of the electrical science, with a minimum of mathematics, in a language that the average reader can understand.

The general scope of this edition has been enlarged to include two new chapters. The first is an introductory summary of the field of electromagnetic radiation and its many practical applications; and the second is an introduction to the design of electrical devices finding ever broadening application in the fields of industrial electronics and automation. Today we can find few electrical fields where electronic devices are not also used. All of the material presented in this book is basic to all electrical fields of specialization, as well as many related fields.

A selection of review questions is appended to each chapter. These questions serve the dual purpose of summary and review of the chapter. Also included in this edition is a Dictionary of Electrical Terms, which simply and clearly explains terms which may cause difficulty.

THE PUBLISHERS

CHAPTER 1

THE NATURE OF ELECTRICITY

THE ELECTRON

The Molecule

All materials, such as water, air, wood, and iron, are made of very small particles. These particles are called *molecules*. The shapes of molecules vary, but for purposes of explanation, we will assume that each molecule is the shape of an oval.

What do we mean when we say that all materials are made of molecules? We mean that every material, regardless of its appearance, shape, or size, is actually a mass of molecules. For example, let us consider common salt. Each little grain of salt is really a vast number of molecules. This example also helps us to understand how small molecules are. In our study of electricity we need not concern ourselves with the size or shape of molecules. We need only understand that all materials, from little grains of salt to the entire earth, are composed of molecules.

The Atom

Let us examine a single grain of salt a little more closely. Scientists tell us that salt contains two chemicals known as *sodium* and *chlorine*, and every molecule of salt contains one part sodium and one part chlorine. We will assume that the oval in Fig. 1 is a molecule of salt magnified many times. The smaller circles within the molecule, which combine to make up this single molecule, are called atoms. One sodium atom and one chlorine atom combine to make up one molecule of salt. (We need not be concerned about how various atoms combine to make up molecules, nor about the shape of the molecule or the atom.)

Size of the Atom. Atoms are so small that their size is difficult to imagine. Experiments show that 200,000,000 atoms may be placed side by side upon a straight line 1 inch long. They are much too small to be seen with the aid of even the most sensitive laboratory apparatus, but their nature has been thoroughly studied by means of the effects they produce upon delicate instruments. Today, therefore, we have a fairly clear idea of what goes on inside of the atom.

Construction of the Atom. We are all familiar with the fact that the earth revolves about the sun, following a regular path. This is indicated in Fig. 2. The dotted line indicates the path around the sun which the earth follows, and this path is known as an *orbit*. The earth is called a *planet* because it revolves about the sun. The earth and sun, in the relationship shown in Fig. 2, are known as a *system*. The sun is the *core* of the system.

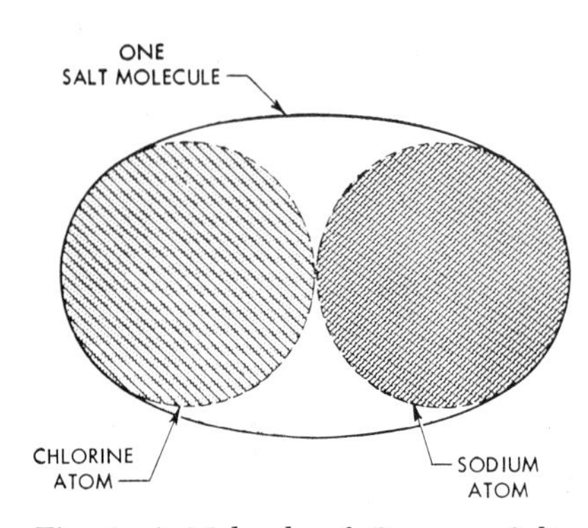

Fig. 1. A Molecule of Common Salt Is Composed of One Part Sodium and One Part Chlorine

An atom is constructed in a manner which greatly resembles the system of the sun and earth taken together. Each atom has a core and one or more planets revolving about the core. Let us examine an atom of *hydrogen* gas, Fig. 3. We select this atom because its construction is the simplest of all the atoms. The hydrogen atom has but a single planet revolving about the core. The planet in the hydrogen atom revolves about the core in a manner similar to the way in which the earth revolves about the sun. In an atom, however, the planet is called an *electron*.

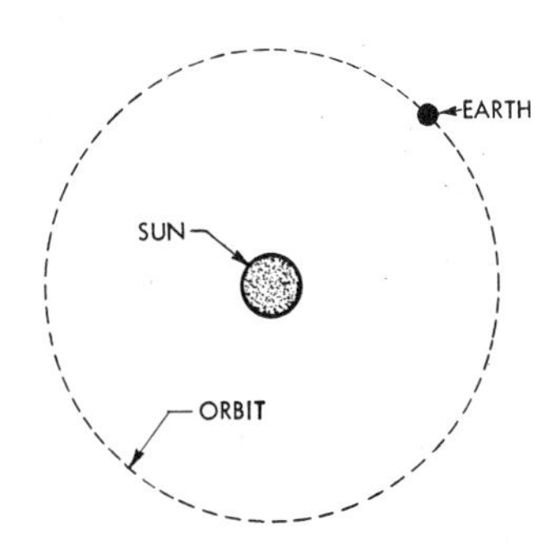

Fig. 2. Illustration of Earth Revolving about the Sun

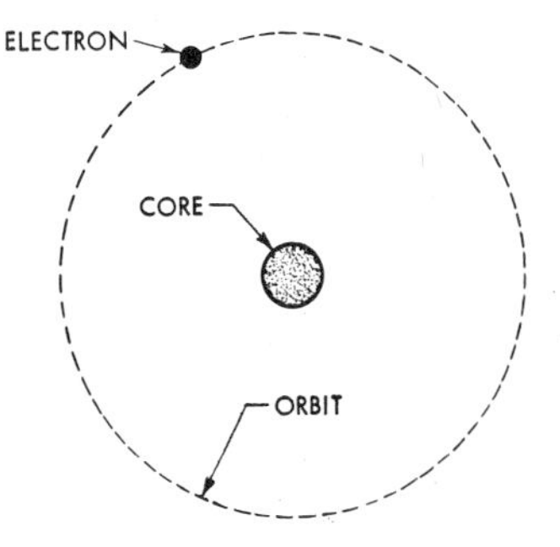

Fig. 3. Illustration Representing Hydrogen Atom

All atoms are very similar in construction, for there is always a core and one or more electrons. The atoms of different substances differ, however, in the size of the core and the number of electrons revolving about it. Fig. 4 represents an atom of *helium*. Helium is also a gas, but it has two revolving electrons.

The system of which the sun and the earth are parts, and which is called the *solar system,* is not quite as simple as Fig. 2. It consists of the sun and nine planets, and each of the planets travels around the sun in a separate path. In a similar way, atoms of solid materials are more complicated than those of the gases. An atom of iron, for example, has 26 revolving electrons, and an atom of copper has 29, Fig. 5.

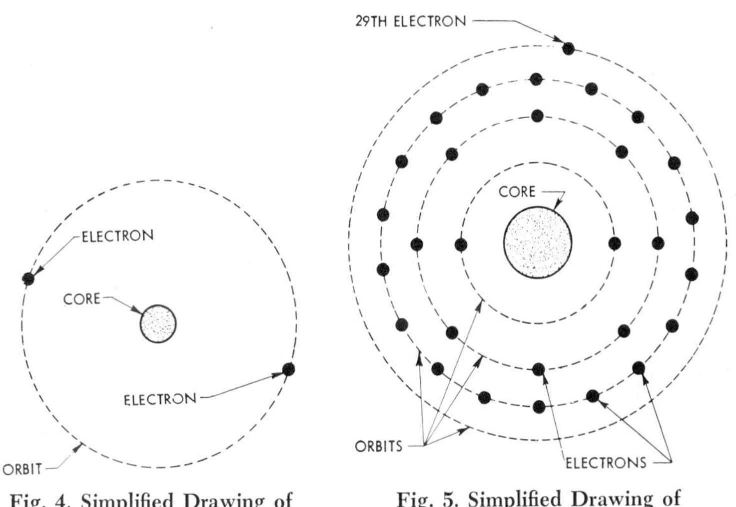

Fig. 4. Simplified Drawing of Helium Atom

Fig. 5. Simplified Drawing of Copper Atom

When the atom contains a number of electrons, some are closer to the core than others. That is, their orbits are not all of the same diameter, Fig. 5. The electrons in the copper atom are arranged at four different distances from the central core. Twenty-eight of the electrons are grouped at three sets of distances. The twenty-ninth electron, which is farthest from the core, revolves alone, Fig. 5. Now, the core exerts a pulling force on the electron, and this is known as a *force of attraction.*

We will discuss this force more thoroughly later on. For the moment, however, it is only necessary to note that attraction between the electron and the core holds the electron in its orbit. Furthermore, this attraction is stronger on those electrons in orbits close to the core than on those farther away, and the attraction is least on the electrons in the outer orbits.

Planetary and Free Electrons

Because this force of attraction is rather weak on an electron in an outer orbit, the electron sometimes escapes from the attraction of the core. Under this condition, it is said to be a *free electron.* So long as the electron continues to revolve about the core of the atom, it is called a *planetary electron.* The term *planetary* is used to describe the revolving electron because the motion of the electron about the core closely resembles the motion of a planet about the sun. A planetary electron which escapes from its atom is a free electron. As we will see later, there are a number of ways in which electrons in outer orbits may be caused to leave their atoms.

Effect of Losing an Electron

When an atom loses an electron, it tries to attract another to replace the one lost. In its normal state, the atom has no effect upon stray free electrons which may surround it. But when one of its electrons is removed, the core of the atom, which is also known as the *nucleus,* sends out a force of attraction. This fact is expressed by saying that the atom has acquired a *charge.*

When the atom captures another electron, it will become uncharged or *neutral* once more. In other words, the new electron will cancel or *neutralize* the charge which the atom showed before.

The attracting force which the nucleus sends out is said to be a *positive* (+) *charge.* The neutralizing force which the electron supplies is said to be a *negative* (−) *charge.* These terms are used to indicate the two types of charges.

Electrical Charges and Electricity

We have examined electrical charges and noted the two types of charge: positive and negative. The term *electricity* is applied to this condition of being charged. It is also applied to the force that results when a free electron tries to neutralize the charge. When it was noted that electricity took on these two forms, and the forms were opposite in character, it was decided to call one positive and the other negative.

Since the positive charge of the nucleus of the atom attracts the negative charge of the electron, we can state this in the form of a rule:

Opposite charges attract. This is a simple way of saying that there is a force of attraction between positive and negative charges.

STATIC CHARGES

Removing Outer Electrons

First, we will consider *static charges.* The term *static* means not moving or at rest. Therefore, static charges are those charges that are at rest.

When two objects are rubbed together, electrons are often removed from the atoms at the surface of one of the materials. The substances from which these materials are made consist of countless atoms, and there are atoms with their planetary electrons at the very surface of the substances. Therefore, when the objects are rubbed together, planetary electrons are physically removed (knocked away) from the surface of one of the substances onto the surface of the other. Since these planetary electrons are taken from their regular orbits when they are moved, they are known as free electrons. Certain substances produce very noticeable results when rubbed together. Rubber and wool are such materials.

If a rubber rod is rubbed with a piece of wool, electrons will be freed, and the free electrons will tend to collect upon the rubber rod. That is, the planetary electrons of some of the atoms on the surface of the wool are knocked out of their orbits, because of the structure of the atoms that make up the wool. These free electrons then leave the wool and collect upon the surface of the rubber rod. If the two materials are then tested, it will be found that the rubber rod shows a strong negative charge, and the wool shows a strong positive charge. We know that a negative charge is the result of a *surplus* of electrons, and a positive charge is the result of a *deficiency* (shortage or lack) of electrons. Therefore, this result was to be expected, for electrons have been given up from the surface of the wool, leaving it positively charged. Because the free electrons from the wool have collected upon the surface of the rubber rod, it has a negative charge.

If we replace the rubber and wool with a glass rod and a piece of silk, the glass rod will receive a positive charge and the silk a negative charge when the two are rubbed together. The glass rod obtains a positive charge because its surface has lost electrons, and the silk obtains a negative charge because it holds an excess of electrons.

Rule of Force between Electrical Charges

We have studied how a condition which we called an electrical charge is developed by removing electrons from their orbits within the atom. We have also mentioned that the atom produces a force as a result of this vacancy in the orbit. This force of the atom tries to draw an electron into the orbit, so the orbit will be filled with the required number of electrons. The electron, on the other hand, which has been removed from one orbit, tries to move into any orbit that has a vacancy. These two forces, the force sent out by the atom and the force sent out by the electron, are different in nature, and the two conditions that set up these forces are called positive and negative electrical charges.

The study of electricity is the study of the methods for removing electrons from their orbits, the forces resulting from this removal, and the control of the movement of electrons back into orbits that have vacancies.

The forces that are set up by positive and negative charges act differently from one another. On the basis of the experiments to be described, it is possible to make up a complete rule governing the forces set up by these positive and negative charges. Since like charges repel one another and unlike charges attract one another, the rule may be stated as follows: *Like charges repel; unlike charges attract.* That is, two positive charges repel one another and two negative charges repel one another, but a positive charge and a negative charge attract one another.

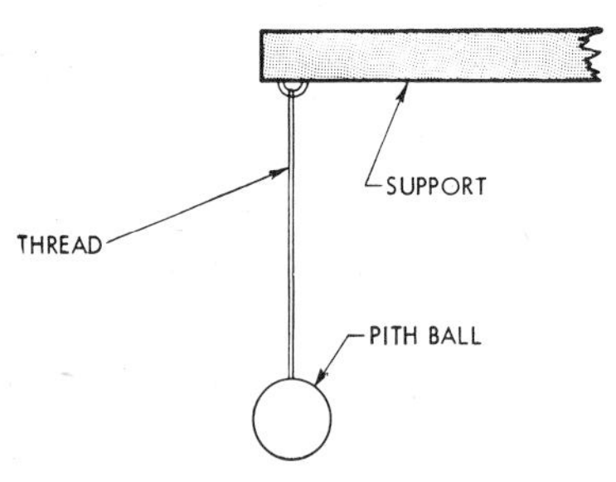

Fig. 6. Showing Pith Ball Suspended by Cotton Thread

Repulsion between Like Charges. A simple experiment will explain a great deal about the nature of electrical charges. Let a small ball of a very light material be suspended from a support by means of a cotton thread, Fig. 6. At the moment, this ball has no electrical charge, for there are as many positive charges as there are negative charges.

The ball is usually made of *pith* (plant pulp). When a positively charged glass rod is touched to the ball, the ball becomes positively charged, Fig. 7. It becomes charged because the strong attractive forces sent out by the many positively charged atoms on the glass rod draw some of the electrons away from the outer orbits of the atoms of pith. When some of the pith atoms have lost electrons, they will send out attractive forces in an effort to find electrons, thus giving a positive charge to the ball.

When a positively charged glass rod has been touched to the ball and quickly withdrawn, it should again be moved in the direction of the ball. The pith ball tends to move away from the glass rod as it approaches. The illustration shows the positively charged rod moving from left to right, toward the ball. As the movement takes place, the positively charged ball is shown moving from left to right, away from

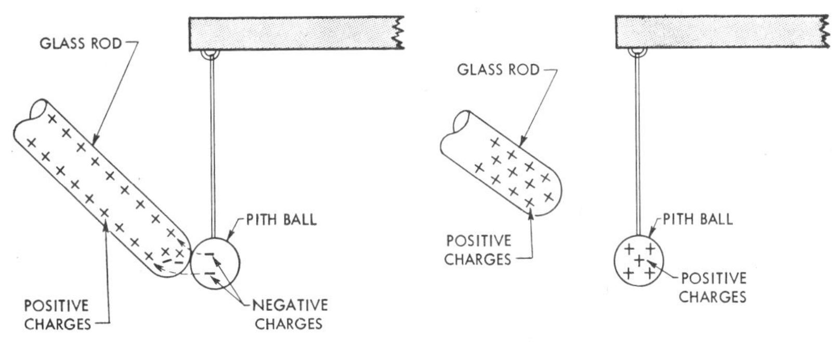

Fig. 7. Method of Positively Charging Pith Ball. View at Left Shows Negative Charges Leaving Pith Ball while Ball and Rod Are Touching. View at Right Shows Positive Charge on Pith Ball after Rod Is Removed

the rod. Since both objects are positively charged, it is quite apparent that one positive charge repels another positive charge, Fig. 8.

The pith ball should now be made neutral again by removing its charge. A simple way of doing this is to touch the ball with the finger. (The reason this makes the ball neutral will be explained shortly.) Now, when a negatively charged rubber rod is touched to the uncharged pith ball, some of the excess electrons on the rubber rod will move onto the ball so that it, too, will have an excess of electrons. This excess of electrons will give the ball a negative charge. If the rod is quickly removed and then returned slowly, the ball will be repelled, Fig. 9. Since both rod and ball are negatively charged, we can conclude that negative charges also repel.

Attraction between Unlike Charges. When we were discussing the result of removing a planetary electron from an atom, we noted that the atom tried to attract another electron. This atom, which is lacking an electron, has a positive charge. The electron which has been removed from the atom has a negative charge. Since the atom tries to draw another electron toward it, and the electron tries to move toward an atom that is missing an electron, we come to the conclusion that opposite charges attract. The positively charged atom attracts the negatively charged electron. The fact may be clearly demonstrated with the aid of the suspended ball. First, the ball should be positively charged by touching it with a positively charged glass rod. Then, if a

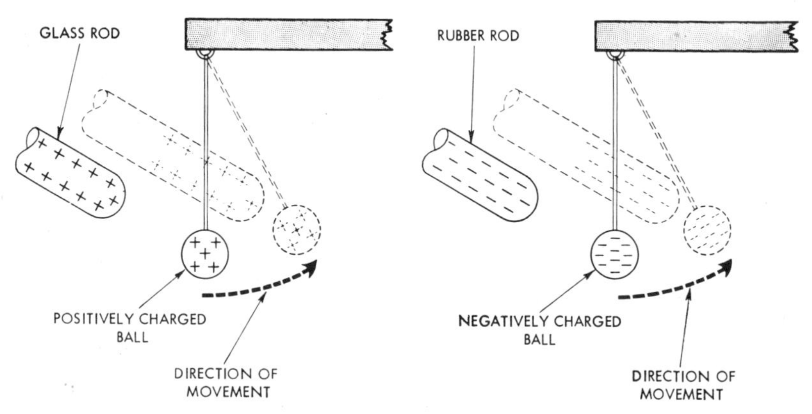

Fig. 8. Illustrating Repulsion between Positive Charges

Fig. 9. Illustrating Repulsion between Negative Charges

negatively charged rubber rod is brought near it, Fig. 10A, the ball will swing toward the rod, showing that the positive charge on the ball is attracted by the negative charge on the rod.

The charge upon the pith ball should now be neutralized by touching it with the finger, and the ball should be touched with a negatively charged rubber rod to give it a negative charge. When a positively charged glass rod is brought close, Fig. 10B, the ball will swing toward it, showing that the negatively charged ball is attracted by the positively charged glass rod.

Removing the Charge. Let a pith ball be positively charged with a charged glass rod. After removing the rod, touch the ball with the finger. Now, if the ball is tested it will no longer be found to be in a charged condition. Touching the ball with the finger removed or neutralized the charge. The reason is not difficult to understand. The earth is a huge reservoir, or storehouse, of free electrons. These electrons spread from the earth onto everything in contact with it. And since we are in contact with the earth, or with something which is itself in contact with the earth, free electrons find their way onto the surface of our bodies. In touching the ball, electrons from our finger are attracted by the positively charged atoms of the ball, so that they obtain enough electrons to satisfy the demand. The ball, then, becomes neutral.

If the ball were negatively charged, it might be neutralized in exactly the same way by touching it with the finger. The excess electrons on the surface of the pith ball would repel one another, and most

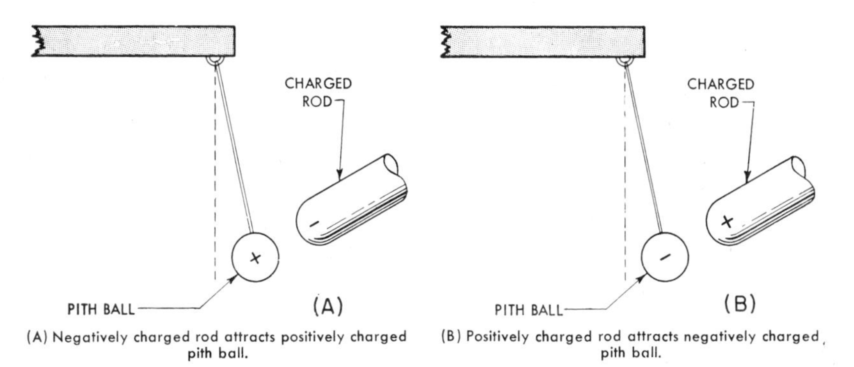

(A) Negatively charged rod attracts positively charged pith ball.

(B) Positively charged rod attracts negatively charged pith ball.

Fig. 10. Illustration of Attraction between Unlike Electrical Charges

of them would find their way onto the finger. For, although the earth contains a great number of free electrons, its surface is so vast that it has a very weak negative charge. In fact, its charge is said to be zero.

When we estimate the strength of a negative charge upon a body, therefore, we do so with respect to the amount of negative charge in excess of that of the earth. When we estimate the strength of a positive charge, we do so with respect to the amount of positive charge in excess of the charge of the earth. If the pith ball has a negative charge in excess of that of the earth, touching it with the finger results in such a transfer of electrons that its amount of negative charge becomes equal to that of the earth, or zero.

Attraction for Light Objects

If small bits of paper are scattered upon a flat surface, and a positively charged glass rod or a negatively charged rubber rod is brought close to them, they will be attracted to the rod. If the glass rod alone had picked up the bits of paper, we would have assumed them to be negatively charged. If the rubber rod alone had attracted them, we would assume them positively charged. But both rods seem to attract them equally well.

The reason for this attraction is shown in Fig. 11. When a positively charged glass rod is brought near a bit of paper, the electrons are drawn from their orbits to the edge of the paper, Fig. 11A. Because the electrons cannot readily flow from the paper to the rod to

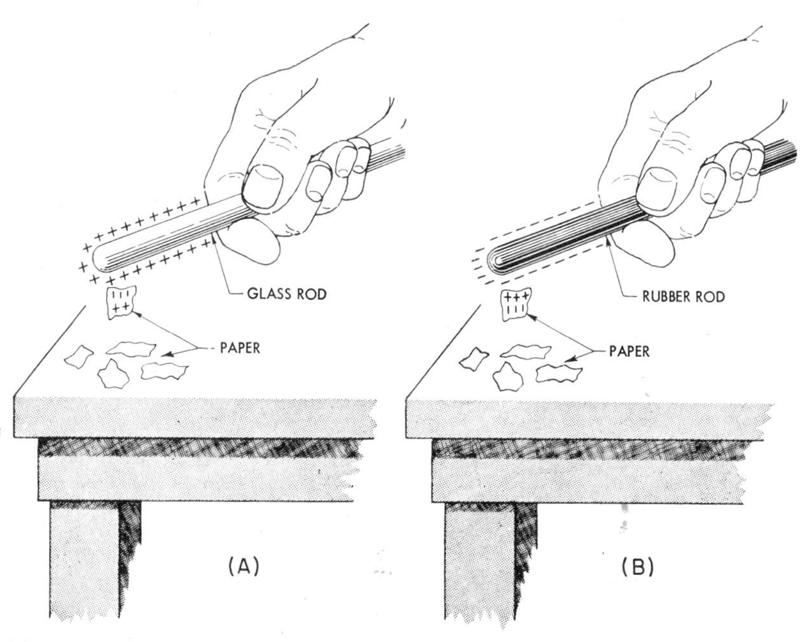

(A) Paper is held to glass rod as a result of attraction between positive charges on glass rod and negative charges which have moved to edge of paper.

(B) Attraction is between negative charges on rubber rod and positive charges caused by electrons being forced from edge of paper.

Fig. 11. Illustrating How Bits of Paper Adhere to Charged Rods

neutralize the positive charge on the rod, there will be attraction between the paper and the rod. The reason for the electrons not being able to travel from the paper to the rod is not of sufficient importance to concern us at this time. We will note, however, that there is attraction between the electrons on the bit of paper and the positively charged atoms of the rod, which results in the paper being drawn to the rod.

Similar results are obtained when a negatively charged rubber rod is placed near the bit of paper. In this case the electrons are repelled (forced away) from the edge of the paper that is near the rod, Fig.

11B. This time there will be attraction between the positively charged atoms on the edge of the paper and the electrons on the rubber rod. This again results in the bit of paper being attracted to the rod.

These experiments have illustrated how static electrical charges—electrical charges that are not moving—act on other static electrical charges. For example, in our first experiment, the positively charged rod pushed away the positively charged pith ball, although no electrons were transferred from one to the other during this repulsion. The positive charges on the rod remained on the rod, and the positive charges on the ball remained on the ball. Because these charges did not move during this, or the other experiments, they are called static charges.

DYNAMIC CHARGES

Flow of Electrons

Now we will turn to a discussion of *dynamic charges.* The term *dynamic* means moving or in motion. Whereas electrical charges have been observed to display certain qualities while at rest, we will see that they display other qualities while in motion. When charges are in motion, they will be considered moving to fill a vacancy in an orbit, or else creating a vacancy by being removed from an orbit. In this discussion we will use a piece of wire that is made of copper. When we examine a length of copper wire, it seems to be a solid piece of material. However, this wire is made up of millions and millions of copper atoms that are very close together. The individual atoms are so small that it is impossible to see them, and they are so close together that the copper seems to be one solid substance. In some respects, we can compare this to viewing a mountain from a distance. When the mountain is miles away, it seems to be one huge mass; but, when we examine it closely, we will see that it is composed of countless grains of sand. Similarly, the copper wire is composed of countless atoms of copper.

Let us turn our attention to an individual copper atom. It was mentioned that there is but a single electron in the outer orbit of a copper atom, and the attraction between this electron and the core, which holds the electron in its orbit, is rather weak. Therefore, this electron can be removed easily, so that it becomes a free electron. Later, we will consider the method employed to remove these electrons. For the moment, however, we will examine what happens to an electron when it is set free from an atom.

Fig. 12 represents an enlarged section of a piece of copper wire, showing the movements of a free electron along the wire. This section shows a representation of only four copper atoms, and all but the outer electrons are omitted for simplification. The four atoms are indicated

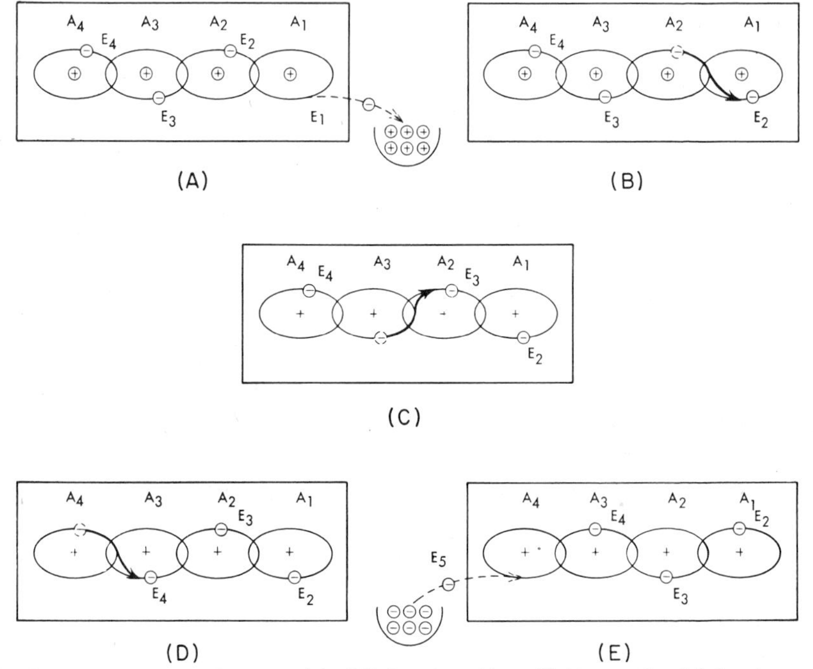

(A) Represents removal of first electron. (B) to (D) Indicate how orbits are filled by attraction of electrons from adjacent atoms. (E) Represents replacement of electron removed at (A).

Fig. 12. Illustrating How Electrons Pass from Atom to Atom in Copper Wire

as A_1, A_2, A_3, and A_4, and the outer electrons of these four atoms are indicated as E_1, E_2, E_3, and E_4. First, we will assume a method of presenting a strong attraction for the electron of atom A_1. The source of this attraction and how it is presented need not concern us at this time—we will just say that it is available. Because of this strong attraction near A_1, the outer electron of this atom is pulled from its orbit, Fig. 12A. Where does this electron go? We will have to be patient for the answer to this question, for the explanation will come a little later. For the moment, we are interested only in the fact that the electron has been removed from A_1.

This leaves A_1 in a positively charged condition; therefore, this atom is trying to attract another electron. While traveling in its orbit, the electron of A_2 passes near A_1, and will be attracted by A_1. Since the attraction of A_2, which holds E_2 in its orbit, is quite weak, E_2 can readily be attracted to A_1, Fig. 12B. Left without an electron, A_2 tries to attract another electron to take the place of E_2. In the same way as E_2 was caused to move to A_1, E_3 is caused to move to A_2, Fig. 12C. Accordingly, Fig. 12D shows E_4 moving from A_4 to A_3. This leaves A_4 without an electron in its outer orbit. Since A_4 will try to attract an electron, we will furnish a supply of electrons from which A_4 may easily attract one to replace E_4, Fig. 12E. This source of electrons is not of importance, for we are interested only in the movement of the electron from atom to atom along the copper wire. This series of events would be repeated by the removal of E_2 from A_1.

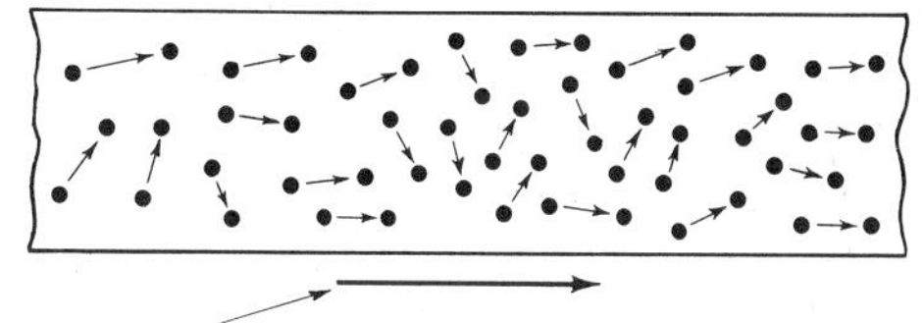

Fig. 13. Random Movement of Electrons along Copper Wire

A larger portion of the piece of copper wire is shown in Fig. 13 which depicts the movement of the electrons along the wire. The electrons do not move directly forward through the wire, but in random fashion, as the arrows show. This movement of electrons is known as an *electron flow*. Electricity, in other words, is based upon the activity of the electron. This negatively charged particle (the electron), when set free of the attraction of the core of its atom, shows certain qualities which we term electrical properties. If it comes to rest upon the surface of an object without being captured again by attraction of some other atom seeking an electron, it becomes a static charge of electricity. If it continues in motion, it becomes a moving or dynamic charge.

Forms of Electricity. The essential thing to note here is the fact that the electricity itself is the same whether in static form or in dynamic form, and it is the electron which is all-important in either case. It might be argued that the positive static charge is not due to the electron but to the core of the atom. Yet, the positive charge is really brought about by the electron, for it is in searching for an electron that the unneutralized core sends out the positive attraction.

Since both static and dynamic electricity are basically the same, it might be expected that one form can be converted into the other. Such is the case. You will recall that when a positively charged pith ball was touched with the forefinger, electrons flowed from the finger to the ball. And when a negatively charged pith ball was touched, electrons flowed from the ball to the finger. In either of these cases, free electrons were set in motion for the instant. The flow of electrons was a flow of electricity. Static electricity, in other words, was changed into dynamic electricity.

Producing Dynamic Electricity

It is necessary that we apply a force to a *conducting wire* to set the electrons in motion. The term conducting wire means a wire through which electrical charges can readily move. In Fig. 12A, we noted that an electron was pulled from the right-hand end of the copper wire. This is an example of a force of attraction or a pulling force. A locomotive exerts a pulling force when it draws the cars behind it. We also noted, Fig. 12E, that an electron was supplied to the left-hand end of the wire. We can say that the electron was pushed into the wire. This is an example of a force of repulsion, or a pushing force—as when we push against a door to close it. Therefore, in electricity we have a force of attraction, which is similar to a pulling force, and we have a force of repulsion, which is similar to a pushing force.

Now, let us return to the copper wire. Before any force is applied, the electrons are confined to orbits around the cores of their atoms. When a force is applied, the electrons are set free and caused to move along the path provided by the copper wire. This force, as shown in Fig. 12, is pulling electrons from one end of the wire, and, at the same time, it is pushing electrons into the other end. The electrons flow in one end of the copper wire at the same rate that they flow from the other; therefore, the copper remains uncharged.

Nature of the Electrical Force

The nature of the force which sets electrons free will be considered in detail later. For the present, it is necessary to understand only its general nature. In Fig. 14A, the force is produced by a *generator*. The generator has two terminals. One is a positive (+) terminal, and the other is a negative (−) terminal.

The path provided by the wire from one terminal of the generator to the other is called a *circuit*. When the generator becomes active, it draws electrons from the wire toward its positive (+) terminal and sends them into the wire from its negative (−) terminal. The generator acts like an electron pump, causing electrons to flow through the circuit provided by the wire in the direction indicated by the arrow.

If the generated force is reversed so that the positive and negative terminals are interchanged, the direction of electron flow in the wire will be reversed, Fig. 14B. This is true because the generating unit

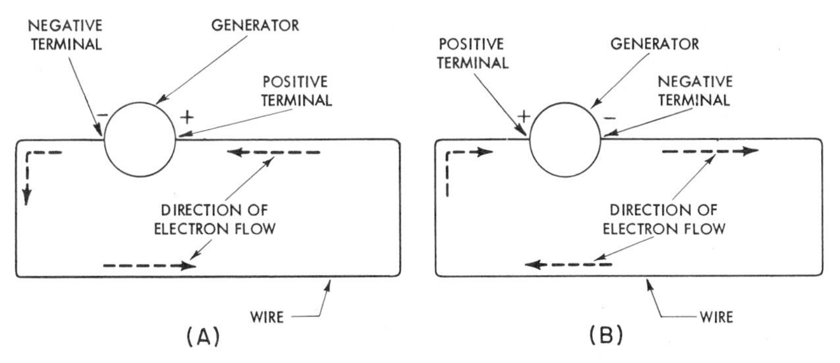

A) Electrons flow from negative terminal counterclockwise through wire to positive terminal.

(B) Reversing generator causes electrons to flow from negative terminal clockwise through wire to positive terminal.

Fig. 14. Showing Direction in which Generator Causes Electrons To Flow through Wire

draws electrons from the wire into its positive terminal and sends them into the wire from its negative terminal.

Early Theory of Electricity

Early experimenters who did not fully understand the nature of electricity, believed it to be an invisible liquid which flowed out of the positive terminal of the battery, or other generating device, into the conducting wire, and around the wire into the negative terminal of the generating unit. Because of the presumed fluid nature of electricity, they said that a flow of current took place in the wire. At this time, the water analogy was often used to explain the flow of electricity. The generator was looked upon as a pump which squirted electricity, similar to water, through a pipe which resembled an electrical conductor. This early theory was only a tentative guess. But unfortunately, by the time that it has been proved to be incorrect, it had become an accepted convention. As laboratory workers performed further experiments, and electrical equipment became part of the industrial scene; a whole body of electrical theory was built upon the incorrect belief that electric current flowed from positive to negative. The positive and negative theory was a natural guess when considered in conjunction with the early current theory, for when a "current" is running "into" a body, this body is receiving something, just as a basin receives water when a stream runs into it. The conventional plus sign indicated an excess charge while the minus sign indicated a deficiency of charge, and the current in flowing from one to the other was thought to balance these unequal charges.

The discovery of the electron and the invention of the vacuum tube conclusively disproved the early theory; but such was the volume of convention that had been built up around the early theory, that a practical compromise had to be reached. This was accomplished by keeping the plus and minus convention, and refering to the flow of electricity now known to consist of electrons as *electron flow,* and stating that this flow took place from negative to positive.

Due to the fact that the original convention caused no serious difficulties in calculations in many branches of electricity, in spite of its inaccuracy the new theory was slow in finding acceptance. Consequently, the two theories have sometimes been used simultaneously, causing considerable confusion. In modern usage, as employed in this volume, the term electron flow is usually used in place of current flow; and it should be remembered that the flow of electrons is from negative to positive. A certain amount of confusion still exists, since some publications continue to use the current flow theory, while still others use the term current, and intend it to refer to the flow of electrons.

Strength of Generating Force

The generating force may be weak or strong, depending upon matters which will be considered later. If it is strong, it will cause a large current flow through the circuit provided by the wire. If the force is weak, however, a smaller current will flow through the circuit. For a certain strength of generating force, the current flowing in the circuit will depend upon the material from which the wire is made. If this wire is made of copper, a large current will be caused with a moderate generating force. If the wire were made of iron instead of copper, this particular generating force would cause a lesser current to flow in the circuit. The reason for this is that it is harder to draw electrons from the outer orbit of iron atoms than from copper atoms, because the attraction between the core and outer electrons of iron is stronger than that of copper.

Conductors and Insulators

Materials in which a current flow is readily established are known as *conductors.* Metals in general are good conductors. Copper and iron are both classed as good conductors even though iron is not quite as good in this respect as copper. Silver is a better conductor than copper, but copper is more generally used for electric circuits because it is relatively cheap.

Substances which do not permit a ready current flow when a generating force is applied are called *insulators.* Paper is an excellent insulator. The reason that paper will not permit current to flow with ease is that it is all but impossible to pull electrons away from their atomic orbits. Insulators, too, vary in this quality. Mica is a far better insulator than paper, because its electrons are more firmly attracted by the cores of its atoms.

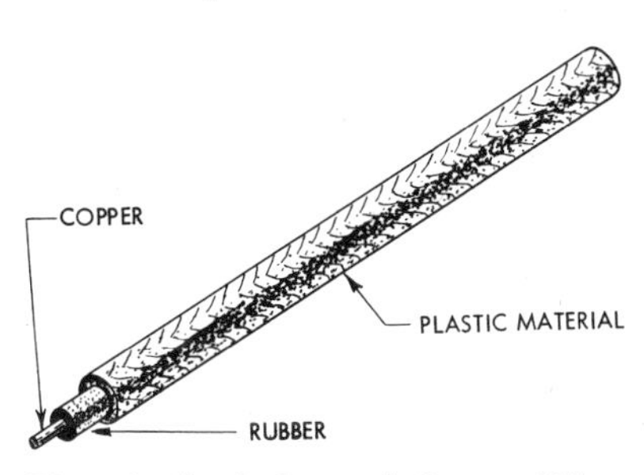

Fig. 15. Plastic-Covered Copper Wire

Conductors are employed where it is desired to transmit electricity from point to point over a given path. Insulators are used where it is desired to prevent the electric current from straying from its desired path. For example, plastic-covered copper wire is used to conduct electric current to the lamps in our homes. Fig. 15 shows a piece of this wire. The copper readily transmits current from the supply line to the lamp. The plastic material which surrounds the copper prevents the current from straying from the copper to surrounding objects, because the current will not readily flow through plastic insulation.

REVIEW QUESTIONS

1. What is the difference between atoms and molecules?
2. Compare the helium and hydrogen atoms.
3. Compare the charge of the core with that of the electron.
4. Define the term electron.
5. How are electric charges established by friction?
6. State the laws of static attraction and repulsion.
7. Briefly explain how a generating unit establishes a flow of electrons in an electrical circuit.
8. Explain why a charged rod attracts bits of paper.

9. Point out the difference between current-flow theory and *electron-flow* theory.

10. Tell how a charged object may be neutralized by merely touching it with the finger.

11. Do you think that one electron would be attracted by another electron? Explain.

12. Define the term electricity.

13. Distinguish between the terms static electricity and dynamic electricity.

14. Explain the purpose of the plastic covering on a piece of copper wire used in house wiring.

15. What is the essential difference between the atoms of conductors and of insulators?

CHAPTER 2

BASIC ELECTRICAL QUANTITIES

ELECTRICAL PRESSURE

What Electrical Pressure Does

There are three important or fundamental items in an electrical circuit. In our study of electricity, we call such items *basic factors.* By the use of these three factors we can explain and understand what is occurring in a particular circuit. These three factors are: *pressure, current,* and *resistance.* In order to use these factors, however, we must define them in terms of units which can be handled in measurements.

A unit of force familiar to everyone is the pound. To open a door it may be necessary to push with a pressure of five pounds. We must use this force in order to obtain the desired movement of an object, whether it is a door, an elevator, or a string of freight cars. This mechanical pressure is required, therefore, to produce mechanical motion.

Similarly, electrical pressure is required to produce electrical motion. Here, electrical motion refers to the movement of electrons along the electrical conductor. Electrical force, or pressure, causes planetary electrons to leave outer orbits of atoms and to surge through the conductor as free electrons.

The Volt

As the pound is the unit of physical force, so the *volt* is the unit of electrical force. This electrical force is known as an *electromotive force* and is indicated with the letters *emf.* It is customary, however, to speak of the electromotive force as the voltage of the circuit. When 1 volt of electromotive force is acting in a circuit, a certain number of electrons are freed from their atomic orbits. When the voltage is increased to 2 volts, twice as many free electrons will be removed from their atomic orbits and will travel around the circuit provided by the electrical conductor. In other words, when the voltage is doubled, the number of electrons flowing in the circuit also doubles.

Definition of the Volt

The volt is defined in terms of two other electrical quantities. The volt is that pressure which will force 1 *ampere* of current through a resistance of 1 *ohm*. We will understand this definition better when the other two terms have been described. The term volt is designated by the letter *v*.

ELECTRICAL CURRENT

Flow of Electrons

When a single free electron moves along the path provided by an electrical conductor, it represents a current of electricity. When a thousand free electrons travel around the conductor, they also represent a current of electricity. We must keep in mind that the current, which is the result of the movement of electrons, consists essentially of movement of electrons of the conductor itself. In the first instance, it would be possible to speak of a flow of one electron; in the second, of a flow of a thousand electrons. Yet, it would be inconvenient to describe the flow in terms of electrons because even the smallest amounts dealt with in practice involve millions and millions of electrons.

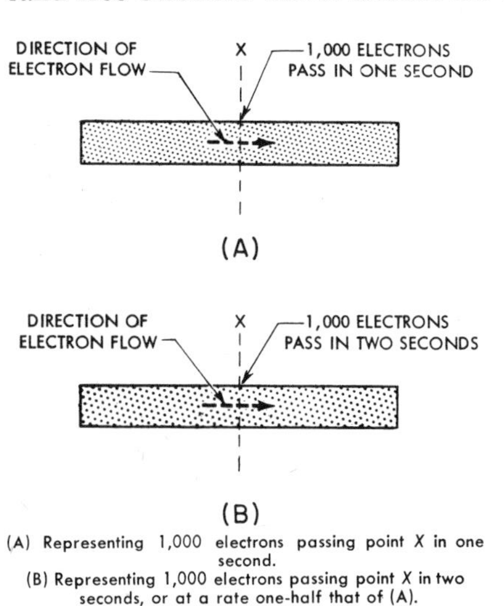

(A) Representing 1,000 electrons passing point *X* in one second.
(B) Representing 1,000 electrons passing point *X* in two seconds, or at a rate one-half that of (A).

Fig. 1. Illustrating Rate of Current Flow through Conductor

Another factor which is important in the determination of current flow is time. Fig. 1 shows sections of two conductors. In Fig. 1A, 1,000 electrons flow past line *X* during a space of one second. In Fig. 1B, 1,000 electrons pass *X* in the space of two seconds. Although the same number of electrons is involved in both cases, the rate at which electrons are traveling around the conductors is twice as great in the first instance as in the second. For, in any particular second, 1,000 electrons will pass in the first instance, while only 500 will pass during that period of time in the second case. As will be explained in detail later, the amount of work which can be done by an electric current depends upon the rate at which electrons are flowing in the conductor rather than upon the mere number of electrons.

The Ampere

As the volt is the unit of electromotive force, so the ampere is the unit of electrical current flow. An ampere of current is said to flow when a certain number of electrons pass along a conductor in the space of 1 second. The actual number of electrons involved is of little practical importance. The essential thing is that this particular quantity of electrons flows during each second of time. The reason the actual number of electrons is unimportant is that current is usually determined by an instrument which indicates current flow directly in amperes. This instrument will be discussed in a later chapter. For the present, it is important to think of current flow in terms of amperes.

Definition of the Ampere

We mentioned that an ampere of current is flowing when a given number of electrons passes a point in 1 second. Although this value is not used in practical applications, it is interesting to note just how large it is: the number being 6,280,000,000,000,000,000 electrons per ampere of current flow.

Since it would be impossible to count such large quantities of electrons, another method of measuring electron flow had to be devised. We know that when silver is used in electroplating, silver is deposited upon the object being plated, and this deposit of silver increases the weight of the object. Furthermore, the rate at which the silver is deposited depends upon the value of current flow used in plating. Now, with delicate scales we can determine the weight of an object with great accuracy. This ability to weigh accurately offers a second definition for the ampere: *An ampere is the current flow which will deposit 0.001118 grams of silver per second.* The term ampere can be written *amp.*

The Coulomb. We have just given the definition of the ampere as a definite number of electrons flowing past a given point in 1 second. This number of electrons, huge as it may be, is considered a definite quantity of electricity. It is comparable to the unit which tells the quantity of water, namely, the gallon.

We can say that when a *coulomb* of electricity passes a given point in the period of 1 second, current is flowing at the rate of 1 ampere.

ELECTRICAL RESISTANCE

Opposition to Current Flow

Let us suppose that a force of 5 pounds is required to open a door. This pressure is required because of the resistance the door offers to being moved from its original position. This resistance is made up of a number of items: the tendency of the door to remain at rest (inertia), the friction of the hinges, and the air which must be moved during the opening process.

Electrical resistance, which opposes the flow of electrons through an electrical conductor, may, to some extent, be compared to mechanical friction. Fig. 2 will help explain what is meant by electrical resistance. The conductor contains countless atoms and electrons. For simplicity, however, only two atoms and three free electrons are indicated in the figure. The atoms are marked A_1 and A_2; the free electrons are marked E_1, E_2, and E_3. In our first discussion of the movement of an electron along a conductor, we considered that the electron moved from one atom to the next. To illustrate the resistance of a conductor, we will employ a slightly different picture.

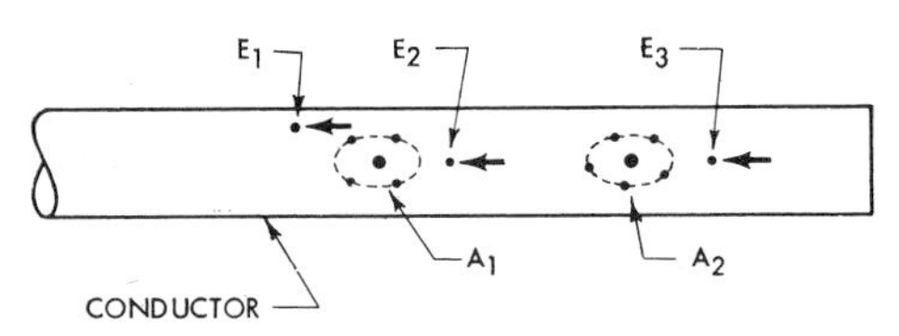

Fig. 2. Representing Opposition Met by Electron in Its Passage through Conductor

The electron of atom A_1 has been set free by the electrical pressure applied to the conductor. Since it was necessary to exert a force to remove this electron from its orbit, this is one form of resistance offered to the flow of electrons.

Atom A_1 has lost an electron and is, therefore, trying to capture one to replace it. Free electron E_1 has avoided the attracting force sent out by A_1 so that it continues to move along the electrical conductor. Electron E_2 coming close to atom A_1 is about to be captured. Electron E_3 is about to collide with neutral atom A_2. A_2 is neutral because it possesses its full number of electrons and, hence, does not send out any attracting force. When electron E_3 collides with the atom, the electron may lose enough speed that it may be captured by some other atom which is in need of an electron.

In the simple case illustrated here, only one of three electrons liberated by the electrical force continues on its way. The stream of free electrons has been interfered with by forces of capture and collision. These interrupting forces make up what we know as electrical resistance.

The Ohm

The voltage is one of two factors which determine the number of amperes flowing in an electrical circuit. The other factor is the resistance of the conductor. The unit of electrical resistance is called the ohm. The value of this unit is chosen to represent the resistance of a conductor which permits 1 amp of current to flow through it when a pressure of 1v is applied to the ends of the wire.

Definition of the Ohm

Our purpose here is to define the ohm with units other than the volt and the ampere. The ohm is that resistance offered by a column of mercury 106.3 centimeters long (about 42 inches, for 1 inch = 2.54 centimeters) and 14.4521 grams mass. This column must be of constant cross section, and the resistance must be measured while the mercury is at the temperature of melting ice (0°C). The Greek letter omega (Ω) is also used to indicate ohms.

Factors Influencing Resistance

The major factors that influence the resistance of a conductor are: *length, cross-sectional area, temperature,* and the *substance* of which the conductor is made. We will discuss each one of these factors in the following paragraphs and show how they influence the resistance of a conductor. Three of these factors are arranged in the form of a rule or *formula* to determine the resistance of a conductor of known length, cross section, and material.

$$R = \frac{KL}{A}$$

The letters in the formula represent the following:

R = the resistance of the conductor in ohms.
L = the length of the conductor.
K = the resistance of the particular material being used.
A = the cross-sectional area of the conductor.

When we have considered each of these factors, we will learn how to apply them to the formula. For example, we will have to know whether to use the number *1* or the number *12* when measuring the length of a conductor. This depends upon whether we must say the conductor is 1 foot long or 12 inches long to use the formula correctly.

The result we get from this formula is the resistance of the conductor at a certain temperature. If the temperature of the conductor we are considering is different from this certain temperature, we will learn to make a correction for the difference in temperature.

Length of Conductor. When an electromotive force of 1v is applied to the ends of the conductor in Fig. 3A, a current of 1 amp will flow through the conductor as long as the resistance remains at a value of 1 ohm. The manner in which this force is applied and the source of the force have been omitted from the illustration for the sake of simplicty. But later on we will consider how this force is applied and what causes it.

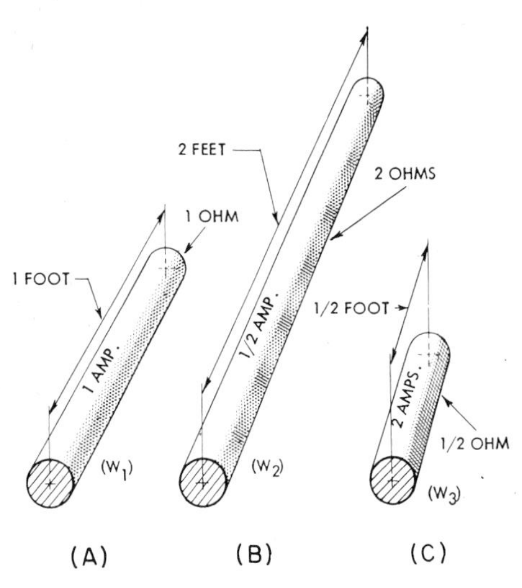

Fig. 3. Resistance of Conductor Varies as Its Length

Suppose now that the length of W_1 is doubled as in Fig. 3B. Here, the conductor is designated as W_2, and the two conductors are the same except for length. The laws of nature are such that a free electron traveling through a certain length of conducting material is subject to the same forces of resistance as in any other similar length of the material. Where the length of the path is doubled, each free electron must meet with twice the forces of resistance. Under this condition, the pressure of 1v is able to maintain a continuous stream of free electrons equal to only ½ amp.

Since it is twice as difficult for any one electron to travel the length of the conductor, it is said that the resistance of the conductor has been doubled. And, since the resistance of W_1 is 1 ohm, the resistance of W_2 must be 2 ohms.

If the length of the conductor is increased to four times that of W_1, an emf of 1v will be able to maintain a flow of electrons equal to only

¼ amp. The resistance of this conductor, therefore, is four times that of conductor W_1, or 4 ohms.

We have seen how doubling the length of a given conductor doubles the resistance of the conductor. In the same way, if we reduce the length of the conductor by one-half, Fig. 3C, the resistance will be reduced by one-half. Therefore, 1v of pressure is able to maintain a flow of twice as many free electrons or a number equal to a current flow of 2 amps. Thus, we can state this as a rule: *The resistance of an electrical conductor varies directly as its length.*

Cross-Sectional Area of a Conductor. The *cross section* of a conductor is its end surface. When the conductor, Fig. 4A, is cut squarely across its diameter, the end surface, or cross section, is circular. The *cross-sectional area* is the area of this squarely cut, circular end. If the conductor is square, Fig. 4B, its cross-sectional area is the area of the square formed by cutting across the conductor. If the conductor is triangular, Fig. 4C, its cross-sectional area is that of a triangle.

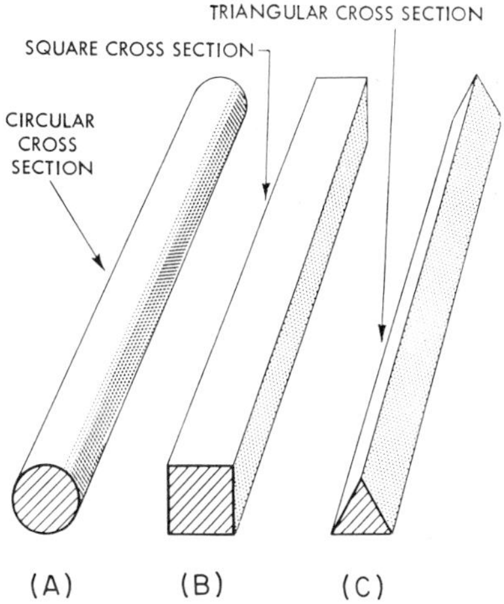

TRIANGULAR CROSS SECTION
SQUARE CROSS SECTION
CIRCULAR CROSS SECTION
(A) (B) (C)

Fig. 4. Electrical Conductors Having Three Types of Cross Section

The cross section of the conductor may have any one of these, or other, shapes, but it is usually circular. Regardless of the shape, however, the resistance of a conductor represented by any one of them varies directly as the length of the conductor.

Suppose the cross-sectional area of the conductor of Fig. 5A is doubled, as in Fig. 5B. Here, any certain number of free electrons traveling through the conductor will have more room to spread out than in the conductor of Fig. 5A. The chances of collision and capture on the part of these electrons are much less than if they were crowded into the smaller cross-sectional area of Fig. 5A. The exactness of nature's laws is such that when the cross-sectional area is twice as great, there are just one-half as many forces of resistance acting on the electron. In other words, when the area is doubled, the resistance of the conductor is halved. If the cross-sectional area is made four times as great, the resistance of the conductor is only one-fourth as much as originally.

If the cross-sectional area of the conductor is decreased to one-half its original value, the stream of electrons will be crowded into one-half the space, Fig. 5C. There will be twice as many chances for capture of individual electrons, and the resistance of the conductor will be twice that of the original case.

Here we see that when the cross-sectional area of a conductor is doubled, the resistance of a certain length of conductor is halved. As the cross-sectional area of a conductor is halved, its resistance is doubled. The resistance of the conductor, then, varies in the opposite direction from the change in cross-sectional area, for the resistance is decreased when the cross-sectional area is increased and the resistance is increased when the cross-sectional area is decreased. When two quantities vary in opposite directions with respect to each other, they are said to vary *inversely*. In view of these facts, it is possible to state the rule of area as follows: *Resistance of an electrical conductor varies inversely as its cross-sectional area.*

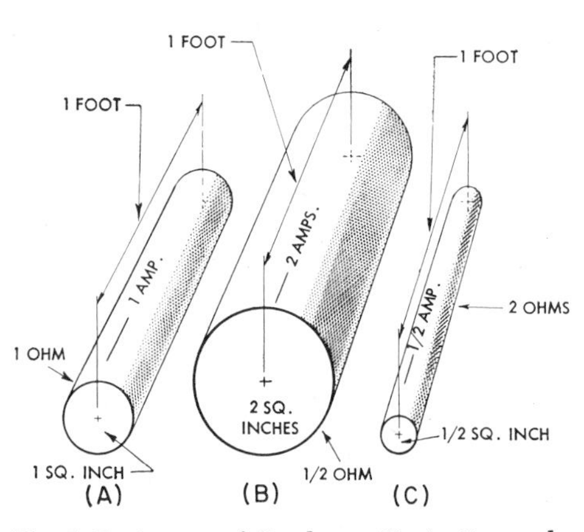

Fig. 5. Resistance of Conductor Varies Inversely as Cross-Sectional Area

Designating Conductor Size. Now that we have seen how the resistance of a conductor varies with its length and cross-sectional area, we will learn how the sizes of conductors are designated. Since copper wire, which has a circular cross section, is the most common conductor, we will limit our discussion to this for the time being. As an aid to understanding how wire sizes are designated, let us refer to Table I, which is a copper wire table of sizes from No. 16 to No. 40, inclusive. The first column lists the sizes of the wire under the American Wire Gauge (AWG) system of designations. The second column lists the diameters of the wires in *mils.* (The mil is $\frac{1}{1,000}$ part of an inch.) The third column is headed *Area in Circular Mils,* and the last column gives the resistance of the wire in ohms per 1,000 feet.

Circular-Mil Area. Let us examine this column more closely and learn the meaning of circular-mil area. For example, No. 36 wire has a diameter of 5.0 mils, and the area in circular mils is listed as 25. From this we see that the area in circular mils is equal to the *diameter in mils squared.* When we say that the diameter is squared, we mean that it is multiplied by itself. Thus, 5 squared means 5×5 and is usually written 5^2. However, diameter in mils squared is a cumbersome expression, so the term circular-mil area was devised to express it.

TABLE I. COPPER WIRE TABLE

AWG *	Diameter in Mils	Area Circular Mils	Ohms per 1000 Feet (20° C)
16	50.8	2583	4.00
17	45.3	2048	5.00
18	40.3	1624	6.39
19	35.9	1288	8.05
20	32.0	1021	10.15
21	28.5	810	12.80
22	25.4	643	16.14
23	22.6	510	20.36
24	20.1	405	25.67
25	17.9	321	32.37
26	15.9	254	40.80
27	14.2	202	51.47
28	12.6	160	64.90
29	11.3	127	81.84
30	10.0	101	103.20
31	8.9	80	130.10
32	8.0	63	164.10
33	7.1	50	206.90
34	6.3	40	260.90
35	5.6	32	329.00
36	5.0	25	414.80
37	4.5	20	523.00
38	4.0	16	660.00
39	3.5	12	832.00
40	3.1	10	1049.00

* American Wire Gauge.

One other point should be noted about the term circular-mil area. It is not a true expression of area, for area is expressed in square units: square inches, square mils, square feet, and the like. Here is a square, Fig. 6, with the sides drawn to represent 5 mils on each side, and the circle inside of the square represents the cross section of a wire which has a diameter of 5 mils. The area of the square is found by squaring the length of the side: $5 \times 5 = 25$ square mils. To find the area of the circle, we must use the rule:

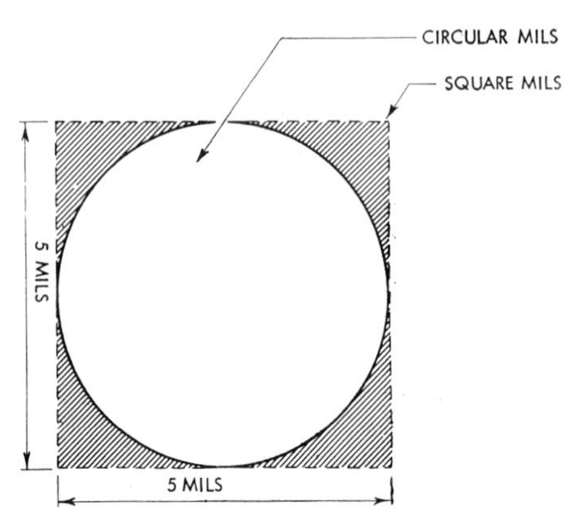

Fig. 6. Showing Relative Areas of Square Mils and Circular Mils

$$A = \frac{\pi d^2}{4}$$

The Greek letter π (pi) is equal to 3.1416, and d is the diameter of the circle. Therefore,

$$A = \frac{3.1416 \times 5^2}{4}$$

and if we divide 3.1416 by 4 we have 0.7854, so that

$$A = 0.7854 \times 5^2$$

Squaring the diameter, we have

$$A = 0.7854 \times 25$$

and

$$A = 19.6 \text{ square mils}$$

From this example we can see that the area of the wire in square mils can be found by multiplying the diameter squared by 0.7854. This number is called a *conversion factor*, for we can use it to convert (change) circular mils to square mils. We can also change square mils to circular mils if we divide the area in square mils by 0.7854.

Now that we have examined the circular mil, we will see how it is used in the following sections.

Conductor Material. Certain materials conduct electrical current more easily than others. Copper is a very good conductor. Lead, which conducts current much less easily, is a poor conductor. Although silver is a better conductor than copper, the cost of silver excludes it from general use.

The less the resistance of a material, the better it serves as a conductor. The property of a material which describes its resistance to the flow of electricity is known as its *resistivity*. When we state the resistivity of a particular material, we must also state its length and cross-sectional area, for resistance varies with length and cross section.

One accepted method of expressing the resistivity of a material is to state the resistance of a material which has a length of 1 foot and a cross-sectional area of 1 circular mil. For annealed copper, the resistance of a 1-foot length having a cross-sectional area of one mil is 10.37 ohms. Therefore, we say that its resistivity is 10.37 *ohms per mil-foot.* The resistivity of silver is 9.9 ohms per mil-foot. It is of interest to note the resistivity of several other conducting materials: aluminum, 17; brass, 42; constantan, 295; gold, 14; cast iron, 54; lead, 132; manganin, 265; mercury, 577; nichrome, 602; and tungsten, 33.

Calculating the Resistance of a Copper Wire. Now that we have examined the various factors to be considered in determining the resistance of conductor, we will apply this information to a sample problem.

Let us first review our rule for determining the resistance of a conductor.

$$R = \frac{KL}{A}$$

R = resistance of conductor in ohms.
L = length of conductor in feet.
A = area of conductor in circular mils. This is equal to d^2.
K = resistivity of conductor in ohms per mil-foot.

We can now employ this rule, or formula, to find the resistance of a certain conductor. Suppose that we have a piece of copper wire which is 200 feet long and 0.032 of an inch in diameter. The diameter of this wire will be 32 mils ($1{,}000 \times 0.032 = 32$), for there are 1,000 mils per inch. If the diameter is 32 mils, the cross-sectional area, in circular mils, is equal to 32^2, or 1,024 circular mils ($32 \times 32 = 1{,}024$). Since the material is copper, the resistivity is 10.37 ohms per mil-foot. Next, we will substitute these values in the formula.

$$R = \frac{KL}{A}$$

$$R = \frac{10.37 \times 200}{1{,}024}$$

Multiplying 10.37 by 200, we have

$$R = \frac{2{,}074}{1{,}024}$$

and dividing 2,074 by 1,024,

$$R = 2.025 \text{ ohms}$$

The formula shows that 200 feet of a 32-mil diameter wire has a resistance of 2.025 ohms. We can compare the resistance of this wire to the resistance of a No. 20 wire, as given in Table I, for the No. 20 wire has a diameter of 32 mils. The fourth column gives the resistance of a No. 20 wire as 10.15 ohms per 1,000 feet. Since 200 feet is $1/5$ of 1,000 feet ($200/1{,}000 = 2/10 = 1/5$), we merely divide the resistance per 1,000 feet by 5. This gives us 2.03 ohms ($10.15 \div 5 = 2.03$), which checks closely with the calculated value.

Effect of Temperature. The resistance of copper conductors increases as temperature increases. In Table I, resistances are measured at 20 degrees Centigrade, which is equivalent to 68 degrees on the Fahrenheit scale employed in the ordinary household thermometer. The rate at which resistance increases with temperature varies in different metals. A length of copper wire that has a resistance of 100 ohms at 20 degrees Centigrade, will have a resistance of approximately 120 ohms at a temperature of 70 degrees Centigrade (158 degrees Fahrenheit).

REVIEW QUESTIONS

1. Name the three basic factors in an electrical circuit.
2. Define the term "volt."
3. How is current expressed?
4. What is an ohm?
5. How does length affect resistance of a conductor?
6. How does cross-sectional area affect resistance?
7. What material is most commonly used for electrical conductors?
8. What is the name of the wire gauge used in measuring copper wire?
9. What is meant by the term "circular mil"?
10. How would you determine the circular-mil area of a round wire?
11. What factors govern resistance of a conductor?
12. What is meant by the term "mil-foot"?
13. How much resistance has a mil-foot of copper?
14. How does resistance vary with temperature?
15. Referring to the formula in the book, determine the resistance of 1000 feet of copper wire which has a diameter of 30 mils (.030 inch).

CHAPTER 3

OHM'S LAW AND ITS APPLICATION

OHM'S LAW

Development of Ohm's Law

During the investigation of the electrical pressure necessary to maintain a flow of current through a conductor, we noted that 1 ampere of current flowed through 1 ohm when 1 v was applied. We also noted that 2 amps of current flowed through 1 ohm when a pressure of 2 v was applied. Since the amount of current flowing in a circuit increases in the same manner as the pressure or voltage in the circuit, we may state this in the form of a rule: *Current flow in a circuit varies directly as the voltage applied to the circuit.*

In connection with the investigation of the effect of length of a conductor upon its resistance, it was noted that an increase in conductor resistance brought about a decrease in rate of current flow; that is, current varied inversely as the resistance. In view of this fact, we may state the rule as follows: *Current flow in a circuit varies inversely as the resistance of the circuit.*

These two rules were first stated by George Simon Ohm, an early German scientist, who combined them into one rule which bears his name: *The current in an electrical circuit varies directly as the voltage and inversely as the resistance.* Ohm's law is the foundation upon which are based all electrical calculations, however simple or however complicated they may be.

Basic Symbols. Before taking up practical examples of Ohm's law, it would be well to learn the three basic symbols used in dealing with electrical quantities. The first of these is the symbol to indicate electrical force, which is known as electromotive force and is measured in volts. Therefore, the expression

$$E = 120 \text{ v}$$

means that the electromotive force (emf) active in a given circuit is equal to 120 volts. The unit of force (the volt) is, as previously explained, represented by the letter *v*.

Electrical resistance is designated by the letter R and is measured in ohms. Thus,

$$R = 5 \text{ ohms}$$

states that the resistance present in a particular circuit amounts to 5 ohms. The unit of resistance may also be represented by the Greek letter Ω (omega). Now the statement may be written

$$R = 5\ \Omega$$

The current flow in an electrical circuit is indicated by the letter I. We may remember this designation by referring to it as the *intensity* of the current flow. Later, we will see that the letter C, which might be expected to be the abbreviation for current, is used to designate a different quantity. The unit of current flow is the ampere, which is abbreviated *amp.* Here, the expression

$$I = 24 \text{ amps}$$

means that the current flowing in the circuit amounts to 24 amps.

Use of Basic Symbols in Ohm's Law. Symbols may be used to represent Ohm's law in simplified form and can be written as

$$I = \frac{E}{R}$$

For the moment, let us replace the letters by the units they stand for. Then the law would be written as

$$\text{Current} = \frac{\text{Voltage}}{\text{Resistance}}$$

When Ohm's law is written in this way, it is called a *formula* and is read as follows: *The current is equal to the voltage divided by the resistance.* When a word, letter, or number is placed above a line over another word, letter, or number, the line has the same meaning as the sign ÷, which is read *divided by.*

Rearrangement of Ohm's Law

When the formula is written in this manner, it can be used only to find the current flowing when the voltage and the resistance are known. The formula can be rearranged, however, and then used to find the voltage or the resistance. Let us see how this rearranging is accomplished. The law was originally written as

$$I = \frac{E}{R}$$

but, in this case, let us suppose that we wish to know what voltage is necessary to force a certain amount of current through a given resistance. Of course, we will first have to know the value of the current and the value of the resistance—in all cases, two of the three values must be known. Therefore, we know that E will equal something, and we know that it will be related to the current and the resistance in some way.

We will examine the original formula, for this is the one we wish to rearrange. We will assume that $E = 10$ v and $R = 5$ ohms. When these values are substituted for their symbols, we have

$$I = \frac{10}{5}$$

We can immediately see that 10 divided by 5 equals 2, but we are not interested in this final result at the moment. We are interested in rearranging the formula. We will start by inserting the value for I in the formula, which we will call an *equation* from now on.

$$2 = \frac{10}{5}$$

This is a true equation, for 10 divided by 5 is 2, and 2, of course, is equal to 2. Now, let us multiply both sides of the equation by 5. Both sides of the equation must be multiplied by the same number to keep the equality, and the value 5 was chosen for a definite reason, as we will soon see.

$$2 \times 5 = \frac{10}{5} \times 5$$

$$10 = \frac{50}{5}$$

This shows that the equation is still true, for $50 \div 5 = 10$. A moment's examination of the first equation will show another point. This equation can also be written

$$2 \times 5 = \frac{10 \times 5}{5}$$

If we perform the division operation on the right-hand side of the equation, that is, divide the 5 (of the 10×5) by 5, we have an answer of 1. This will give

$$2 \times 5 = 10 \times 1$$

$$10 = 10$$

This shows that the equality holds true after multiplying both sides by 5. Instead of actually performing the division, we can cancel the number so that

$$2 \times 5 = \frac{10 \times 5}{5}$$

and

$$2 \times 5 = \frac{10 \times \not{5}}{\not{5}}$$

$$2 \times 5 = 10$$

This can be done because a number divided by the same number is equal to 1, and 1 times a number is equal to that same number ($1 \times 10 = 10$).

After seeing how an equation can be changed by using numbers, we will return to the letters of Ohm's law.

$$I = \frac{E}{R}$$

This time, instead of multiplying both sides of the equation by 5, we will multiply it by the letter R, for $R = 5$ ohms. Now,

$$I \times R = \frac{E \times R}{R}$$

Since $R \div R = 1$, just as $5 \div 5 = 1$, we can write the equation as

$$I \times R = \frac{E \times 1}{1}$$

or

$$I \times R = E$$

This tells us that the current flowing in a circuit multiplied by the resistance in that circuit is equal to the voltage applied to the circuit. Therefore, if we know the values of the current and the resistance, we can find the voltage. Because we are finding the voltage, the formula is turned about and written

$$E = I \times R$$

so that it reads: The voltage is equal to current times resistance. When letters are used in an equation in place of numbers, the multiplication sign is not used. The letters to be multiplied are placed together.

$$E = IR$$

Thus far, we have arranged Ohm's law for finding current and for finding voltage:

$$I = \frac{E}{R}$$

$$E = IR$$

The next step is to arrange the equation of Ohm's law for finding resistance. This can be done very easily by using

$$E = IR$$

For the moment, we will rewrite this as

$$IR = E$$

If we divide both sides of the equation by I, we will have

$$\frac{IR}{I} = \frac{E}{I}$$

When we cancel the I's on the left-hand side of the equation, we have

$$R = \frac{E}{I}$$

This gives us the third of the three arrangements of Ohm's law.

$$I = \frac{E}{R} \qquad E = IR \qquad R = \frac{E}{I}$$

APPLICATIONS OF OHM'S LAW

Simple Applications of Ohm's Law

The generator in Fig. 1 develops an electromotive force of 50 v and is employed to operate a small searchlight. We will assume that the resistance of the wires connecting the generator to the searchlight is zero, or so small that it need not be considered. We will determine how much current the 50-v generator will force through the searchlight; for when the light is in operation, it has a resistance of 10 ohms. In Fig. 1A we have a pictorial view of the generator and searchlight. Fig. 1B shows how this can be represented in an electrical drawing. Since we are interested only in the resistance of the searchlight, we will consider it as a resistor. Accordingly, we will indicate it by a wavy line, which is the symbol for a resistor in an electrical drawing. When an electrical drawing is made in this manner, it is called a *schematic.*

The first step is to write the formula for finding current. The next step is to replace the symbols with known quantities wherever possible. Since the value of E is given as 50 v, and that of R as 10 ohms, we will write the formula

$$I = \frac{E}{R}$$

$$I = \frac{50}{10}$$

$$I = 5 \text{ amps}$$

This tells us that 5 amps will flow through the 10-ohm resistor searchlight when 50 v is applied. This current will not only flow through the resistor but will also flow through the entire *circuit*. A circuit is the path through which the current flows. In Fig. 2 the circuit would be from the negative terminal of the generator to the resistor, through the resistor, and to the positive terminal of the generator. The current then flows through the generator from the positive terminal to the negative terminal.

Now let us operate a light that has a resistance of 5 ohms, while keeping the electromotive force at 50 v. In the following schematic drawings we will consider these searchlights merely as resistors and

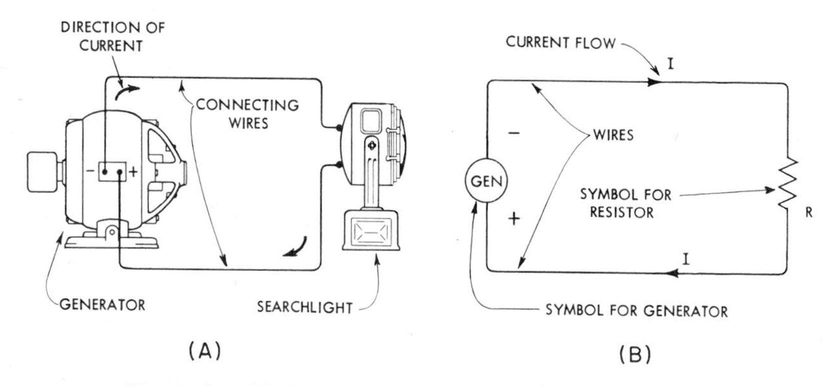

Fig. 1. Searchlight Being Operated by Electrical Generator

speak of them as such. When we substitute the values of Fig. 2 in Ohm's law,

$$I = \frac{E}{R}$$

$$I = \frac{50}{5}$$

$$I = 10 \text{ amps}$$

we find that the current is now 10 amps. This shows that reducing the resistance in a circuit, while holding the emf constant, will cause an increase in current. This is as was expected.

This time we will increase the resistance to 10 ohms, and we will also increase the emf to 100 v, Fig. 3. Here we have doubled the resistance and also the applied voltage. Increasing the resistance should cause a reduction in the current; but, increasing the emf should cause the current to increase. We can see what change is caused in the current flowing in this circuit by substituting these new values in Ohm's law.

$$I = \frac{E}{R}$$

$$I = \frac{100}{10}$$

$$I = 10 \text{ amps}$$

This shows that the current is the same. Doubling the resistance would cause the current to reduce one-half, or 5 amps. Then doubling the emf would cause the current to double from 5 amps to 10 amps. Therefore, the current remains unchanged.

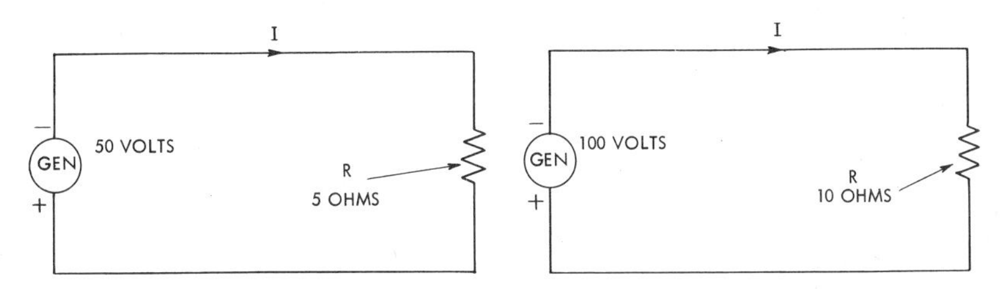

Fig. 2. Schematic Drawing of Circuit Containing 50-v Generator and 5-Ohm Resistor

Fig. 3. Schematic Drawing of Circuit Containing 100-v Generator and 10-Ohm Resistor

Further Applications of Ohm's Law

From these examples, it is apparent that the value of current flowing in an electrical circuit can be determined in every case, provided that the voltage active in the circuit and the resistance of the circuit are known. Sometimes, however, the voltage and the current are given, and it is desired to find the resistance of the circuit.

In this case, Fig. 4, the applied voltage is 75 v, the current is 5 amps, and we wish to determine the resistance of the circuit. Therefore, we will employ the arrangement of Ohm's law that states what R is equal to and substitute the values for the voltage in the current.

$$R = \frac{E}{I}$$

$$R = \frac{75}{5}$$

$$R = 15 \text{ ohms}$$

This tells us that the resistor in the circuit has a value of 15 ohms.

In the third type of problem, the current and the resistance are known, and the voltage is unknown. These problems can be solved with the third arrangement of Ohm's law. In Fig. 5 the current is 5 amps and the resistor has a value of 25 ohms.

$$E = IR$$

$$E = 5 \times 25$$

$$E = 125 \text{ v}$$

The voltage required to send a current of 5 amps through a resistance of 25 ohms is found to be 125 v.

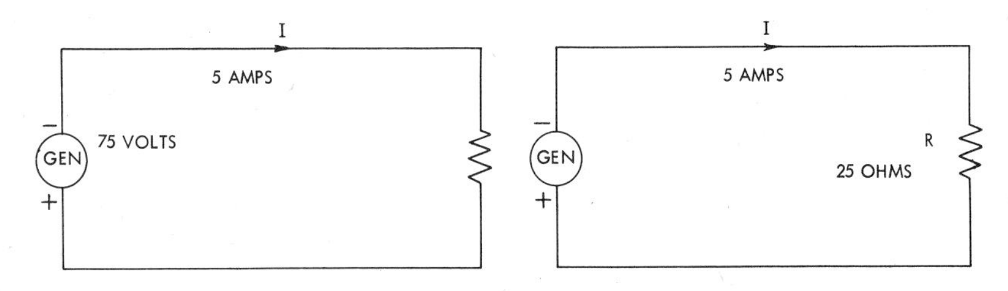

Fig. 4. Schematic of Circuit in Which Resistance Is Unknown

Fig. 5. Schematic of Circuit in Which Voltage Is Unknown

Voltage Drop

It was mentioned earlier that the effect of the voltage active in the circuit is to liberate electrons from the atoms and force these electrons around the electrical circuit. The term *voltage drop* is used to designate the loss in electrical pressure caused by forcing current through a resistance. Fig. 6 will help illustrate this condition. This shows a resistor connected to a generator by means of conducting wires, which can also be called *leads*. The resistor in this illustration is a long piece of high-resistance wire wound spirally on an insulating form. The resistor is mounted by two brackets which are attached to the cylindrical form. The resistance of the leads, however, is so low that it is considered to be zero. In this case, the generator develops an emf of 200 v and the resistor has a value of 50 ohms. According to Ohm's law,

$$I = \frac{E}{R}$$

$$I = \frac{200}{50}$$

$$I = 4 \text{ amps}$$

The value of the current flowing is 4 amps. This is noted near the arrows on the conducting wires, the arrows indicating the direction of current flow.

Since the generator develops an emf of 200 v, we have an electrical pressure of 200 v at the negative terminal of the generator. This voltage is also present at point *A* on the resistor, because there is no resistance in the lead and, accordingly, no loss in electrical pressure. When the current flows through the resistor, however, there will be a loss of electrical pressure. This pressure or voltage is lost in forcing current through the resistor. We will divide the resistor into four unequal sec-

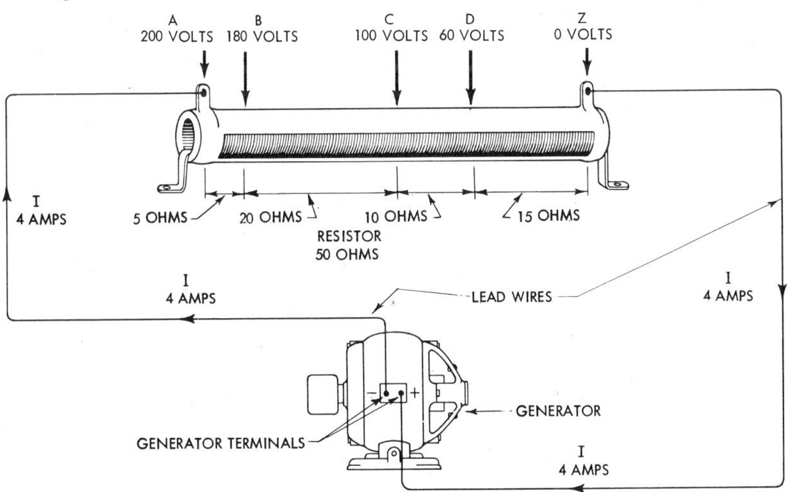

Fig. 6. Illustrating How Voltage Drop Occurs along Coil of Resistance Wire

tions to see how the voltage drop occurs. Between point *A* and point *B*, there is 5 ohms of resistance; and if a current of 4 amps is flowing through the resistor there will be a voltage drop between points A and B. Employing Ohm's law,

$$E = IR$$
$$E = 4 \times 5$$
$$E = 20 \text{ v}$$

we see that there will be a loss in voltage of 20 v in forcing current through this portion of the resistor. Therefore, the voltage at point B will be 180 v (200 − 20 = 180) instead of the original 200 v.

As the current is forced through the resistor from point B to point C, there will be an additional voltage drop. With 20 ohms of resistance between these points, the voltage drop is determined by Ohm's law.

$$E = IR$$
$$E = 4 \times 20$$
$$E = 80 \text{ v}$$

With the voltage dropping 80 v from point B to point C, the voltage at point C will be 100 v (180 − 80 = 100). Then the voltage drop between points C and D will be 40 v,

$$E = IR$$
$$E = 4 \times 10$$
$$E = 40 \text{ v}$$

and the voltage at point D is 60 v. Finally, the voltage drop between points D and Z will be 60 v.

$$E = \text{IR}$$
$$E = 4 \times 15$$
$$E = 60 \text{ v}$$

so the voltage at point Z is 0 v (60 − 60 = 0).

This shows how there is a loss in voltage as current is forced through a resistance. The different points along the resistor in Fig. 6 were chosen at random. We could include additional check points along the resistor, if we so desired, and it would show the voltage drop along the resistance at closer intervals.

Practical Example of Voltage Drop. Fig. 7 shows an electrical circuit consisting of a generator, an electric lamp, and the connecting wires W_1 and W_2. The voltage of the generator is 120 v, and the current required by the lamp is 10 amps. That portion of the conductor between the negative terminal of the generator and point *A*, at one end of the lamp, has a resistance of 1 ohm. The other conductor from the positive terminal to the *B* end of the lamp also has a resistance of 1 ohm. Now, since the brightness of the lamp depends upon the voltage applied, it is desired to know how much voltage is present between points *A* and *B*. The importance of the applied voltage on the output of the lamp will be considered in greater detail later on.

Here, 10 amps flow through the lamp. Since the current is the same throughout every portion of the circuit, the generator must send forth 10 amps of current from its negative (−) terminal and must receive 10 amps at its positive (+) terminal. In order to supply the lamp, this 10 amps of current must flow through the two conductors. To find

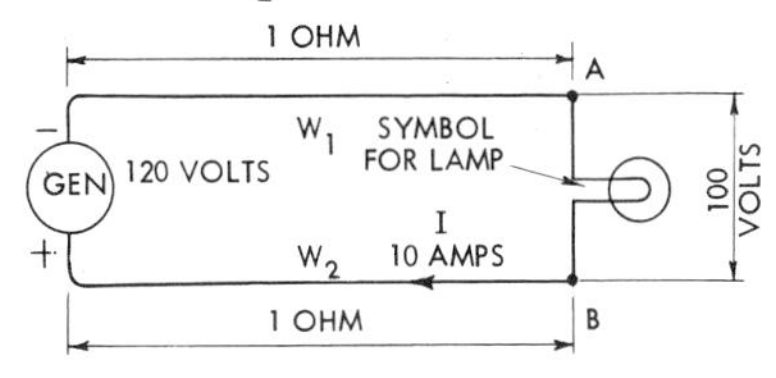

Fig. 7. Showing Voltage Drop along 1-Ohm Conductors Which Are Supplying Electric Lamp

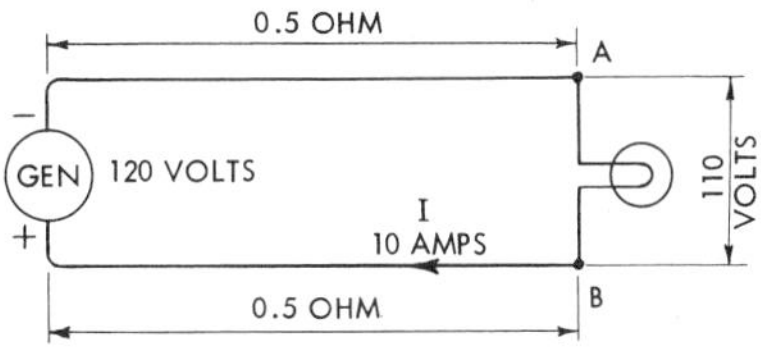

Fig. 8. Showing Voltage Drop along ½-Ohm Conductors Which Are Supplying Electric Lamp

the voltage drop in each of these conductors, it is necessary to apply Ohm's law as follows:

$$E = IR$$
$$E = 10 \times 1$$
$$E = 10 \text{ v}$$

From the formula, it is seen that the voltage drop from the negative terminal to point *A* is 10 v, and the voltage drop from *B* to the positive terminal is also 10 v. Thus, 20 v are consumed in the conductors, and only 100 v will be present across *A* and *B*. If this remaining voltage is insufficient for the lamps, it may be necessary to replace the conductors with ones of larger cross section which will, of course, have less resistance.

Suppose that larger conductors are substituted, Fig. 8, having a resistance of 0.5 ohm each instead of 1 ohm. What is the effect upon the voltage applied to the lamps? Referring again to the formula,

$$E = IR$$
$$E = 10 \times 0.5$$
$$E = 5 \text{ v}$$

the voltage drop in each conductor is found to be 5 v. In the two conductors, twice this amount will be lost, or 10 v. In this case, the voltage applied to ends A and B is 110 ($120 - 10 = 110$) which would prove much more satisfactory than the original value of 100 v.

REVIEW QUESTIONS

1. State how current varies as voltage increases.
2. How does current vary as voltage decreases?
3. How does current vary as resistance increases?
4. How does voltage change as resistance decreases?
5. How did Ohm express the relationship between these quantities?
6. Write out the form of Ohm's law used in determining current, employing the symbols E, I, and R.
7. Write out the form used in determining resistance.
8. Write out the form for determining voltage.
9. How much current will 100 volts force through a resistance of 7.5 ohms?
10. How much additional resistance would be required to reduce this current to 5 amperes?
11. How much voltage would be required to increase this 5-ampere current to 20 amperes?
12. How much will current change in a circuit if the resistance and the voltage are both doubled?
13. How much will current increase or decrease if voltage is cut in half and resistance is doubled?
14. How much will the voltage drop in a supply conductor be reduced if the diameter of the conductor is doubled?
15. Make a rough schematic diagram of a generator connected to a resistor, indicating polarities, and showing direction of electron flow by means of arrows marked on the wires.

CHAPTER 4

ELECTRICAL CIRCUITS

SERIES CIRCUITS

Circuit Features

The three basic circuits in electricity are: *series, parallel,* and *series-parallel.* The distinguishing feature of each is the way in which the electrical equipment is connected, and their names describe these connections. We will discuss each type separately and learn what their differences are.

Arrangement of Series Circuit. The circuits we have been using to examine current flow and voltage drop are of the series type. Figs. 1

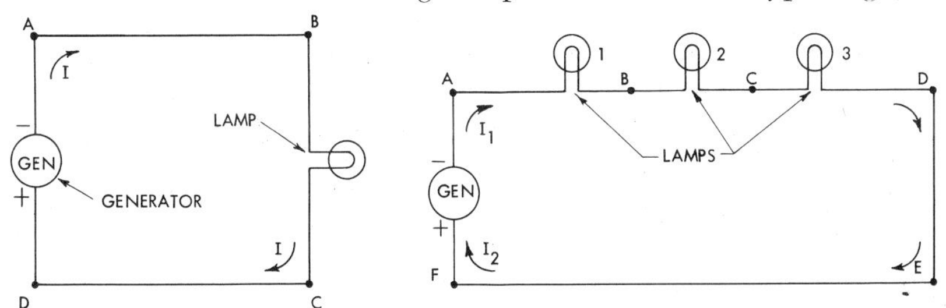

Fig. 1. Simple Series Circuit **Fig. 2. Series Circuit with Three Lamps**

and 2 show two series circuits. There is but a single lamp in Fig. 1, but there are three lamps in the circuit of Fig. 2. The lamps of Fig 2 are connected end to end, or in series; therefore, this is called a series connection. Fig. 1 is a simple series circuit, but it is easier to see the arrangement of a series circuit when two or more units are used, Fig. 2. When the units (generators, lamps, or other electrical equipment) are connected end to end, so there is only one path for the current, they are said to be in series.

Current in Series Circuit

These two circuits have one condition in common: the path through which the current flows. Both of these circuits have but one path for the current. The complete path for the current, Fig. 1, is *ABCDA*. In Fig. 2 the path is *ABCDEFA*.

The current I_1, Fig. 2, shown flowing from the negative terminal of the generator, must be the same as the current I_2, shown flowing into the negative terminal of the generator. These values must be the same, for they are one and the same current. The reason for this is that the current cannot accumulate anywhere along the circuit. We can state this in the form of a rule: *The current is the same at all points around a series circuit.*

Resistance of a Series Circuit

We will use Fig. 3 as an aid for understanding the resistance in a series circuit. In Fig. 3A, we see one long resistor. This is again a length

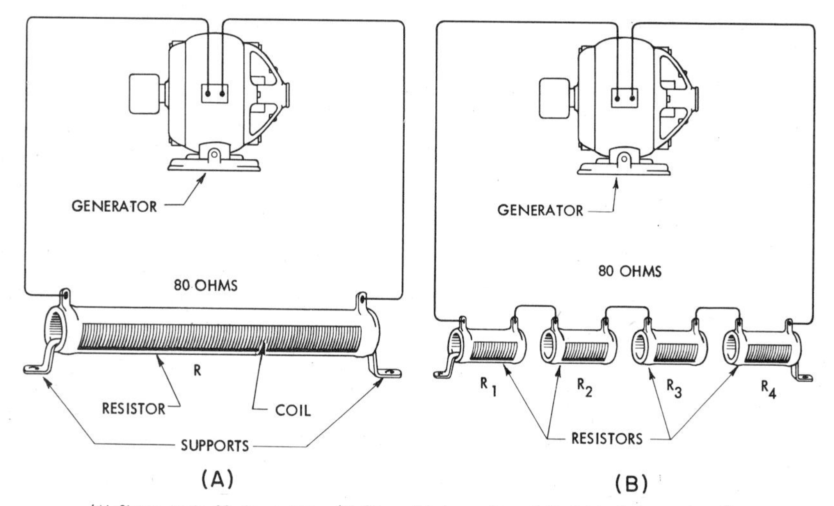

(A) Shows single 80-ohm resistor. (B) Shows 80-ohm resistor divided into four equal portions.

Fig. 3. Illustrating How Total Resistance of Series Circuit Is Determined

of resistance wire that is wound on an insulating form, and its length is such that its total resistance is 80 ohms. The figure also shows a generator connected to the resistor, but, for the moment, we will direct our attention to the resistor itself.

In Fig. 3B, the form has been separated at three points, dividing the resistor into four equal sections. These four sections are marked R_1, R_2, R_3, and R_4. There has been no change made in the total resistance of the circuit by dividing it into four separate sections; therefore, we can say that R, Fig. 3A, is equal to the sum of R_1, R_2, R_3, and R_4 of Fig. 3B. This can be written in formula style to account for any number of resistors in a series circuit.

$$R = R_1 + R_2 + R_3 + R_4$$

If each of the resistors in Fig. 3B were 20 ohms, the total resistance in the circuit would be 80 ohms.

$$R = R_1 + R_2 + R_3 + R_4$$
$$R = 20 + 20 + 20 + 20$$
$$R = 80 \text{ ohms}$$

Voltage Drop in a Series Circuit

If the generator in Fig. 3 is rated at 160 volts, the current flowing in the circuit is equal to E/R, or 160/80, which is 2 amps. The voltage drop across resistor R_1 equals 2×20, or 40 volts ($E = I \times R$). In the same way, the voltage drop across each of the small resistors R_2, R_3, and R_4 is 40 volts. When these four voltage drops are added (the small drop in connecting wires being ignored) the total is equal to 160 volts. A rule may be stated, therefore, as follows: The sum of the voltage drops in a series circuit is equal to the applied voltage.

PARALLEL CIRCUITS

Arrangement of Parallel Circuit

The parallel circuit is employed in our homes; lights, television, refrigerator, and kitchen appliances being connected in this manner. A parallel circuit has as many paths as there are devices. In Fig. 4, three

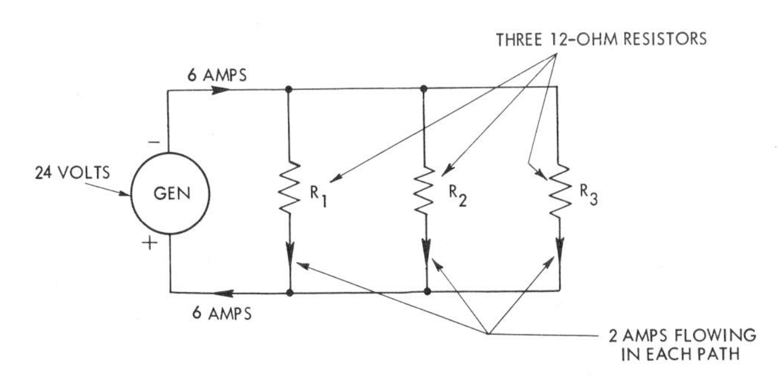

Fig. 4. Simple Parallel Circuit

resistors R_1, R_2, and R_3 are connected across the line wires from the generator, offering three separate paths to the flow of current.

If the generator is rated at 24 volts, and the resistance of each of the three resistors is 12 ohms, the current flowing through each path is equal to the voltage at its terminals divided by its resistance. Since the voltage here is 24 and the resistance is 12 ohms, the current in R_1 is equal to $^{24}/_{12}$, or 2 amps. The currents flowing through R_2 and R_3 are also 2 amps each, the total current flowing in the circuit amounting to the sum of the three, or 6 amps.

Resistance of Parallel Circuits

With a voltage of 24, and a total current of 6 amperes, Ohm's law tells us that the combined resistance of the three resistors must be equal to $^{24}/_{6}$ (E/I), or 4 ohms. This value is termed the *equivalent resistance.* In order to determine the amount of current flowing in any parallel circuit, it is necessary to determine the current flowing through each part and to add them together, or else to find the equivalent resistance and to divide the voltage by this quantity. With a simple circuit, it is possible to use either method, but in the somewhat more complicated circuits of the next section, you will find it impossible to use the first method.

The second method will be made clear with the help of Fig. 5 which shows a 24-volt generator supplying current to two 4-ohm resistors connected in parallel. To determine the equivalent resistance of these two

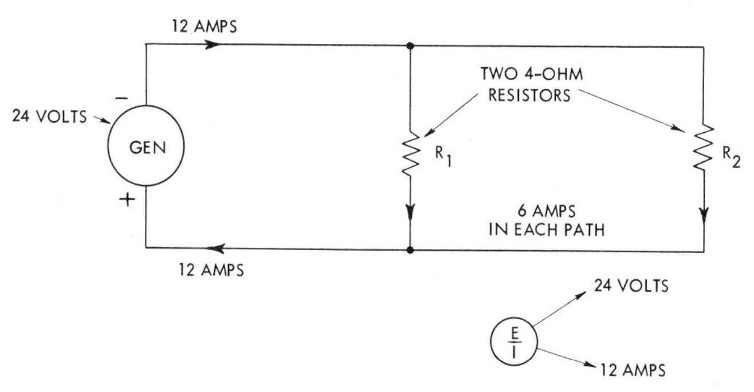

Fig. 5. Equivalent Resistance in Parallel Circuit

equal resistors, we shall perform three simple steps. *First,* we invert the two resistance values, or turn them upside down. With the 4-ohm resistor, we place the figure "1" over the "4" and get the fraction $\frac{1}{4}$. The second resistor, having the same resistance, provides a second fraction of $\frac{1}{4}$. *Second,* we add the two fractions: $\frac{1}{4} + \frac{1}{4} = \frac{2}{4}$ or $\frac{1}{2}$. *Third,* we turn the resulting fraction upside down, or invert it, to obtain the value of the equivalent resistance in ohms.

The equivalent resistance of the combination of two 4-ohm resistors connected in parallel is seen to be 2 ohms. Hence, the current flowing in the circuit must be equal to E/R, or $^{24}/_{2}$, which is 12 amperes. Checking this result by means of the first method, the current through each resistor is equal to $^{24}/_{4}$, or 6 amperes. The current through both, together, must be twice this amount, or 12 amperes, as before. This method for determining equivalent resistance may be used with any number of resistors which are connected in parallel if the steps are carried out in "one-two-three" order.

A further example will emphasize the principle. In Fig. 6 a 24-volt generator supplies current to three resistors which are connected in parallel, their respective resistances being 2 ohms, 3 ohms, and 6 ohms.

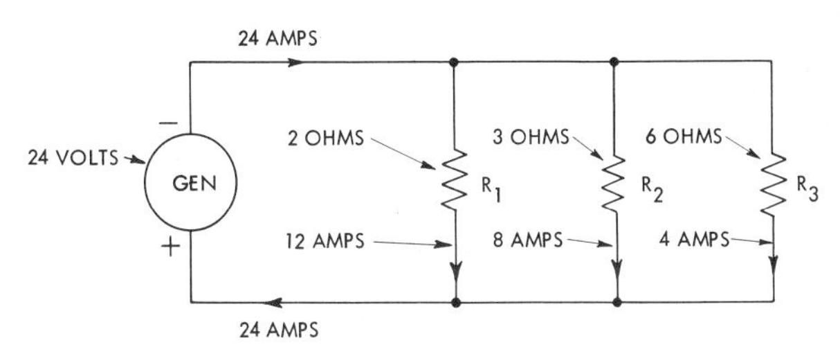

Fig. 6. Equivalent Resistance—Three Resistors in Parallel

Following the plan developed in connection with Fig. 5, *Step One* is to invert each resistance value, giving the three fractions, $^{1}/_{2}$, $^{1}/_{3}$, and $^{1}/_{6}$. *Step Two* calls for adding the fractions, thus, $^{1}/_{2} + ^{1}/_{3} + ^{1}/_{6}$. Now, fractions can only be added if the values at the bottom of each fraction (called their denominators) are equal. Here, the denominators are all different, being 2, 3, and 6.

To make the denominators equal, it is merely necessary to find some number into which all will divide a whole number of times. The numbers 6, 12, or 24 would be satisfactory. Let us choose 12, and write three fractions with 12's on the bottoms as denominators, and leaving the upper (numerator) parts blank: $/_{12} + /_{12} + /_{12}$.

Next, divide the new denominator by the old denominator in each case, and write the answer as the top or numerator of one of the fractions. Thus, 12 divided by 2 equals 6, so that 6 will be written over the 12 in the first fraction, making it $^{6}/_{12}$. Again, 12 divided by 3 equals 4, so that 2 will be written as the numerator of the second fraction, making it $^{4}/_{12}$. And 12 divided by 6 equals 2, so that the third fraction becomes $^{2}/_{12}$.

Step Two may be completed, now, by adding the fractions: $\frac{6}{12} + \frac{4}{12} + \frac{2}{12} = \frac{12}{12}$, which is equal to 1. *Step Three,* which requires the answer to be inverted, is hardly necessary here, because inverting the figure "1" gives the answer "1."

The equivalent resistance of these three resistors, then, is equal to 1 ohm, and the current flowing in the whole circuit is equal to E/R, or $\frac{24}{1}$, which is 24 amperes. When checked by the first method, this answer is seen to be correct.

SERIES-PARALLEL CIRCUITS

A Common Type of Series-Parallel Circuit

Fig. 7A represents a series-parallel arrangement which gets its name from the fact that certain combinations of resistors which are in parallel

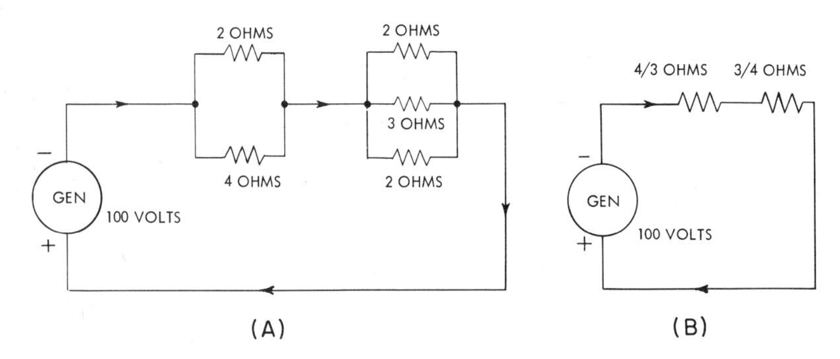

Fig. 7. A–Series-Parallel Circuit; B–Series Circuit Which Is Electrically Equivalent to the Series-Parallel Circuit of Fig. 7A

with each other, are connected in series. In the figure, a 2-ohm and a 4-ohm resistor are in parallel with each other. In a second group two 2-ohm resistors are in parallel with each other and also with a 3-ohm resistor. The two groups are connected in series with a 100-volt generator.

To determine circuit resistance, it is first necessary to find the equivalent resistance of each combination, and then to add these equivalent values. Starting with the left-hand group, *Step One* yields the fractions $\frac{1}{2}$ and $\frac{1}{4}$. Adding them, under *Step Two,* $\frac{1}{2} + \frac{1}{4} = \frac{2}{4} + \frac{1}{4}$, or $\frac{3}{4}$. Inverting this resultant fraction, in accordance with *Step Three,* 1 divided by $\frac{3}{4}$ equals $\frac{4}{3}$ ohm.

The equivalent resistance of the right-hand group is now determined. *Step One* gives $\frac{1}{2}$, $\frac{1}{3}$, and $\frac{1}{2}$. Adding the fractions, as per *Step Two*, $\frac{1}{2} + \frac{1}{3} + \frac{1}{2} = \frac{3}{6} + \frac{2}{6} + \frac{3}{6}$, or $\frac{4}{3}$. Inverting this fraction, *Step Three*, gives: 1 divided by $\frac{4}{3}$ equals $\frac{3}{4}$ ohm.

The circuit then becomes the same as that shown in Fig. 7B, where a $\frac{4}{3}$-ohm resistor is connected in series with a $\frac{3}{4}$-ohm resistor. Adding them, $\frac{4}{3}$ ohm + $\frac{3}{4}$ ohm = $\frac{16}{12}$ ohm + $\frac{9}{12}$ ohm, or $\frac{25}{12}$ ohm. The amount of current flowing in the circuit is equal to E/R, or 100 divided by $\frac{25}{12}$, which, according to simple arithmetic, is equal to $100 \times \frac{12}{25}$, or 48 amperes.

This current passes from the negative terminal of the generator through each of the two resistance groups, in series, to the positive terminal of the generator. The voltage drop across the left-hand group is equal to $I \times R = 48 \times \frac{4}{3}$, or 64 volts. The voltage drop across the second group is equal to $48 \times \frac{3}{4}$, or 36 volts.

Another Form of Series-Parallel Circuit

Fig. 8 illustrates a type of circuit which comes under the general heading of series-parallel combinations, and which is sometimes called a parallel-series grouping. Two or more resistors are connected in series, in each leg, and the legs are connected in parallel. A moment's reflection will show that the total resistance of each leg should first be obtained, and the problem solved as a simple combination of parallel resistors.

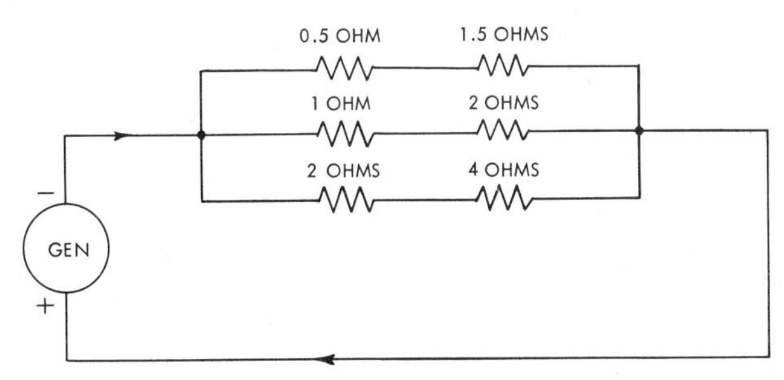

Fig. 8. Parallel-Series Circuit

Adding the resistors in the upper leg of Fig. 8, 0.5 ohm + 1.5 ohm = 2 ohms. The middle leg is equal to 1 ohm + 2 ohms = 3 ohms. And the bottom leg is equal to 2 ohms + 4 ohms = 6 ohms. Thus, three resistors of 2 ohms, 3 ohms, and 6 ohms, respectively, are connected in parallel, the identical problem that was presented and solved in connection with Fig. 6.

Problems involving any combination of series and parallel resistors may be solved readily through application of the simple principles explained above.

REVIEW QUESTIONS

1. Two 5-ohm resistors are connected in series with a 150-volt generator. What is the voltage drop across each resistor (neglecting the small loss in connecting wires)?
2. If another 5-ohm resistor is connected in series with them, what is the voltage drop across each of the three?
3. A 10-ohm resistor, a 5-ohm resistor, and an unknown resistor are connected in series with the 150-volt generator, and a current of 5 amperes flows in the circuit. What is the value of the unknown resistor?
4. Find the voltage drop across each resistor in problem 3.
5. The 150-volt generator sends a current of 5 amperes through a series of four unknown resistors. The drop across the first resistor is 25 volts, across the second 35 volts, across the third 40 volts, and across the fourth 50 volts. Find the resistance of each unit.
6. Add the three fractions: $\frac{1}{4}$, $\frac{1}{6}$, and $\frac{1}{8}$.
7. Find the equivalent resistance of three resistors of 8 ohms, 6 ohms, and 4 ohms which are connected in parallel.
8. If the generator supplying the load of problem 7 is rated at 26 volts, how much current flows in the circuit?
9. Will circuit resistance be increased or decreased by connecting another resistor in parallel with an existing combination of resistors?
10. Two equal resistors are connected in parallel. If the resistance of one is doubled while that of the other is halved, will circuit resistance remain the same as before?
11. One of two parallel resistors is 2 ohms. The value of the second resistor is unknown, but the equivalent resistance of the parallel combination is $\frac{5}{6}$ ohm. What is the value of the unknown resistor?
12. Five resistors are arranged in a series-parallel grouping similar to that of Fig. 7A, except that the generator is rated at 138 volts. The left-hand group has a 2-ohm and a 3-ohm resistor in parallel. The right-hand group has a 3-ohm, a 4-ohm, and a 2-ohm resistor in parallel. What is the equivalent resistance of the left-hand group?
13. What is the equivalent resistance of the right-hand group?
14. How much current flows through the circuit?
15. What is the voltage drop across each group?

CHAPTER 5

MAGNETISM AND ELECTROMAGNETISM

MAGNETISM

Early History

The early Greeks first noticed certain qualities in the type of iron ore called *lodestone.* When two lumps of the ore were placed together, a noticeable effort was sometimes required to separate them. A larger piece of the ore oftentimes attracted smaller pieces of the same material. The Greeks named the peculiar and invisible quality *magnetism.*

Another interesting feature of lodestone was that if a piece of iron were stroked several times with this ore, Fig. 1, the iron seemed to acquire properties which resembled those of lodestone. This condition of the iron which now shows evidence of magnetism, is expressed by saying that it has become *magnetized.*

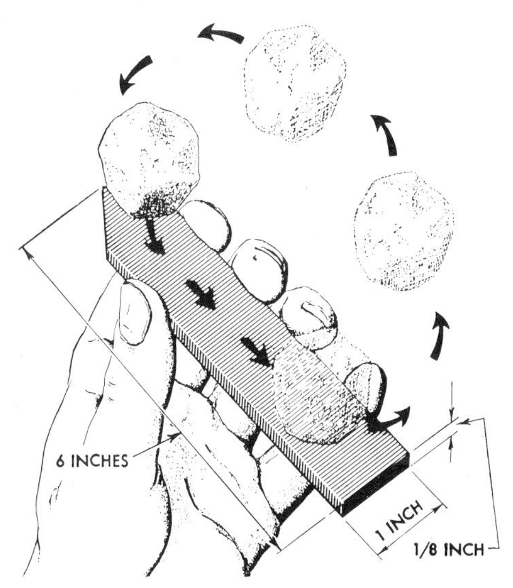

Fig. 1. Magnetizing Iron Strip by Stroking with Lodestone

North and South Poles

Experiments with pieces of lodestone led to no definite conclusions. One reason lay in the fact that the ore was found in a variety of shapes. They were so varied that results were often confusing or even contradictory. With the aid of a thin strip of magnetized iron, Fig. 1, experimenters learned many facts about magnetism and about magnetized objects.

When the thin strip of magnetized iron was suspended at its middle so as to be free to turn, it was found that one particular end always came to rest when it pointed toward the north pole of the earth as in Fig. 2. This end was termed the *north-seeking end* because it appeared to hunt for the north pole of the earth. And, since the opposite half of the strip was necessarily turned toward the south pole of the earth, it was termed the *south-seeking end.* The terms were shortened, with the passage of time, to *north end* and *south end.* Later, the term *pole* was substituted for the term end, so that a magnetized strip was said to have a *north pole* and a *south pole.* These terms are the ones used today and are written *N pole* and *S pole.*

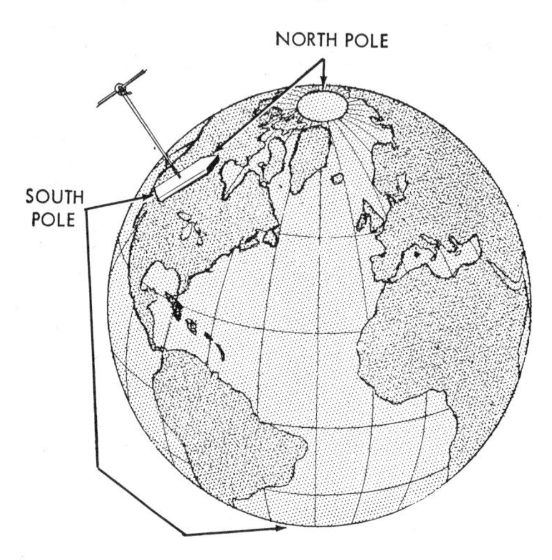

Fig. 2. One End of Magnetized Strip Points North

Attraction and Repulsion

Magnetized strips react upon one another in certain definite ways. If the S pole of one is brought close to the N pole of another, the two strips tend to draw together, Fig. 3A. The same result will be noted if the strips are reversed so that the N pole of the first is brought close to the S pole of the second.

On the other hand, if the N pole of one is presented to the N pole of the other, Fig. 3B, they tend to draw away from, or to repel, one another. The same thing occurs if two S magnetic poles are presented to one another, Fig. 3C. It is evident that when the adjacent poles of the two magnetized strips are of opposite polarities, that is, one north and the other south, a force of attraction is present, for the strips tend to draw together. If the adjacent poles are of the same polarity, a force of repulsion is noted.

Upon the basis of these observations, it is possible to state the following fundamental rule of magnetism: *Unlike magnetic poles attract; like magnetic poles repel.*

Lines of Force

Since the force of attraction or of repulsion, as the case may be, is noticeable when the magnetized pieces are yet some distance apart, it is evident that a kind of force passes through space between them. Invisible *lines of force* are believed to spread out from magnetic poles.

Fig. 4 illustrates an experiment which gave rise to the idea of lines of magnetic force. A piece of cardboard is sprinkled with iron filings which are distributed evenly upon the surface of the cardboard in a thin layer. If the magnetized bar is now placed upon the central portion

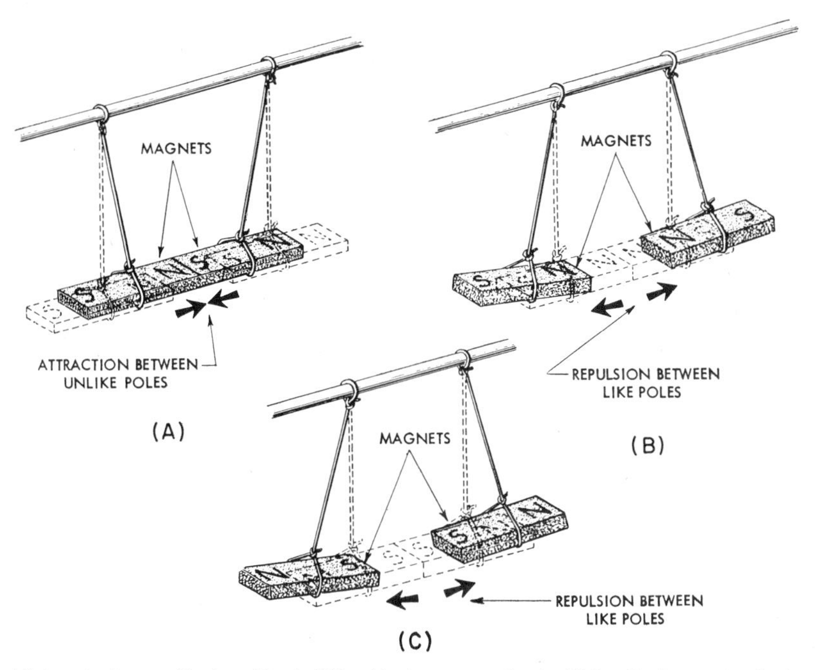

(A) Attraction between N pole and S pole. (B) Repulsion between two N poles. (C) Repulsion between two S poles

Fig. 3. Illustrating Law of Magnetic Attraction and Repulsion

of the cardboard and the cardboard is tapped gently to agitate the filings, they will form a pattern of magnetic lines.

The lines spread out most thickly in the regions of the poles and form two elliptical figures, one along each side of the magnetized bar. Close observation shows that the lines are continuous in each case from one magnetic pole to the other. It is concluded, therefore, that magnetic force exists in the form of continuous lines which emerge from one end of the magnet, then pass through the air to the opposite pole, and complete the path through the bar. Fig. 4 shows only one plane, but if the magnet were rolled on its side, the lines of force would be similar.

Magnetic Patterns. Fig. 5A shows the pattern developed in a layer of iron filings when the N pole of one magnetized piece is brought near to the S pole of another. It is clear that the lines of force from the N pole of one pass into the S pole of the other. Some of the lines still swing around the sides from the N pole of each bar to its S pole; but many of the lines do not. If the sheet of cardboard were large enough, it would be seen that lines from the N pole of the right-hand bar make a wide sweep around the sides of the two bars to enter the S pole of the left-hand bar.

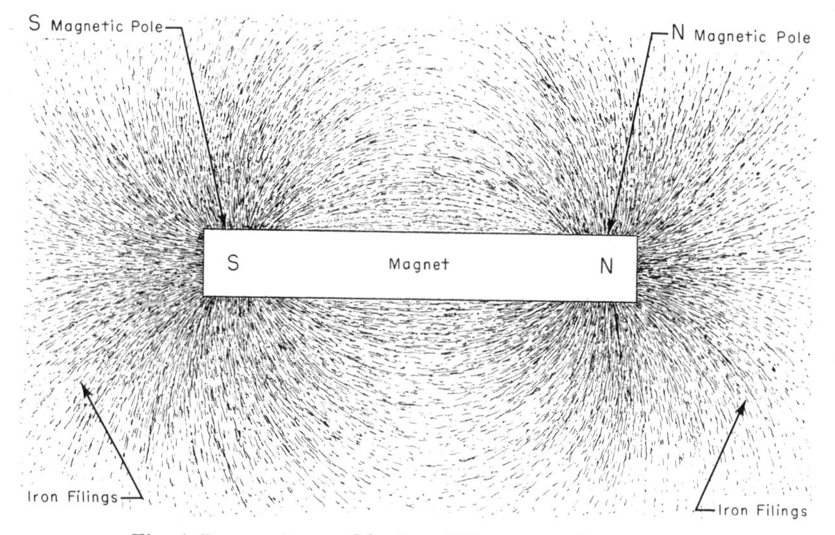

Fig. 4. Pattern Assumed by Iron Filings around Bar Magnet

Fig. 5B shows the pattern developed when a N pole of one bar is presented to the N pole of the other. It is evident that lines from a N pole are repelled by those of the other N pole.

From these two patterns it may be concluded that an attractive force results when the lines of force from two magnetic poles find themselves in agreement and that a force of repulsion results when the two sets of magnetic lines find themselves in opposition. It is possible to arrive at a hasty and incorrect conclusion in regard to this matter of agreement and disagreement. For it might be thought that the lines from two N poles would be in agreement, since the poles are alike. A moment's reflection, however, will disclose the error. If we assume, for the time being, that the lines of force emerge from N poles and enter S poles,

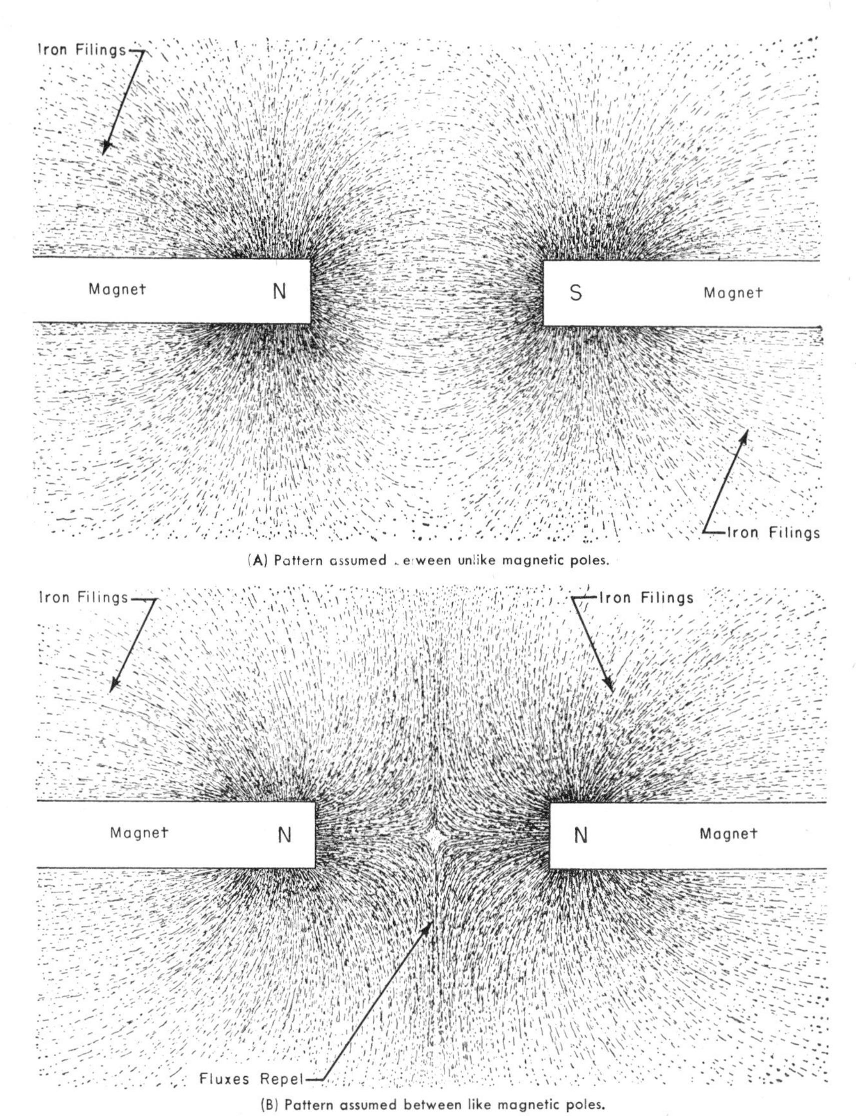

Fig. 5. Pattern Assumed by Iron Filings between Magnetic Poles

it is evident that the lines from the two N poles will be coming out of the pole in each bar so that they will clash with one another. On the other hand, since the lines emerge from a N pole and enter a S pole, the lines from a N and a S pole will be in agreement with one another when the two are brought near.

Direction of Lines of Force. When the line theory of magnetic force was proposed, it was assumed that magnetic loops, or lines, emerged from N poles and entered S poles as indicated in Fig. 6. Magnetic theory founded upon this belief has never been disproved. It may be stated in the form of a rule: *Lines of magnetic force leave magnetized objects at N poles and re-enter the objects at S poles.*

It should be emphasized here that magnetic lines are really closed loops of force. In practice, it is sometimes more convenient to forget

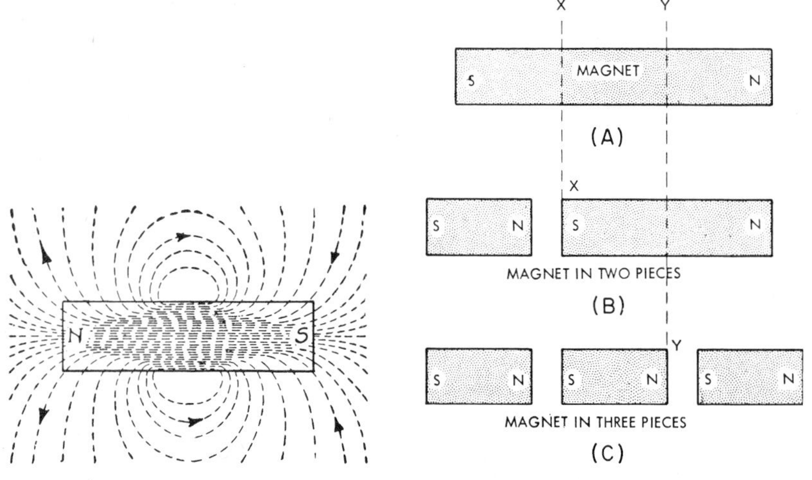

Fig. 6. Showing Direction of Magnetic Lines of Force

Fig. 7. Effect of Dividing Magnet into Parts

that they are loops and to think of them as two sets of magnetic lines, one emerging from the N pole and the other entering the S pole in the same way. However, the basic fact should not be forgotten.

Weber-Ewing Theory of Magnetism

Fig. 7 shows what occurs when a magnetized bar is broken into pieces. In Fig. 7A the bar has a S pole at one end and a N pole at the other. Two dotted lines are drawn across it at points *X* and *Y*. If a break is made at line *X*, so that there are two separate pieces, it will be found that the small piece at the left, Fig. 7B, has a N and a S pole. The larger piece also has a N and a S pole.

If the larger piece is now cut along line *Y*, Fig. 7C, it will be found that both pieces have a N and a S pole. Before the bar was cut, it had a single N pole and a single S pole. Now, when it is cut into three pieces, each one has a N and a S pole, so that there are now three N poles and three S poles. As a matter of fact, the result will be much the same if the original bar is cut into 1,000 pieces. For, however small the pieces may be cut, each will be found to have a N and a S pole.

To account for this fact, two scientists, J. A. Weber and Wilhelm Ewing, suggested that magnetized objects are made up of magnetized

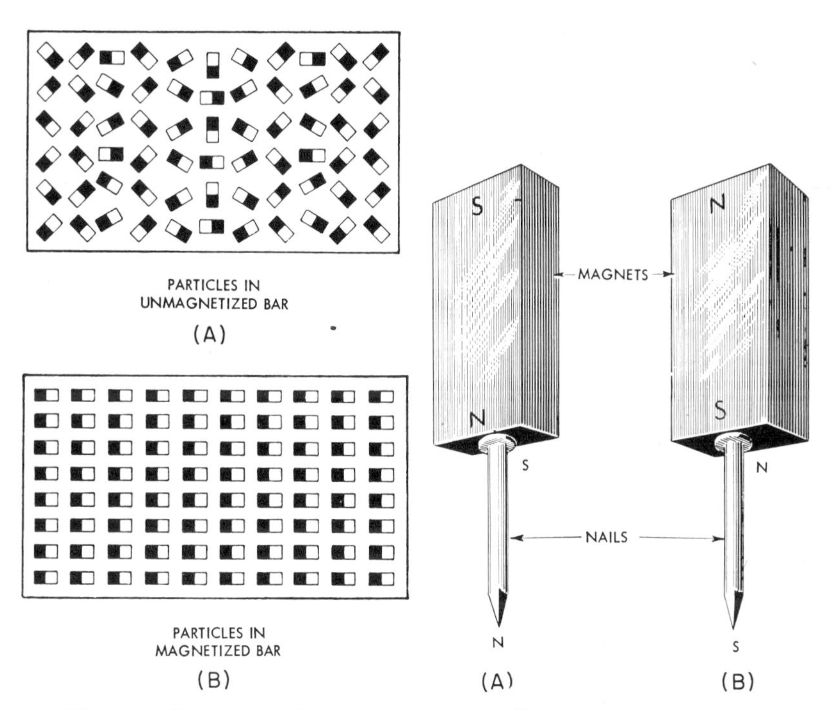

Fig. 8. Weber-Ewing Theory of Magnetism

Fig. 9. Illustrating Magnetic Induction

particles. When a bar of iron is unmagnetized, the particles are arranged in a random fashion. Fig. 8A shows such an unmagnetized bar. When it is magnetized, the particles are caused to line up, Fig. 8B, so that all N poles face one direction and all S poles the opposite direction. The magnetic forces of individual particles are added together so that lines of force emerge from the N pole and re-enter the S pole, thus showing signs of magnetism. When it was learned that particles still showed signs of magnetism even when ground to powder, scientists expressed the belief that each molecule was magnetized.

Electron Theory of Magnetism

Research shows that magnetism, like electricity, is a product of the electron; a circle of force being associated with each electron. Within the atom, some of the circles of force oppose those of other electrons, cancelling out the magnetic effect; and resulting in a net magnetic "charge."

Each atom may be thought of as one of the small magnets used in explanation of the Weber-Ewing theory. The atomic structure of materials which can be magnetized is such that the atoms readily swing into positions of magnetic agreement under the influence of a magnetizing force. Materials easily magnetized are said to be paramagnetic.

Permanent Magnets. A magnetized piece of metal is commonly termed a *magnet*. If a piece of iron which contains carbon is heated to a red temperature and then quickly immersed in water or oil, the surface will be found more resistant to the action of a file than it was before being treated. The metal is then said to be hardened. When a hardened piece of iron is once magnetized, it retains its magnetism for days, months, or even years. On the other hand, if an unhardened piece of iron is magnetized, it will lose its magnetism in a very short time, sometimes in a fraction of a second. The piece which retains its magnetism for a long period of time is called a *permanent magnet*. The soft piece is not a permanent magnet but only a *temporary magnet*.

Permanent magnets are used in any number of applications. Small generators in special electrical applications often use permanent magnets, and electrical measuring instruments also employ them. Another common use is in loud-speakers for public address systems.

Magnetic Induction. If a common wire nail is brought into contact with one pole of a magnetized bar, Fig. 9A, the nail will cling to the magnetic pole. If the pole happens to be the N pole of the magnet, a N pole will be found at the lower end of the nail. If the nail is touched to the S pole of the magnet, Fig. 9B, the lower end of the nail will have a S pole. If taken away from the magnet, the nail will lose its magnetic properties. In other words, the nail is but a temporary magnet.

The lines of force of the magnet cause the particles of the nail to arrange themselves in such a way that their magnetic lines agree with those coming from the magnet. Therefore, a S magnetic pole will be formed at that end of the nail which is in contact with the N pole of the magnet, and a N pole will be formed at the lower end. When the nail touches the S pole of a magnet, a N pole is formed at that end of the nail which is in contact with it, and a S pole is formed at the opposite end. This method of causing magnetism in one piece of metal by contact with a magnetized piece is called *magnetic induction.* Here, the poles in the nail were said to be *induced* by the magnetic lines from the magnetized bar.

At this time we might note one point about magnetic materials. Hard materials, which retain their magnetism for long periods of time, are usually more difficult to magnetize, while soft materials, which do not retain their magnetism, are easily magnetized. Stated another way, materials that are easily magnetized generally lose their magnetism quickly, and materials that are difficult to magnetize usually retain their magnetism. Therefore, the nails, which are easily magnetized, do not retain their magnetism.

Types of Magnets. For the sake of simplicity, the magnets used in the illustrations have all been of the strip or bar type, but magnets are produced in a variety of shapes. Fig. 10 shows a *horseshoe magnet.* The pattern assumed by the magnetic lines of force is indicated, the greater majority of lines passing directly across the open end from one pole to the other. Circular magnets are used for loading scrap iron onto railroad cars. Cylindrical magnets are used for removing scraps of iron from material which passes over the magnets.

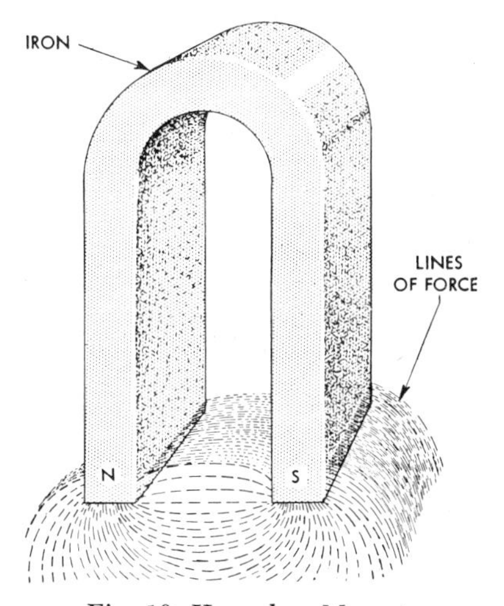

Fig. 10. Horseshoe Magnet

Magnetic Resistance

Magnetic lines of force can pass through any material, but they pass more readily through magnetic materials: iron, cobalt, and nickel. In this respect, the classifications of magnetic and nonmagnetic are similar to the classifications of conductors and nonconductors as applied to the flow of electric current.

Nonmagnetic materials offer resistance to the flow of magnetic lines just as nonconductors offer great resistance to the flow of current. Magnetic resistance is called *reluctance.* There is a term for magnetic pressure, but since it is not in everyday use, it may be omitted at this point.

The quantity of magnetic flow, or the number of magnetic loops or lines produced in a given piece of material, depends upon the strength of the magnetic pressure and the reluctance of the material, as the flow of current depends upon the electrical pressure and the resistance of the conductor. The reluctance of air and other nonmagnetic substances equals thousands of times the reluctance of iron.

The lines of force try to use the easiest available path in completing their circles or loops. In the familiar bar magnet, the iron core provides an exceedingly smooth path for that part of the loop contained in it.

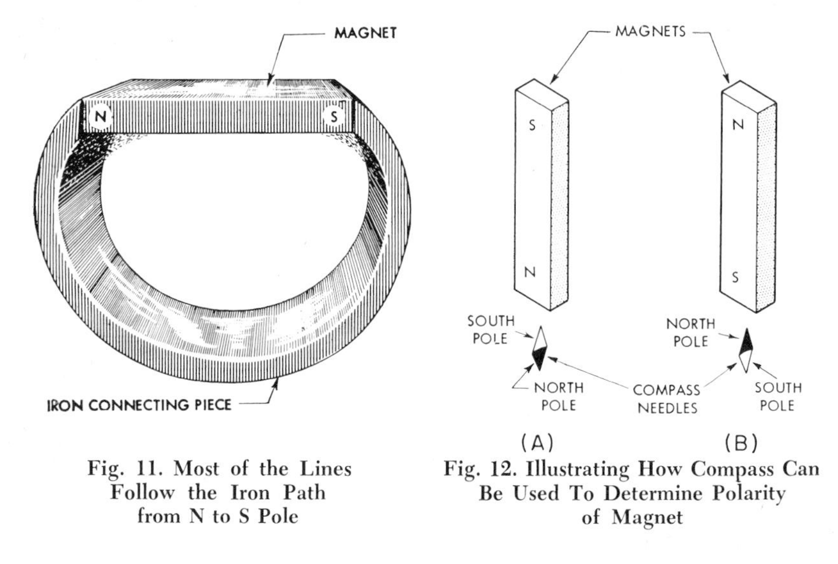

Fig. 11. Most of the Lines Follow the Iron Path from N to S Pole

Fig. 12. Illustrating How Compass Can Be Used To Determine Polarity of Magnet

The remaining portion must take the best path it can find through the air from one pole tip to the other. If it were not for the repulsion between lines causing their need for space through which to pass, they would cling to the surface of the magnet. Because of this space requirement, the lines bulge out as noted in the pattern of iron filings. If the return path from one pole to the other is made of iron, as in Fig. 11, practically all of the magnetic lines will choose this path instead of jumping across the air space.

Use of Magnetic Compass

For many centuries, the compass was the principal aid by means of which mariners were able to guide their ships. Since the N pole of the compass always turns toward the general direction of the north geographical pole, the navigator was able to tell if his ship was proceeding in the desired direction. It should be noted that the magnetic polarity of this pole, which attracts the N pole of the compass, must be S, since unlike poles attract. In other words, the magnetic pole adjacent to the north geographical pole is a south magnetic pole. The confusion here arises from the fact that the term north-seeking pole, originally employed to designate the pole of the lodestone or compass, was shortened to north pole. This apparent confusion, however, is of little practical importance.

The fact that unlike poles attract is utilized to determine the nature of a magnetic pole in a magnet with the aid of the compass. Fig. 12 shows how this is done. When the compass is brought near the N pole of a bar magnet, Fig. 12A, the S pole of the compass is attracted to it. When brought near to the S pole of the magnet, Fig. 12B, the N pole of the compass is attracted. The compass provides the quickest possible check upon polarity of magnetic poles.

Magnetizing and Demagnetizing a Piece of Iron

A bar of iron may be magnetized by any method which causes atoms of the material to arrange themselves in such a way that the magnetic loops from electrons may assist one another. As previously mentioned, one of the earliest methods was to stroke the iron with a piece of lodestone. Magnetic lines from the lodestone helped atoms of iron to assume the desired positions. Mechanical friction alone sometimes produces this effect; but the most common way to magnetize an object is with the aid of an electric current. The next section, which tells about electromagnetism, will explain how this is accomplished.

A magnet can have its magnetic condition altered, so that it is no longer magnetic. When the magnetism is removed from an iron bar, it is said to be *demagnetized.* One of the simplest ways of demagnetizing an object is to heat it. If the heating is carried to even a moderately high value, the atoms of the material are caused to abandon the fixed positions into which they have grouped themselves, so that the loops no longer agree in direction.

Another way to demagnetize a magnet is to strike it repeatedly with a hammer. The mechanical vibration often has the same effect as heating. Another method is to employ an electric current in such a manner that magnetism established by the current opposes that in the magnet. When this is done, the atoms of the material swing from their positions just as in the case of heating or vibration.

Another important factor in the demagnetization of magnetized objects is time, for the natural tendency of atoms is to assume nonfixed positions. When a bar of iron is magnetized and the atoms are caused to arrange themselves in a certain definite pattern in order to maintain the magnetic condition of the material, they will remain in this pattern only so long as forced to do so. Those which are more loosely retained than others will tend to swing back to original positions. As more and more of them swing back, the total magnetism of the bar decreases. In time, even a permanent magnet will become demagnetized.

ELECTROMAGNETISM

Magnetic Effect of Current Flow

When free electrons pass along an electrical conductor, evidences of magnetism may be detected. Magnetism created by a flow of electric current is called *electromagnetism.* A magnet kept in a magnetic condition by the continuous flow of an electric current is called an *electromagnet.* Electromagnets are used in numerous pieces of electrical equipment.

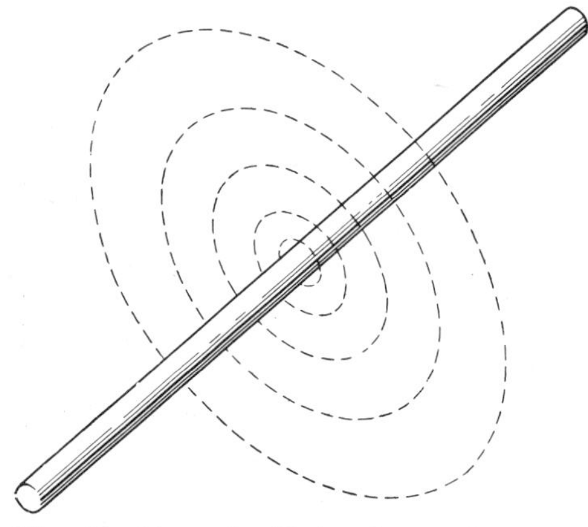

Fig. 13. Magnetic Circles Surrounding Conductor through which Current Is Flowing

Circles of Force about an Electrical Conductor. When current flows through an electrical conductor, magnetic lines of force are set up at right angles to the direction of current flow. During our examination of the lines of force in a bar magnet, Fig. 6, we observed that these lines had no beginning and no end. The magnetic lines set up by a current flow have the same property, for they are circular. For this reason, they are called *circles of force,* Fig. 13. This shape will be assumed whenever the entire path is through one kind of material. Air is a nonmagnetic substance, and all nonmagnetic substances offer the same degree of resistance to the passage of magnetic lines.

It should be noted that some of the circles are close to the surface of the conductor, while others are at a distance from it. The reason for this is much the same as the reason for the spreading of lines through air adjacent to the bar magnet. Each circle requires sufficient space in which to act, and, if it cannot find this space close to the conductor, it must expand until its space requirements are satisfied. This reveals another important characteristic of magnetic lines: these lines are extremely flexible—they may be stretched or expanded to immense proportions.

So long as current flows in the conductor, the circles of force surround it; but when the current ceases to flow, the circles collapse and the magnetism near the conductor disappears. This result follows from

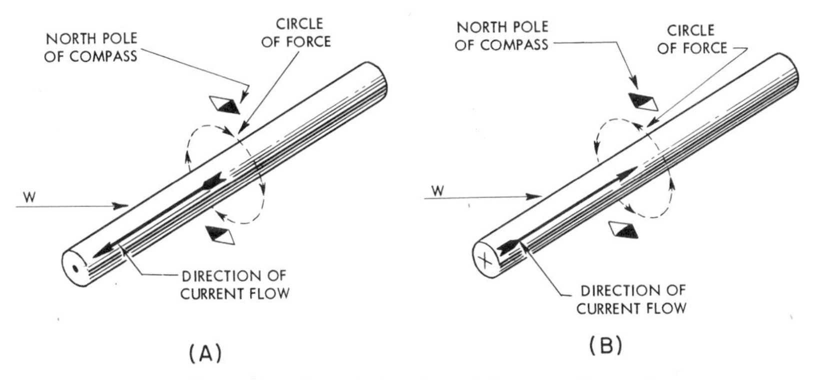

Fig. 14. Illustrating How Indication of Compass Depends upon Direction of Current Flow

the fact that the free electrons which made up the flow of electric current have become absorbed into the atomic structure of the material of the conductor.

Direction in which Circles of Force Act. It is now time to consider the direction in which circles of force act or travel around the conductor. A simple way to determine this direction is with a magnetic compass. But the compass acts because of a reason different from that noted in connection with the testing of magnetic poles in Fig. 12. There, the compass needle was moved by the attraction between unlike magnetic poles. Here, the reason for the movement of the compass needle may be explained somewhat differently.

If the compass needle, Fig. 14A, is held directly above the circle of force, the N pole of the needle will swing so that it points in the direction along which the circle of force moves. Since the compass needle is a small magnet, with lines of force traveling along its body from the S end to the N end inside the metal, it will turn until the direction of these lines or loops agrees with the direction of the circle of force. The direction of the circle of force at the top, where it touches the needle, is from left to right. The compass needle must swing around, then, until the direction of the magnetic lines within its body are from left to right, thus placing the N pole of the needle so that it points in the direction of the circle of force at that point.

Transferring the compass to the bottom of the circle of force, Fig. 14B, will result in a change in direction of the N end of the compass needle. This result is to be expected, for the N pole of the needle will now point in the direction of the force circle at this point, which is opposite from the direction at the top of the circle.

This illustration also introduces a new symbol, one to indicate direction of electron or current flow. The arrow shown here may be pictured as having a cone-shaped head which comes to a sharp point, and a tail with stabilizing fins whose cross-section is in the form of a cross. Viewed from the head end, the sharp point may be represented by a dot, and from the opposite end the tail may be represented by a cross. In Fig. 14A the dot at the end of the wire indicates that current is flowing out of it. In Fig. 14B, on the other hand, a cross on the end of the wire indicates that current is flowing into it.

Determining Direction of Current Flow in Electrical Conductor

Referring back to Fig. 14A, it will be seen that the direction of the force circle is clockwise and that the current is moving toward the observer. Investigations have led to the conclusion that this is the correct direction of activity of the circle of force. If the current were moving away from the observer, the circle of force would appear to act in a counterclockwise direction. In other words, when the direction of current changes, the motion of the circle of force also changes.

This fact makes it possible to determine the direction of current flow in a conductor with the aid of the magnetic compass. With the compass held above the conductor in which current is flowing, Fig. 14A, the N pole of the needle points to the right. The direction of the compass needle indicates that the circles of force which surround the conductor act in a clockwise direction. Since the circle is clockwise, the direction of the current flow in the conductor is toward the observer. If the compass is held bneath the conductor, the N pole of the needle will point to the left, which is the direction of a clockwise circle of force at that point. The same result is obtained, then, regardless of the place where the rest is made.

Should the compass test give the opposite indication, Fig. 14B, it would be evident that the direction of the circle of force was counterclockwise, and the current flow is away from the observer. Thus, it is possible to determine the direction of current flow in a conductor merely by a test with a magnetic compass.

The Left-Hand Rule. A method commonly used for determining the direction of the magnetic circles when the direction of current flow is known is shown in Fig. 15. If the conductor is grasped in the left

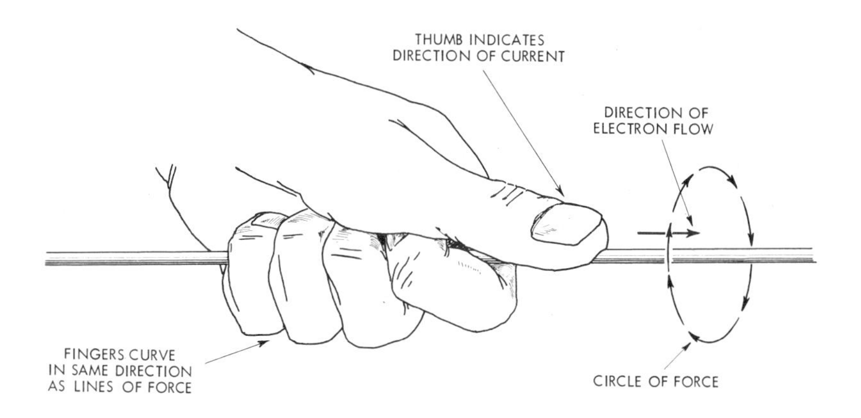

Fig. 15. Left-Hand Rule for Determining Direction of Magnetic Lines Set Up by Electron Flow in Conductor

hand, with the thumb pointing in the direction of the current, the fingers will wrap around the conductor in the same direction as that of the circles of force. If only the direction of the circles of force are known, the left hand may be wrapped around the conductor with the fingers in the direction of the circles of force, and the thumb will then indicate the direction of current flow. It is possible to recall the relationship between direction of current flow and direction of circle of force of Fig. 14, but it is sometimes quicker to call upon the left-hand rule.

Motion of Circles of Force. It has been suggested that the circle of force has direction. The statement might lead one to think that the circle of force was in continuous motion. Such is not the case, for although the circle of force has a tendency to act in a clockwise or a counterclockwise direction, the circle of force is stationary with regard to its source. In connection with electrical radiation, the circle of force is a form of energy, and energy is the ability to perform work. The energy represented by the circle of force tends to release itself in a certain direction, but it is not continuously revolving in that direction.

There is another motion of the circle of force that is of interest to us, however, and that is its motion radially, Fig. 16. When no current is flowing in the conductor, there are no circles of force surrounding it. Now we will cause a small amount of current to flow through the conductor, and we will have a circle of force at F_1. If we increase the current flow, the circle of force will increase in size until it occupies the position at F_2. A further increase in current flow will cause it to expand until it occupies the position at point F_3.

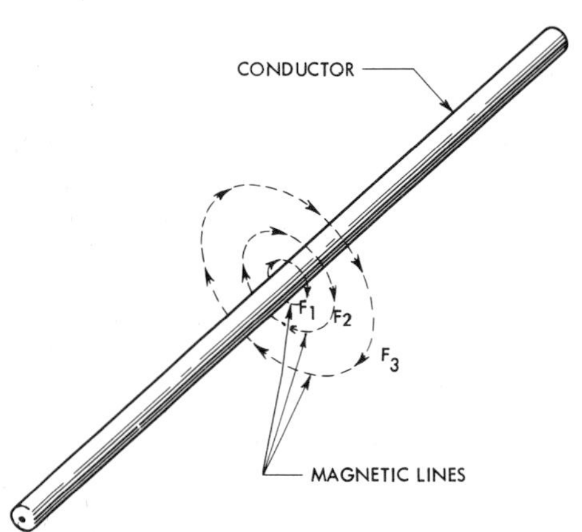

Fig. 16. Showing Expansion of Lines with Increase in Current Flow

As the original circle of force moves from F_1 to F_2 and F_3, new circles of force take up its place at F_1 and F_2. In other words, as the current increases, the number of circles of force increases, forcing the outer circles of force farther and farther from the surface of the conductor.

Should the current flow be stopped, as by opening a switch, these circles of force would quickly reduce in size until they no longer existed. This growth and reduction in the size of the circles of force are usually spoken of as the *expansion* and *collapse* of the lines of force. Expansion and collapse of the circle is a form of motion which will prove very important later on. It is to be noted, however, that this motion, too, differs from that of rotation.

Magnetic Effect of Current Flowing in Wire Loop

In Fig. 17 a loop of copper wire is bent to the indicated shape. The loop in Fig. 17A is connected to an electrical generator or other source of current so that current flows in the loop in a direction indicated by the large arrows. By carefully applying the left-hand rule so that the thumb points in the direction of current flow, it will be found that the fingers wrap around the wire so that they are on the inside of the loop at all times. In other words, the direction of the circles of force is such that they act always in a direction which is downward on the inside of the loop, Fig. 17A.

If a magnetic compass is brought toward the upper surface of the loop, holding it approximately in the center of the open space, the N pole of the needle will be attracted. Were the loop of wire a bar magnet, the needle would indicate that the upper surface was a S pole,

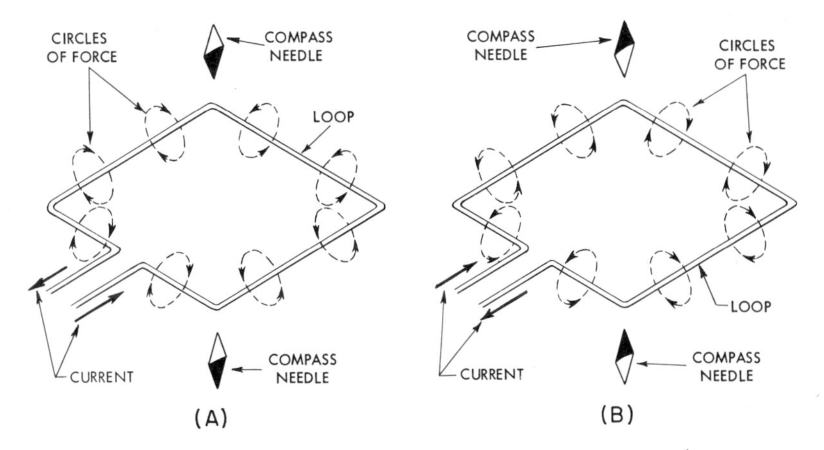

Fig. 17. Using Compass Needle To Show Magnetic Effect of Current Flow in Wire Loop

because of the attraction between unlike poles. Actually, the wire loop has become the equivalent of the bar magnet, the force of all the circles adding up to produce a S pole at the top.

When the compass is held near the center of the lower face of the loop, the S pole of the needle will be attracted, Fig. 17A, indicating that a N pole has been formed here. If the current flow is discontinued, the compass test will show that the loop possesses no magnetism whatsoever. The magnetic condition, then, was altogether a product of the flow of electric current. Such magnetism is called electromagnetism, and the wire loop represents a simple form of electromagnet.

Reversing Direction of Current Flow in Loop. Should the direction of current flow in the loop be reversed, Fig. 17B, the left-hand rule will show that the direction of the circles of force is upward in the interior of the loop; for if the thumb is pointed in the direction of current flow, the fingers will wrap around the wire so that they are upward inside the loop instead of downward as in the first case. The S pole of the compass needle is now attracted toward the upper face of the loop, showing that a N pole has been formed there. The N pole of the compass is attracted toward the lower face of the loop, thus indicating that a S pole has been formed there.

It would be well to take note of the relationships between direction of current flow and polarity of the wire loop. In Fig. 17A, where the direction of current flow in the loop is in a counterclockwise direction, a S pole is formed at the upper face of the loop. In Fig. 17B, where the direction of current flow at the upper face is clockwise, a N pole is formed here. If the loop of Fig. 17A is observed from below, so that one is looking at the lower face, the direction of current flow in the loop will be clockwise, and a N pole will be formed there. In the same way, observing the loop of Fig. 17B from the lower face shows the current circling the loop in a counterclockwise direction, and a S pole is formed there.

These relationships may be memorized. It is easier to concentrate upon memorizing only one of the two relationships, since one follows from the other. For this purpose, it may be remembered that a N pole forms at the upper surface of the loop when the current flows through it in a clockwise direction. Or, if it is noted that the observer is always in such position that he is gazing at that surface of the loop in front of which he has mentally placed himself, the question of whether it is the upper or the lower face of the loop is unimportant. Under this condition, an easily remembered rule may be stated: *clockwise direction of current forms a N pole.* Knowing this rule, it becomes a simple matter to tell at a glance the polarity of an electromagnet.

In everyday electrical applications, the simple electromagnet is met with infrequently. The strength of the magnetic poles formed by the loop of wire alone is rather weak for practical purposes. The air offers so high a resistance to the passage of magnetic lines that considerable strength of current flow is necessary to produce a noticeable effect.

Effect of Introducing Iron Core

The magnetizing effect of a wire loop may be greatly increased by the use of an iron centerpiece or core. Fig. 18A shows a wire loop which is formed around a rectangular central core of iron. Since the current in the loop flows in a clockwise direction, when viewed from the top surface, a N pole would be formed there if it were a plain loop. The introduction of the iron core does not alter this fact. A N pole will be formed at the upper face of the iron core, but the strength of the N pole thus formed is many times as great as it would be without the iron core.

The reason for the tremendous increase in magnetism depends upon two facts: First, the iron provides an easier path for the circles of force to travel in. Second, the magnetic circles induce the atoms of iron to assume positions which allow the magnetic forces of the iron particles to add together in much the same way as when a bar of unmagnetized iron was stroked with a piece of lodestone. Since the direction of the circles on the inside of the loop is upward, magnetic loops are caused to form in the iron in such direction that they agree with that of the circles of force. The effect is similar to that produced when the N pole of the compass needle is caused to point in the direction in which the circle of force acts.

When a number of loops of force have been formed in the iron core, they assist the circles of force in causing or inducing more loops to form, with the result that the number of magnetic loops is tremendously increased over those formed by the wire loop alone. In Fig. 18A the magnetic loops leaving the N pole and those entering the S pole are shown as lines rather than as complete loops. As mentioned before, it is often convenient to think of them as lines rather than as loops. Any factual error caused in this manner is more apparent than real, for in electrical apparatus, the return path from the N pole to the S pole is usually through iron instead of through air. At any point in the complete magnetic circuit, therefore, the magnetic loops are essentially lines of force. Hereafter, the phrase *lines of force* will be used.

Reversing Direction of Current Flow around Core. When the direction of current flow in the loop is reversed, as in Fig. 18B, the polarity of the iron core will be reversed in the same way that the polarity of the simple loop was reversed. Since the direction of activity of the magnetic circles of forces is downward inside the loop, atoms of iron will choose positions so that magnetic lines will tend to emerge from the lower face of the core and to enter the upper face. Thus, a N pole will be formed at the lower surface, and a S pole at the upper. Knowing the direction in which current in the loop is flowing when observed from one face or the other of the core, the polarity at the end is readily determined with the rule: *clockwise direction of current forms a N pole.*

Increasing Strength of Electromagnet. As noted before, the quantity of magnetism produced in a piece of iron depends upon the reluctance (magnetic resistance) of the iron and the strength of the magnetizing force. The easiest way to increase the magnetizing force is to increase the amount of current flowing in the loop. The unit of magnetic force which corresponds to the volt as a unit of electrical force, is the *ampere-turn.* By *turn* is meant a complete loop. In Fig. 18,

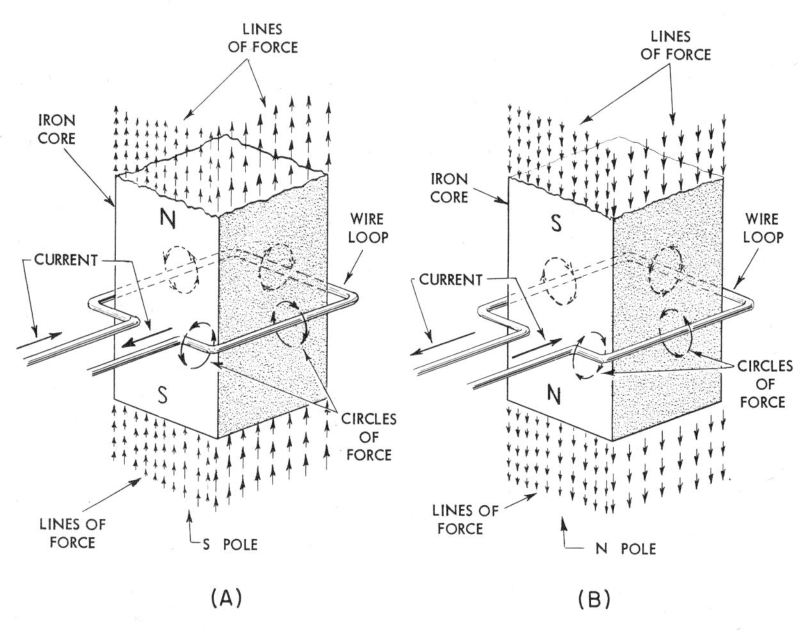

Fig. 18. Illustrating How Magnetic Effect Is Increased by Magnetic Forces of Iron Particles Adding to Circles of Loop

where the wire makes one complete loop around the iron core, the loop is said to consist of one turn. If 1 ampere of current flows in the loop, the magnetic force thereby established will be 1 ampere × 1 turn, or 1 ampere-turn. With 2 amperes flowing through the loop, there will be 2 × 1, or 2 ampere-turns. In the same way, 5 amperes will produce a force of 5 ampere-turns. With an increase in current strength, an increased number of magnetic circles are formed around the wire, and a greater number of magnetic lines are caused to form in the iron core.

The same result may be obtained by increasing the number of turns in the loop while the current remains at the original value. A loop, especially if it consists of more than a single turn, is usually termed a *coil.* Now, the coil which surrounds the iron core in Fig. 19 consists of 4 turns. When current flows in the coil, circles of force are caused to form along each of the 4 wires along any one side of the core so that 4 times as many circles of force will result as would be the case in a coil of 1 turn. The magnetic force or pressure for a current of 1 ampere would be 1 ampere × 4 turns, or 4 ampere-turns. The current of 1 ampere flowing through a coil of 4 turns produces the same quantity of magnetism as 4 amperes flowing through a coil of 1 turn. Eight times as much magnetism will be produced by a current of 2 amperes flowing through 4 turns as by a current of 1 ampere, and 20 times as much by a current of 5 amperes. Electromagnetic coils may have a great number of turns. They may have hundreds or thousands of turns.

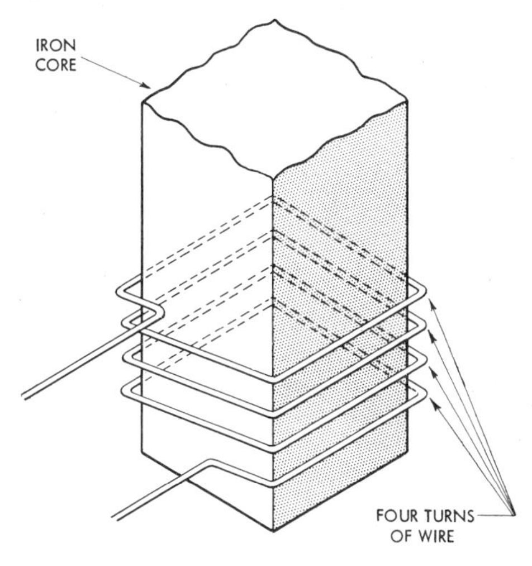

Fig. 19. Showing Iron Core with Four Turns of Wire. Strength of Electromagnet Is Determined by Number of Ampere-Turns

Other Factors which Determine Strength of Magnetism. The amount of magnetism established by a certain number of ampere-turns depends upon the reluctance of the magnetic path. Reluctance depends upon the length and the cross section of the magnetic path in much the same way as the strength of an electric current depends upon the length and cross-sectional area of the electrical conductor.

Reluctance is largely dependent upon the nature of the material which forms the core of the electromagnet. The core is usually made of some kind of iron, and the reluctance of any particular kind of iron depends upon its chemical composition. There are a great number of grades of iron, varying from soft to hard, the degree of softness or of hardness depending largely upon the amount of carbon which the iron possesses. Steel, of course, is a form of iron. The cores of electromagnets used in electrical apparatus are usually made of soft grades of steel which have very low magnetic reluctance. With these materials, a moderate value of current may establish a very high value of magnetism.

It might be well to mention at this point that a great number of magnetic lines considered together are spoken of as magnetic *flux*. A single line might be spoken of as a line of force, but when the magnetism issuing from the face of a magnetic core is considered as a whole it is called magnetic flux. Thus, one may say that the magnetic flux established by a coil surrounding an iron core is much greater than the flux established by the coil when the iron core has been removed. Hereafter, the quantity of flux will be spoken of, rather than the amount of magnetism.

REVIEW QUESTIONS

1. What is a line of force?
2. What causes magnetic attraction and repulsion between poles of two magnets?
3. State the Weber-Ewing theory of magnetism.
4. Describe the process of magnetic induction.
5. Why do lines of force of a bar magnet bulge out in returning from the N pole to the S pole?
6. How would you test the polarities of a magnetized bar with a magnetic compass?
7. Discuss permanence of the magnetic condition.
8. What is the path of a line of force?
9. How do circles of force build up around an electrical conductor?
10. What happens to circles of force when current ceases to flow?
11. Discuss possible movement of the circle of force.
12. Explain the left-hand rule.
13. Describe the formation of poles in a simple electromagnet.
14. How does the introduction of an iron core increase the flux of the electromagnet?
15. An electromagnetic core is surrounded by two coils. One, consisting of 100 turns of wire, carries a current of 1 amp which flows in a clockwise direction. The other, consisting of 75 turns of wire, carries a current of 2 amps in a counterclockwise direction. What is the value of the magnetic force?

CHAPTER 6
SIMPLE ELECTRICAL GENERATORS

STATIC GENERATORS

Simple Static Generator

The simplest method of generating static electricity is to make some bodily movement with regard to surrounding objects. Raising one's hand from a paper which lies upon a desk removes electrons from the surface of the paper, leaving a small positive charge upon the paper and an excess of negative electrons, or a negative charge, upon the surface of the hand. A much greater effect is produced by walking across the room. Friction of shoe soles upon a carpet causes considerable displacement of electrons. After drawing a rubber comb through the hair a few times, especially in a very dry climate, the comb may become so highly charged that the hair will be caused to rise merely by bringing the comb near to it. Thus, one may generate some static electricity by almost any kind of physical movement which involves contact with surrounding objects. In all these cases, it should be noted the static charge is brought about through friction between adjacent surfaces.

Frictional Generator

Friction is used to produce static electricity in the machine illustrated in Fig. 1. Basically, the machine consists of a glass disk which

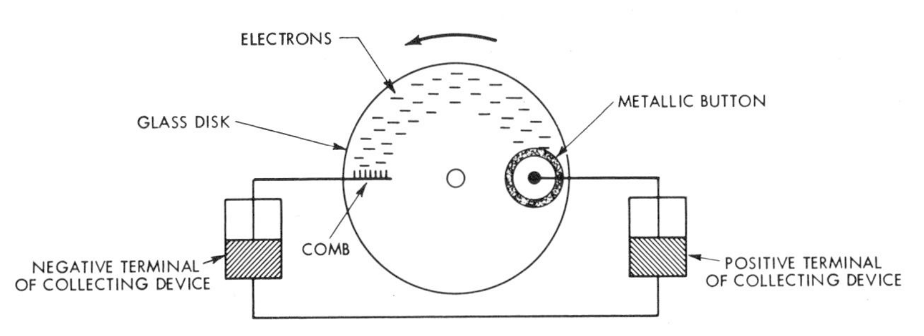

Fig. 1. Frictional Static Generator

turns upon a shaft, a metallic button, which is faced with leather on the surface and is in contact with the glass disk, and one collecting brush. The brush is a metallic comb which is touching the glass disk at one end and leading to the negative (−) terminal of the collecting device at the other. The button is connected to the positive (+) terminal of this collecting device, which is termed a *capacitor,* or *condenser,* will be discussed later.

In operation, the glass disk is forced to turn upon its shaft against the friction of the leather on the button. Friction between glass and leather causes electrons to be rubbed off the leather and to be deposited upon the glass. As the disk continues to turn, the charged area on its surface comes into contact with the brush, and the excess electrons are transferred to the collecting device, giving an increased negative charge to this half of the device. Meanwhile, the leather absorbs

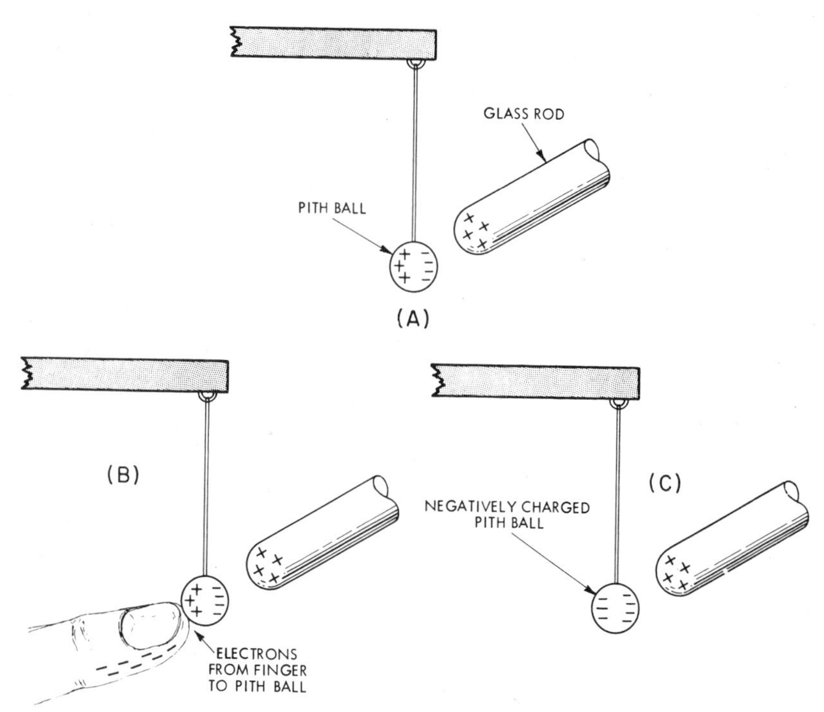

Fig. 2. Static Induction

electrons from the metallic button to replace those rubbed off onto the glass disk. However, the button can supply these electrons only by drawing them from the positive terminal of the collecting-device, to which it is attached. In doing so, the positive terminal of the device acquires a higher positive charge, since its shortage of electrons is made more severe. Thus, the static charge on the collecting device builds up to a higher and higher value as the machine continues to operate.

Static Induction

Other static generators operate upon the principle of *static induction.* One object is said to induce a charge in another object when it causes such a charge to exist without making direct contact with the other object. Fig. 2 will help explain the process.

When the positively charged glass rod is brought near to the neutral pith ball, Fig. 2A, some negatively charged electrons are attracted to that side of the ball nearest the rod, while positively charged atoms remain as far from it as possible. If the finger is now touched to that side of the ball, Fig. 2B, negative electrons from the finger neutralize the positive charge on that side of the ball, giving it an excess of electrons. If the finger is now removed, the ball will be left with a negative charge, Fig. 2C.

Influence Machines. Static generators which make use of the principle of static induction are called *influence machines.* One of the simplest of these is the *electrophorus.* It is composed of but two parts, Fig. 3A: a stationary circular member which is made of hard rubber

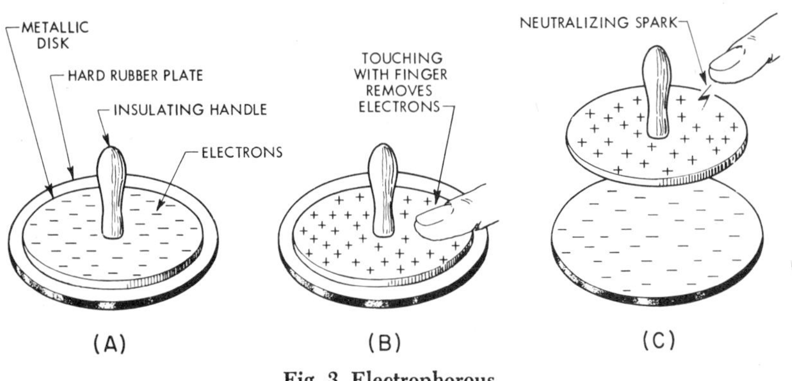

Fig. 3. Electrophorous

or of some resinous material—such as bakelite—and a metallic disk, whose insulated handle permits it to be placed upon and to be removed from the stationary disk.

The rubber disk is given a frictional negative charge by rubbing it vigorously with wool or similar material. Then the metallic disk is set down upon it. Actually, the metal of the disk touches the rubber in very few spots. These spots will become neutralized by contact with the disk which supplies sufficient positive charge to absorb electrons actually in contact with it. But the greater part of the disk will be at a slight distance from the lower member. The negative charge on the rubber plate will attract positively charged atoms to the lower face of the metallic disk and will repel excess electrons to the upper face. Touching the upper face of this disk removes the excess electrons and it will be left with a strong positive charge, Fig. 3B.

When the handle is raised, Fig. 3C, and the finger brought near the disk, a spark may be drawn between the finger and the metal as electrons are attracted through the air to neutralize the positive charge upon the disk. Here, the finger removed the excess electrons as shown, Fig. 3B. Now, when the finger is brought near to the disk, Fig. 3C, it supplies electrons to neutralize a positive charge. The reason the finger may perform both tasks was explained in the first chapter, where it was pointed out that the surface of the earth is a huge storehouse of free electrons. The finger, being attached to a body which is always in contact with the earth, serves as a transfer agent, taking off an excess of electrons in one case, and furnishing sufficient electrons to make up for a deficiency in another.

The experiment with the electrophorus may be repeated a great many times before it must again be charged. Many rotating influence machines make use of the principle of the electrophorus.

Van de Graaff Static Generator

A static machine widely used today is the Van de Graaff generator, Fig. 4. It employs a different principle than that of either the friction or the influence type. There is a hollow insulating column held in position by a supporting base and covered with a metal dome. Within the base is a high-voltage device which supplies a continuous stream of electrons to a metallic comb. It is placed a short distance from the belt which moves, in the direction of the arrows, around two pulleys. Within the dome is the negative transfer unit, which carries electrons from the moving belt to the inner surface of the dome. There are air spaces separating the unit from both dome and the belt. Another transfer unit is fastened to the dome directly above the upper pulley, its lower end approaching quite close to the belt.

In operation, the lower pulley is driven at high speed by an electric motor. The device in the base supplies electrons to the comb. These electrons are repelled continuously from the pointed tips of the comb onto the surface of the belt, which carries them upward toward the negative transfer rod. Here, electrons pass from the belt onto the rod, and are repelled onto the inner surface of the dome. Repulsion between like charges causes the negatively charged electrons

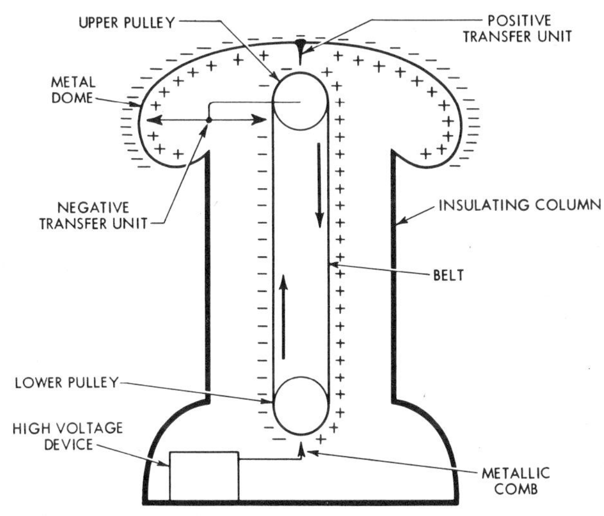

Fig. 4. Van de Graaff Static Generator

to collect upon the outer surface of the dome and to build up a heavy charge there. Since a strong negative charge is built up on the outer surface of the dome by electrostatic repulsion, a positive charge tends to build up on the inner surface. The positive transfer rod fastened to this inner surface, becomes charged. Since it is very close to the belt, it absorbs electrons from it so that the belt will be positively charged as it passes. When the belt reaches the bottom pulley, the positive charge on its surface is neutralized, and an excess of electrons is supplied by the comb.

Extremely high voltages are built up by this machine for use in special X-ray machines and for experimental work in atomic research operations. It should be noted that the dome may be made to take a positive charge rather than a negative one, if so desired.

Removing Static Charges From Belts. Static electricity is sometimes generated unintentionally and its presence can be highly undesirable since it may cause severe electrical damage or even prove hazardous to human life. Perhaps the most common source of trouble is from static created by friction between belts and pulleys. Fig. 5A shows a motor driving its load by means of a belt and two pulleys. Friction between the surface of the belt and the surfaces of the pulleys, friction between particles of the material of which the belt is composed, and even friction between the belt and the surrounding air, builds up a charge upon the surface of the belt as indicated in the figure.

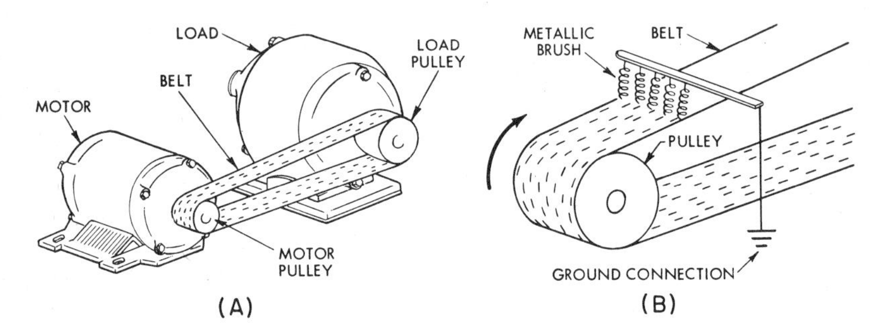

Fig. 5. Removing Static Charges from Belt

When the static charge attains a high value, it will find some means of neutralizing itself, perhaps by jumping through the air in the form of a spark. In doing so, it selects the easiest available path. If this path happens to include the motor windings, the spark may rupture the insulation, causing an expensive breakdown.

Such trouble is often avoided by arranging a metallic brush to remove the charge from the belt as it is formed. Fig. 5B shows how this is accomplished. The brush is placed near the belt, and it carries off excess electrons to the earth. The brush may be in the form of a comb with sharp teeth, which project close to the surface of the belt, or it may have short, flexible springs, the springs making direct contact with the belt. Connection to the earth is called a *ground connection* or, more simply, a *ground.* The belt is said to be *grounded.*

Other Static Hazards. Static electricity often causes fires or explosions in grain elevators. Friction between grain and metal chutes builds up a negative charge upon the grain and a positive charge upon the metal. When the charge becomes sufficiently great, a spark from a mass of grain to a piece of metal may cause fire or explosion. The remedy here, of course, is to make sure that metal objects are well grounded.

In paper mills and in printing establishments, static charges on the surface of the paper may cause sheets to stick together. Sometimes this condition results in great expense. It is often counteracted by air-conditioning the plant to keep the air moist. When moist, air is a better conductor than when dry. Static charge can neutralize itself by passing through moist air directly to the earth. Where this method is impractical or ineffective, the paper is caused to pass over combs or brushes which are connected to a negative or a positive source of supply similar to that used in the Van de Graaff generator. Discharge from the brushes neutralizes any charge upon the paper.

Serious, and often fatal, explosions have occurred in hospital operating rooms because of static discharge. Static built up by friction of rubber-soled shoes with the floor, or by friction of the anaesthetic with nozzles or hoses, was the principal source of this trouble. A static spark near explosive gas sometimes injured the attendants or even killed the patient. Grounding, here, did not provide complete protection because the problem was so complicated. Today, however, the difficulty has been solved with the aid of conducting rubber. Ordinary rubber is an insulator which allows static charges to build up on it or through its use. Conducting rubber is a form of rubber which is a sufficiently good conductor that static charges pass to ground before they can become sufficiently concentrated to cause a spark.

Fires in gasoline filling stations sometimes result from static sparks. Rubber automobile tires, speeding over asphalt pavements, acquire a strong negative charge, which is transferred to the body of the car. A spark between the body of the car and the metal nozzle of the gasoline hose may occur if the charge on the car is not removed before the hose is inserted into the gas tank. The charge is usually removed, however,

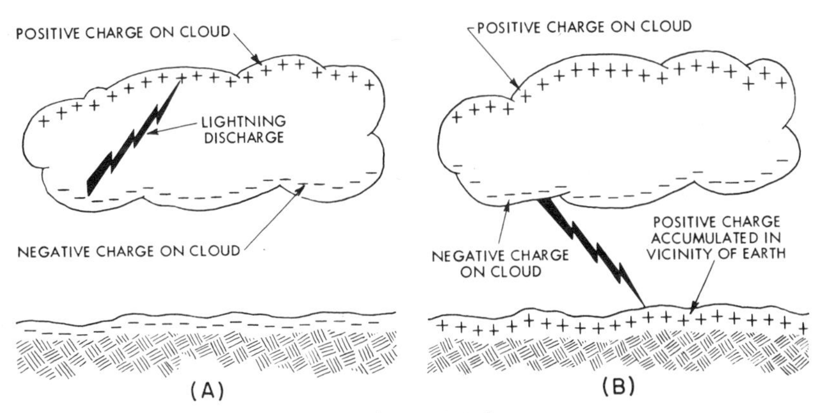

Fig. 6. Lightning Discharges

by touching the nozzle to the metal of the car, the electrons being carried off by a grounding wire embedded in the fabric of the hose.

Lightning. One of the most common static hazards is not man-made. Lightning, in some areas, is decidedly hazardous to property and life. Fig. 6 will help explain its nature. Fig. 6A shows a storm cloud passing above the earth. This cloud has a negative charge on the upper surface and a positive charge on the lower surface. Different theories explain how these charges accumulate, but they are beyond the scope of this book. Therefore, we will say that under certain conditions the charges are collected in this manner. When the charges are arranged in this way, the accumulation continues until there is sufficient voltage to cause a heavy flow of electrons from the negative to the positive side of the cloud through the misty interior. This flow of current may amount to a million amperes for a fraction of a second, and the intense spark makes the flash which is known as lightning.

Under other conditions, however, the charges are collected as shown in Fig. 6B. Investigations have indicated that when the charges have this arrangement the lightning is more apt to travel between the

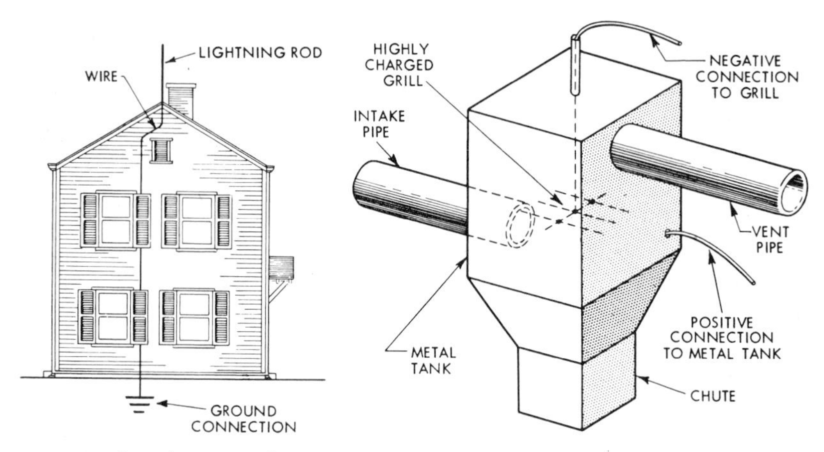

Fig. 7. Lightning Rod **Fig. 8. Dust Precipitator**

earth and the cloud than between the two oppositely charged surfaces of the cloud. This very heavy flow through the air develops intense heat and heats the air through which it travels. The heated air expands rapidly and moves away. Cold air rushes in to take its place, and they meet with the resounding crash known as thunder.

When a lightning discharge takes place between a cloud and earth, or something on it, considerable damage can result from the intense heat. The discharge generally strikes the highest object in the vicinity in which the cloud and the earth have built up pressure.

Structures are sometimes protected by means of *lightning rods.* A lightning rod is a sharp-pointed metal rod which projects above the highest point of a structure. Fig. 7 shows a rod fastened to the peak of a gable roof. The rod is connected to a heavy wire which follows along the roof and down the side of the house to the ground. The wire should make a connection between the rod and ground as nearly vertical as possible. It was once supposed that the rod sent electrons from the earth to neutralize the cloud. Investigation has disproved this. All the rod does is provide an easy path for the high momentary current which results when lightning strikes near by. If the rod were not present, the lightning would strike the gable and damage the house.

Dust Precipitator

Before leaving the subject of static electricity, we will examine one case where static charges are used to great advantage. Many large manufacturing plants create a great deal of dust as a waste product. The dust sometimes accumulates upon the surface of the country for miles around, ruining farm lands and damaging the appearance of the landscape. Costly lawsuits sometimes result from this matter, and communities have passed laws to combat the nuisance. Cement plants, and others of a similar nature, have managed to cure the ailment with the aid of *dust precipitators.*

A precipitator, such as in Fig. 8, is inserted in the stack which carries off fumes from the plant. The gas enters the lower part of the metal tank through the intake pipe and discharges into the atmosphere through the vent pipe. The gas rises through a grill which is attached to a source of negative charges by means of an insulated wire. As the dust particles rise, they become negatively charged through contact with, or nearness to, the grill. The positive connection from the static generator is attached to the shell of the tank. The negatively charged particles of dust are attracted to the positively charged walls and cling there while the clean gas or air passes out through the vent pipe. When the particles of dust have built up a thick layer upon the walls, the weight of the mass becomes greater than the attractive force, and the thick lumps drop through the chute for disposal.

PRIMARY CELLS

Elementary Voltaic Cell

The invention of the voltaic cell really started man along the road to electrical knowledge. The term *voltaic* was obtained from the name of the Italian scientist, Alessandro Volta, who first devised a successful *cell* of this type. Basically, a voltaic cell consists of two dissimilar metals which are immersed in a chemical solution called an *electrolyte*. Fig. 9 represents such a cell.

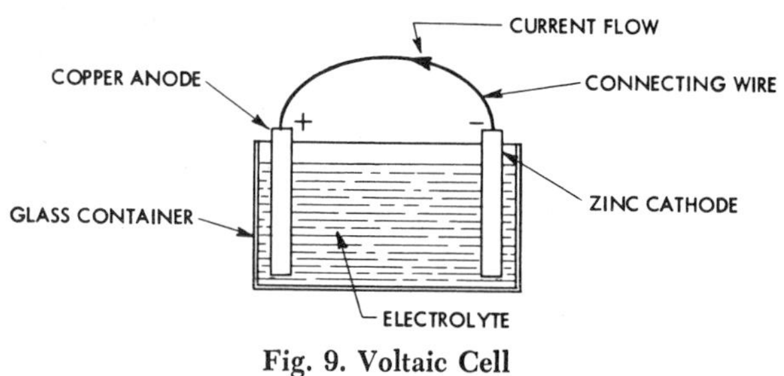

Fig. 9. Voltaic Cell

A glass container holds a quantity of electrolyte, in this case sulfuric acid diluted with water. Sulfuric acid is made up of sulfur, hydrogen, and oxygen and is chemically indicated as H_2SO_4. The positive (+) element of the cell is made of copper and is called the *anode*. The negative (−) element is of zinc and is called the *cathode*. When a circuit is connected across the elements or plates, a current will flow.

Principles of the Elementary Cell

The electrolyte removes electrons from the positive plate and deposits electrons on the negative plate throughout the whole time the cell is functioning. It is believed that the acid breaks up chemically into two kinds of atomic particles, or *ions* as they are called, one of them being positively charged, the other negatively.

The electrolyte starts working on the plates as soon as the two metals are placed in the solution, and a certain amount of action takes place. But it ceases shortly, and nothing more happens until a wire is connected from one electrode to the other as shown in the figure. At this time, negative charges on the zinc plate repel electrons into the wire, and these free electrons pass along the conductor because of attractive forces on the copper plate, which is in need of electrons. Meanwhile, particles of the electrolyte become activated again, removing electrons from the positive plate and depositing electrons on the negative plate.

Although it presents an over-simplified picture of actual processes, one may look upon the operation as a transfer of electrons from the positive plate directly to the negative plate inside the cell, and a transfer of electrons from the negative plate to the positive plate by way of the external conductor. We have considered the activity of but a single molecule of sulfuric acid, but there is actually an enormous quantity of molecules taking part in this activity.

Operating Features of the Elementary Cell. The voltage or pressure of this simple cell is approximately 1 volt. This voltage may not be raised by increasing the size of the plates or the amount of electrolyte. Voltaic cells may be made with metals other than copper and zinc. Some of these will form pairs which have a higher voltage than copper and zinc, while others will form pairs having a lower voltage. In any case, the voltage established by any pair is a fixed quantity, for it appears that any two metals create only a certain total amount of electrical force, and this total force is the electromotive force of the cell.

Internal Resistance

The current in a circuit depends upon the total resistance in the circuit as was mentioned in our study of Ohm's law. This total resistance, however, can be divided into two parts: the internal resistance and the external resistance. The internal resistance is that resistance which is within the cell. Ions encounter opposition to movement through the electrolyte as do electrons in their passage through a conductor or resistor.

After the cell has operated for a time, its internal resistance increases considerably because of the bubbles of hydrogen gas that collect upon the copper plate. These bubbles prevent the electrolyte from making contact with the anode and, consequently, stop the transfer of electrons from the anode to the hydrogen ions. This action is known as *polarization.* Polarization may be counteracted, as will be seen later, by the use of chemical substances which absorb the hydrogen bubbles.

Another important feature in the operation of the voltaic cell is the fact that the zinc plate gradually dissolves into the electrolyte as the cell is used and must, therefore, be renewed periodically. The copper plate remains altogether unaffected during operation of the cell.

The external resistance of the circuit is that resistance which is connected across the terminals of the cell. Lamps, heaters, and the like usually make up the external resistance of a circuit.

Fig. 10A represents a circuit consisting of a cell and a small lamp. The lamp and the conducting wires make up the total external resistance. A cell is represented in a schematic diagram with one short line

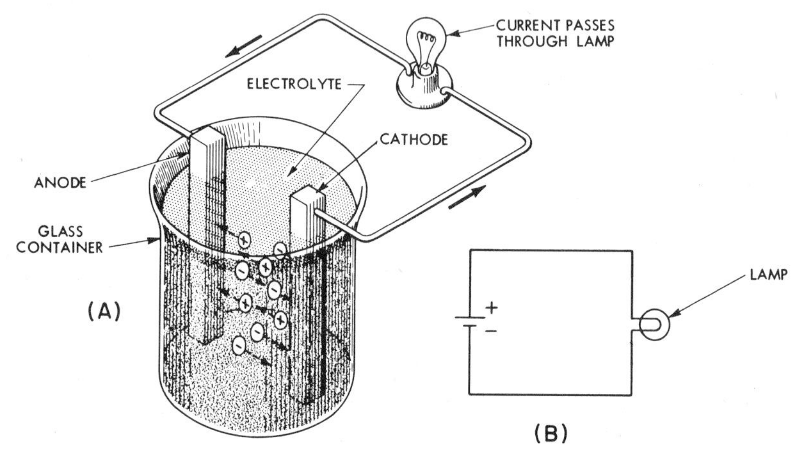

Fig. 10. Lamp Connected to Voltaic Cell

and one long line drawn parallel, as shown to the right. The long line is always the positive terminal, and the short line is the negative terminal. These terminals are also called *plates*. Drawn in schematic form, the circuit of Fig. 10A will be indicated as in Fig. 10B.

The Gravity Cell

A commercially successful cell in which copper and zinc are used for plates, or *electrodes*, is the *gravity cell*. Fig. 11 illustrates the general construction of the unit. The glass contains an electrolyte which is made of three chemical substances: zinc sulfate, copper sulfate, and sulfuric acid. It also contains two electrodes; the zinc one is placed in the upper portion of the cell, being in the form of a crow's-foot, while the copper one in the bottom of the cell is of ribbed construction.

The cell receives its name from the fact that, when copper sulfate is poured into the bottom portion of the cell and zinc sulfate is poured on top of it, gravity keeps the liquids apart. Since copper sulfate is heavier, it remains in the bottom of the cell and the zinc sulfate floats on top of it. Although the zinc sulfate solution assists greatly in operation of the unit, the really important element is the sulfuric acid, just as it is in the operation of an elementary voltaic cell. The copper sulfate acts as a depolarizer; that is, it absorbs the hydrogen bubbles which collect on

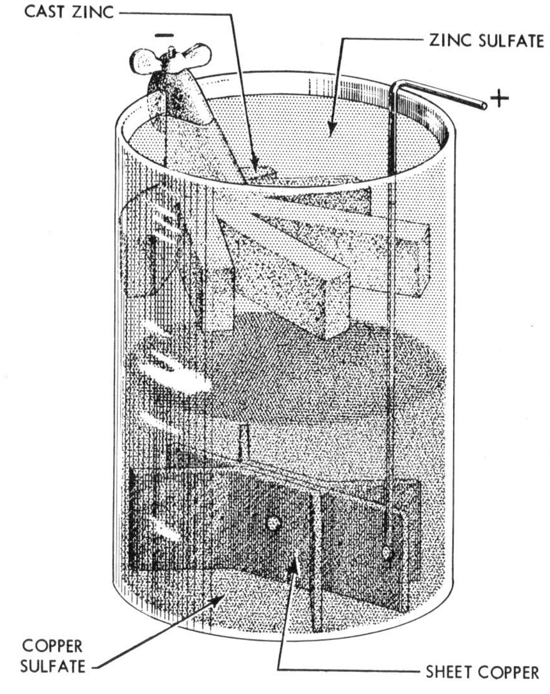

Fig. 11. Gravity Cell

the copper electrode and prevents the electrolyte from coming in contact with it. This, as we have noted, was called polarization. The copper sulfate depolarizer, therefore, tends to prevent polarization.

The Leclanché Cell

Although the gravity cell has been widely used in certain fields, especially that of telegraphy, a cell that has proved of far greater commercial importance is the *Leclanché* cell, Fig. 12. In this unit the positive electrode is made of carbon, while the negative is of zinc. The electrolyte is a solution of water and ammonium chloride. This cell creates a pressure of approximately 1.5 v. In operation, hydrogen bubbles collect upon the carbon electrode, causing polarization unless steps are taken to prevent it. It is customary to employ a substance called manganese dioxide. In Fig. 12 there is a porous cup containing a quantity of manganese dioxide, which prevents the electrolyte from depositing hydrogen bubbles upon the surface of the electrode.

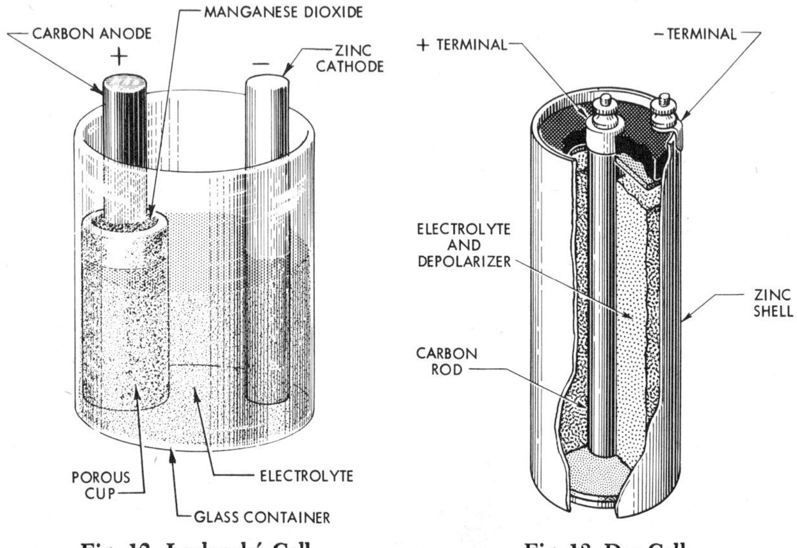

Fig. 12. Leclanché Cell

Fig. 13. Dry Cell

The Dry Cell

The Leclanché cell provided the basis for the modern *dry cell* which has such a vast field of application. Actually, the dry cell is not dry; but when the top of the cell has been sealed with compound, and a cardboard cover has been placed over the outer surface, it appears so. One of these cells is shown in Fig. 13. The positive carbon electrode is placed in the middle of the unit, and the negative zinc electrods forms the outer shell of the cylindrical container. Inside the zinc sheath, a layer of cardboard is soaked with ammonium chloride paste which serves as the electrolyte. Between the carbon rod and the cardboard is a mass of soft material composed of manganese dioxide, the depolarizing agent, and a mixture of ammonium chloride and zinc chloride solution. A terminal lug is fastened to the carbon rod, forming the positive (+) connection, and another is fastened to the zinc shell to form the negative (−) connection of the cell.

The voltage of the unit is the same as that of the Leclanché wet cell, or 1.5 v. Dry cells are useful for applications where small amounts of current are required for short periods of time. Where they are required to give even a small amount of current continuously, their useful life is shortened.

In operation, the depolarizing agent gradually loses its effectiveness through absorption of hydrogen gas, and the liquid materials eventually dry out. Both of these occurrences have the effect of increasing internal resistance of the cell and thus lowering its useful output. The processes of deterioration are speeded up by heating. If the cell is required, therefore, to carry a great deal of current, or if it is kept in use for long periods of time, the heat thus generated will greatly shorten the life of the cell.

CELLS AND BATTERIES

Combinations of Cells

A single unit is properly called a cell, while a group of cells connected in one way or another is properly called a *battery*. The term battery, however, is often applied to a single unit as well. Many applications call for a voltage greater than that of a single cell. To meet these different needs, a group of cells is employed, and the method of arranging the cells depends upon the needs.

Series Combinations of Cells. When a higher voltage is required than is afforded by a single cell, the cells are connected as in Fig. 14A.

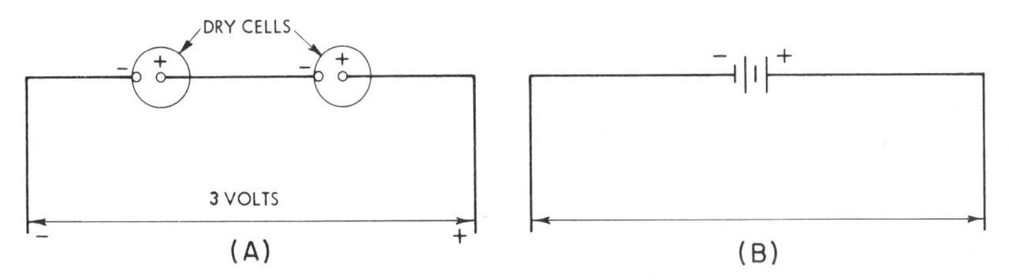

Fig. 14. Series Combination of Two Cells

The zinc terminal of one cell is connected to a circuit wire. The carbon terminal of this cell is connected to the zinc terminal of the other cell. And the carbon terminal of the second cell is connected to the other circuit wire. When connected in this manner, the cells form a battery whose voltage is 3 v instead of 1.5 v. Fig. 14B illustrates the manner of indicating these cells in a schematic drawing.

If a pressure of 6 v is required, four cells may be connected as in

Fig. 15A. This connection would be indicated in schematic diagram as shown in Fig. 15B.

This method of connecting cells is termed a *series connection*. Keeping in mind the fact that the zinc terminal is negative and the carbon positive, it becomes an easy matter to connect a number of cells in series

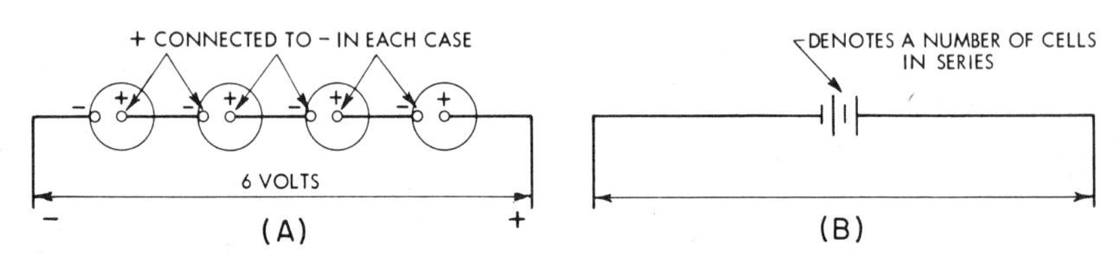

Fig. 15. Series Combination of Four Cells

to provide any desired voltage. All that is required is that the positive (+) terminal of one cell be connected to the negative (–) terminal of the next, and that the positive (+) terminal of the second be connected to the negative (–) terminal of the third, this process being carried on until the desired number of cells are connected together. The two end terminals remaining, that is the negative (–) terminal of the first cell, and the positive (+) terminal of the last, become the battery terminals which connect to the circuit which is supplied.

Parallel Combination of Cells. Fig. 16A illustrates another method of connecting cells. If 1.5 v is sufficient pressure, but it is desired to

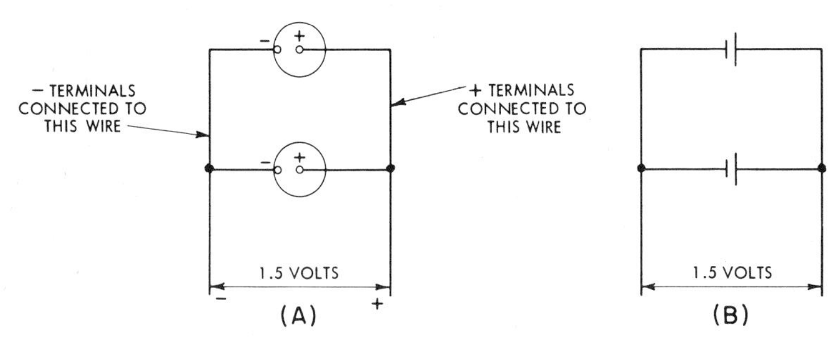

Fig. 16. Two Cells Connected in Parallel

reduce the current drain upon the unit, so that its life will not be unduly shortened, a second one may be connected with it as shown, the negative terminals being connected to one circuit wire, the positive terminals to the other. The current taken from each cell will be only one-half that which flows in the circuit wires. Fig. 16B is the schematic representation of this connection.

If the drain on each cell is to be reduced still further, any number of cells may be connected in the same way. This arrangement, is termed a *parallel connection.*

Other Types of Voltaic Cells

There are numerous other types of voltaic cells, many built to suit a particular type of service. In most, the voltage is somewhat lower than that obtained with the Leclanché type of cell. Regardless of the kind of electrodes or electrolyte used, the principle of operation is identical with those described here.

SECONDARY CELLS

Principle of the Storage Cell

In principle, the storage cell is exactly the same as the voltaic cell. The storage cell uses electrodes (plates of different materials) and an electrolyte which carries electrons from the positive plate to the negative plate. The essential difference between the two types of cell is found in the electrodes. The positive (+) copper electrode of the voltaic cell remains copper so long as the cell exists, and the negative (−) zinc electrode remains zinc, although it must be replaced from time to time as it dissolves.

But, in the storage cell, the positive (+) electrode changes into a somewhat different metal as it discharges, and the negative (−) plate also changes its nature. When the cell has become discharged, its plates may be restored to their original condition by a current sent through the cell in the direction opposite to that of the discharge current. This process is called *charging* the cell. There are, in general, two types of storage cell: the *lead-acid cell* and the *nickel-iron-alkaline cell.* The first type is simply designated as a lead cell, but the second is often called an *Edison cell* because of its inventor.

The Lead-Acid Cell

The lead cell employs sulfuric acid as the electrolyte and electrodes which are made of a lead compound. When the storage cell is in a charged state, the positive electrode is of lead peroxide, while the negative electrode is of pure lead.

Lead Cell on Discharge. When the cell is connected to a load, current flows through the circuit, and chemical changes take place in the cell as shown in Fig. 17. The positive electrode, which was originally composed of lead peroxide (PbO_2), is changed into lead sulfate ($PbSO_4$). The negative electrode, on the other hand, changes from pure lead (Pb) to lead sulfate. And the electrolyte is gradually transformed from sulfuric acid (H_2SO_4) into water (H_2O). In this process the negative electrode gives up electrons and the positive electrode absorbs electrons.

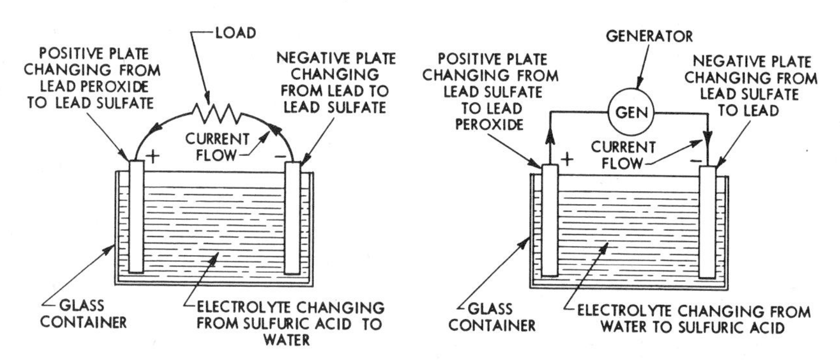

Fig. 17. Lead Cell During Discharge

Fig. 18. Lead Cell During Charge

Charging the Lead Cell. The discharged cell has been connected to a generator in Fig. 18. It will be noted that current now flows through the circuit in the direction opposite to that during discharge. Current from the generator flows to the negative plate through the liquid of the electrolyte to the positive plate, and thence to the positive terminal of the generator.

As current flows through the cell, chemical changes again take place. This process is the reverse of that taking place during discharge. Electrons are forced onto the negative plate by the generator, and electrons are removed from the positive electrode. In this process, the negative plate is changed from lead sulfate ($PbSO_4$) back to pure lead (Pb). At the same time, the positive plate is being changed from lead sulfate ($PbSO_4$) to lead peroxide (PbO_2), and the electrolyte is returning to its originally acidic state (H_2SO_4).

Commercial Lead Cell. The commercial lead cell has a number of positive plates and a number of negative plates, Fig. 19. They are arranged in two groups, with positive and negative plates quite close to one another. The placement in the cells is such that a negative plate lies on either side of each positive plate, the two sets being prevented from touching by means of thin wooden or hard rubber sheets called separators. There is one more negative than positive plate. The reason for

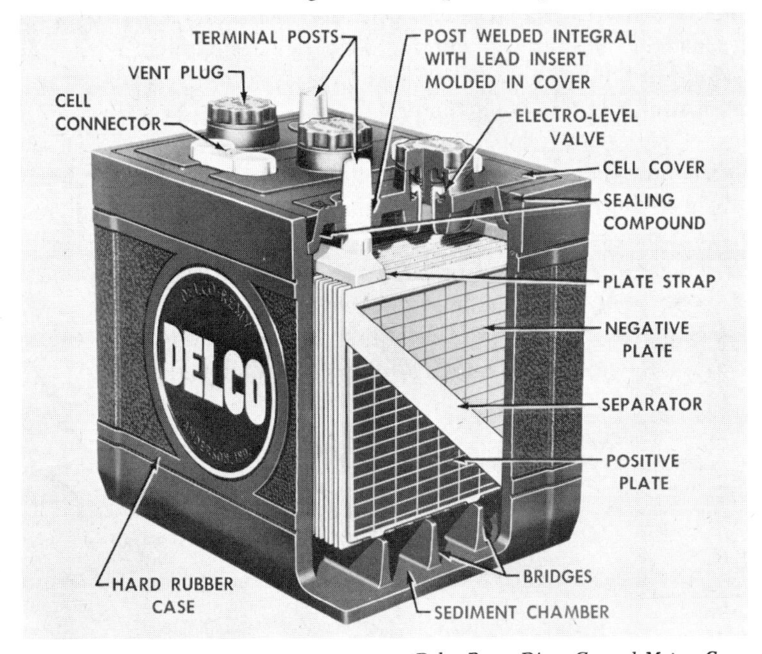

Delco-Remy Div.—General Motors Corp.

Fig. 19. Construction of a Storage Battery

this is that only one side of an end positive plate would be used if there were the same number of plates in each set. The positive plates are more costly than the negative, and they are usually thicker. Therefore, it is cheaper to use an additional negative plate rather than to sacrifice one-half of a positive plate.

In one form, the surfaces of both positive and negative plates are ridged with a special tool in order to give more exposed surface for the electrolyte to work upon. Other cells use this type of negative plate but employ a positive unit which has ribbons of lead set into holes in a metallic grid. The automobile battery makes use of a grid type of plate in which the spaces are filled with a soft lead paste, which is somewhat porous. The goal of all these types of construction is to obtain the greatest amount of working area for the electrolyte.

After a certain amount of operation, material which peels off the plates gathers in the bottom of the cell as sediment, to such a depth that it forms a connection between positive and negative plates. For this reason, the plate assembly is elevated from the bottom. The enclosing cases for stationary commercial cells are made of glass; for portable cells, such as those used in automobiles, they are made of hard rubber.

Operating Facts about the Lead Cell. The voltage of the lead cell is approximately 2 v, being slightly greater than this value when fully charged, and slightly less when discharged. The state of charge of the cell is not judged, however, by its voltage, for this is not a good indicator. The best method is to check the density of the electrolyte. By *density* is meant the weight of the liquid as compared to the weight of an equal volume of water. For as the electrolyte gives up its sulfate content to the plates of the cell on discharge, it decreases in density. But it is not necessary to weigh the liquid in order to determine this fact. Instead, a device known as a *hydrometer* is employed.

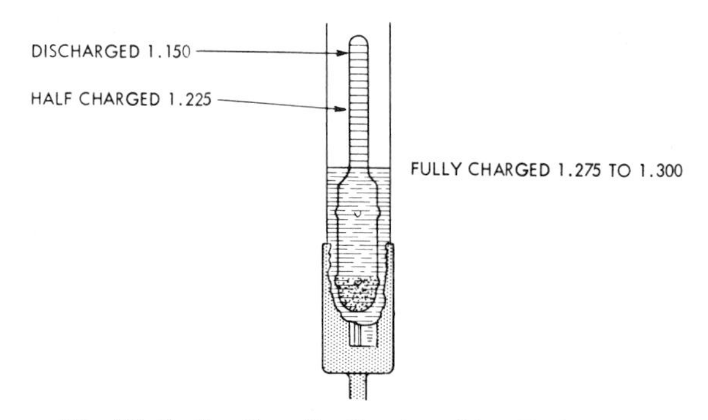

Fig. 20. Testing Specific Gravity with a Hydrometer

Fig. 20 represents a hydrometer. It consists of an air-filled glass bulb which has a lead weight in the bottom. When the hydrometer is placed in the liquid of the cell, it sinks into the liquid to a distance which depends upon the density of the liquid. If placed in the electrolyte of a fully charged cell, it will read, perhaps, 1275. When the cell is fully discharged, it will read approximately 1150. The hydrometer is usually placed inside a syringe so that a quantity of the electrolyte can be drawn up from the cell.

The density reading thus obtained is called the *specific gravity* of the cell. It affords an accurate indication of the general state of charge of the cell, for the density of the electrolyte slowly alters between full charge and discharge. When a low specific gravity reading of 1150 is reached, it is no longer safe to discharge the cell. After this value has been reached, further discharging will result in permanent *sulfation* of the plates. This is when the lead sulfate becomes crystalline and is no longer chemically active.

Capacity of Cell. The ability of a storage cell to hold an electrical charge is expressed in *ampere-hours.* A 100 ampere-hour cell will supply 12.5 amps for a period of 8 hours ($12.5 \times 8 = 100$). Hence, an ampere-hour is simply 1 amp $\times$ 1 hour, or ½ amp $\times$ 2 hours. Storage cells are usually rated on an 8-hour basis. Thus, a 200 ampere-hour cell would put forth a current of 25 amps steadily for a period of 8 hours. This ability of the cell to supply electricity is termed its *capacity.* And the capacity of a cell is always expressed in ampere-hours.

Storage Batteries. Storage cells are not often used singly. They are invariably assembled into batteries which consist of two or more cells. The 6-volt automobile battery consists of three separate cells connected in series. The 12-volt battery consists of six cells connected in series. In commercial applications where stationary batteries are required, as in stand-by service for power stations, they may be grouped into batteries of 50 or more cells connected in series. The term storage battery is much more common, therefore, than the term storage cell.

The Edison Cell

Fig. 21 shows a cutaway view of the Edison Cell. The positive plates are made up of a number of nickelled tubes which contain the active material, nickel oxide. In order to give the electrolyte free access to the active material, the tubes are given numerous perforations. To obtain improved electrical conductivity the nickel oxide is alternated with layers of nickel flake at the time it is tamped into the tube.

The negative plate is of similar construction except that finely divided iron oxide is used as the active ingredient and is contained in regular perforated pockets instead of tubes. The electrolyte in this cell consists of potassium hydroxide and a small quantity of lithium hydroxide, dissolved in water.

Operation of the Edison Cell. When the cell is charged, the iron oxide is changed into iron, and the positive plate is nickel peroxide. As the cell delivers current to a load, the positive plate changes from nickel peroxide to nickel oxide, and the negative plate changes from iron to iron oxide.

Charging reverses this process, namely, the positive plate again becomes nickel peroxide, and the negative plate becomes iron. The electrolyte does not take part in these changes, and the density varies only slightly during these changes.

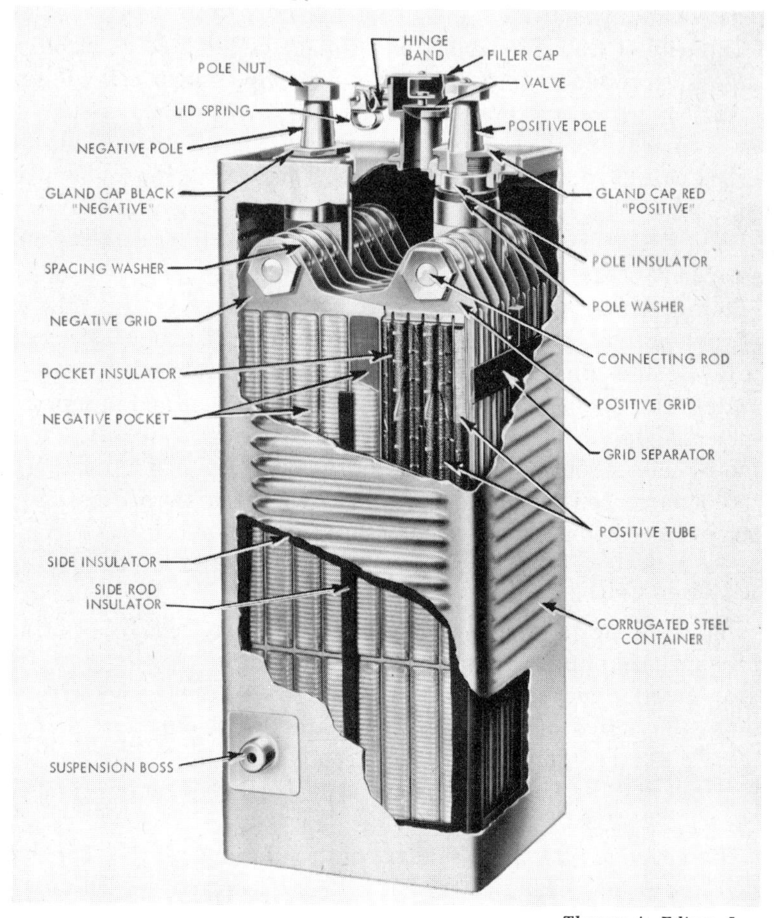

Thomas A. Edison, Inc.

Fig. 21. Cutaway View of the Edison Cell

Facts about the Edison Cell. It is not possible to determine the state of charge of an Edison cell by means of a hydrometer reading because the density of the electrolyte varies but slightly between charge and discharge. The voltage of this cell is somewhat less than that of the lead cell, being approximately 1.4 v when fully charged and 1 v when discharged. The capacity of this cell, although rated in ampere-hours like the lead cell, is usually based on a 5-hour discharge period. It is more rugged than the lead cell, and it will stand considerable abuse. It may be roughly handled; it may be overcharged and overdischarged without permanent damage. Edison cells can be frozen solid, yet operate without difficulty when thawed out.

These cells, like the lead acid cells, are usually grouped into batteries. Since their voltage is lower than that of the lead cell, it is necessary to connect a greater number of Edison cells in series to obtain a given voltage.

OTHER SIMPLE METHODS OF GENERATING ELECTRICITY

Thermoelectricity

When two dissimilar metals are joined together, and the junction between them heated, an electrical pressure is created. In Fig. 22A

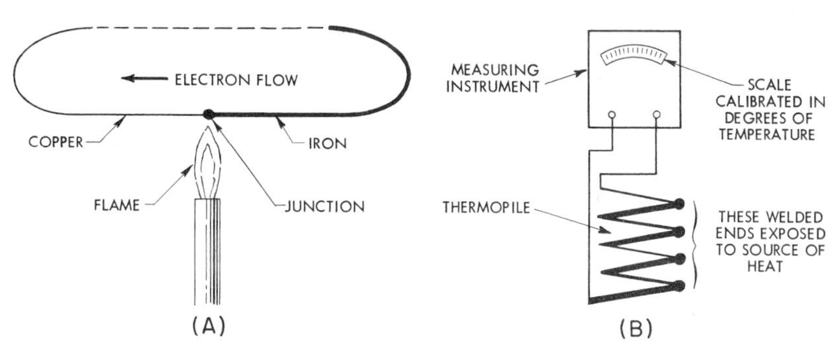

Fig. 22. A–Thermocouple; B–Thermoelectric Pyrometer

a piece of copper wire has been welded to a piece of iron wire. If a gas flame is applied to the junction point, electrical pressure is created, and a current of electricity will flow if the free ends of the wires are connected, the direction of current flow being from iron to copper. Such a combination of metals is called a *thermocouple*, or a thermel.

What actually happens when the junction point of the two metals is heated, is not definitely known. It is quite likely, however, that planetary orbits of one metal interfere with those of the other so that electron collisions result, with consequent freeing of electrons. The electrical pressure thus created is of a very low value, but a number of thermocouples may be connected in series just as was done in the case of dry cells. If all the junctions are heated at the same time, a higher pressure is thus obtained. The series of thermocouples is termed a *thermopile.*

Fig. 22B represents an instrument, called a pyrometer, which is employed in measuring high temperatures such as those inside an electric furnace. In the figure, a sensitive electrical meter is calibrated to show degrees of temperature on the scale. The thermopile is exposed to the source of heat. As the temperature varies, the number of free electrons varies to the same extent, the current flowing through the circuit rising or falling with the temperature.

If the junction between the two metals is cooled instead of heated, a similar result will follow as in the case of heating except that the electrons will flow in the opposite direction in the circuit. This effect has not been used commercially to any great extent.

Other pairs of metals than iron and copper may be used to form a thermocouple. In practice, nickel-iron alloys are commonly paired with a dissimilar metal, each particular combination producing its own characteristic temperature-voltage curve of values.

Piezoelectricity

Mechanical pressure, alone, is sufficient to cause a flow of electrons in many substances, Rochelle salts, Tourmaline, and Quartz being materials of this type. Current flow occasioned in this manner is termed *piezoelectricity.* The atomic structures of these substances is so delicately balanced that pressure causes orbits of planetary electrons to overlap, bringing about collisions which free electrons.

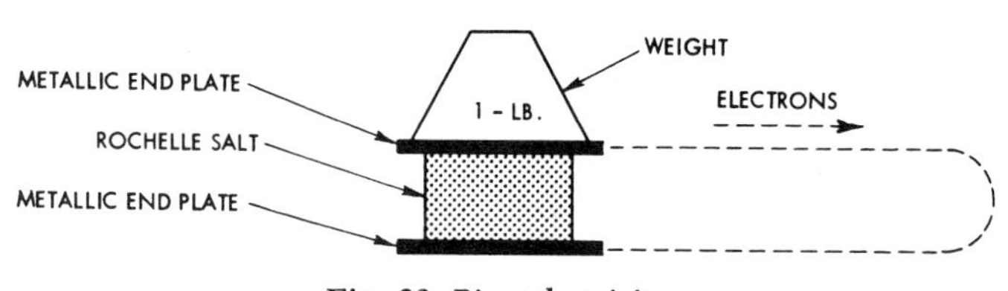

Fig. 23. Piezoelectricity

In Fig. 23, a 1-pound weight is imposed upon a block of Rochelle salt, this pressure causing a flow of current between metallic end plates which are connected by a copper wire. If the weight is increased to 2 pounds, the flow of current will be increased, although not in direct proportion to the values of the weights. This principle is made use of in the crystal microphone which is sometimes used in connection with radio or public speaking systems.

Photoelectricity

When a ray of light strikes upon certain materials, electrons are set free. Those which show this quality to a marked degree are termed *photoelectric* substances. It is likely that all materials are more or less photoelectric although the metals are comparatively far more sensitive than non-metals. Zinc, of the common metals, is quite responsive, Caesium and Selenium more so. This subject will be discussed in some detail in a later chapter.

REVIEW QUESTIONS

1. Explain how static electricity is generated by friction.
2. What happens if the electrophorous is touched with a finger after raising the disk?
3. Describe the Van de Graaff generator.
4. How may static charge be removed from a leather belt?
5. State two methods of removing static charge from paper.
6. Tell how lightning discharge takes place between a cloud and the Earth.
7. How does a dust precipitator operate?
8. Outline principles of the voltaic cell.
9. Describe the Leclanché cell.
10. Make simple sketches showing two voltaic cells in series, and two in parallel.
11. Plates of a charged lead storage cell are composed of what two materials?
12. What changes take place when the storage cell is discharged?
13. Describe the Edison storage cell.
14. Explain how thermal electricity is generated.
15. What kind of force gives rise to piezoelectricity?

CHAPTER 7

ELECTROMAGNETIC GENERATORS

PRODUCING CURRENT FLOW MAGNETICALLY

Effect of Magnetic Lines on Moving Conductor

Magnetic lines of force are a form of energy. They have power to act upon metallic substances so as to free electrons from planetary orbits when relative motion exists. In Fig. 1A, for example, when copper wire *W* moves across the magnetic field established by pole N, electrons are freed in *W*. Their direction of flow, if the ends of *W* are connected together to form a complete circuit, is such that magnetic circles will form about the conductor as shown, the circles moving counter-clockwise in this particular case.

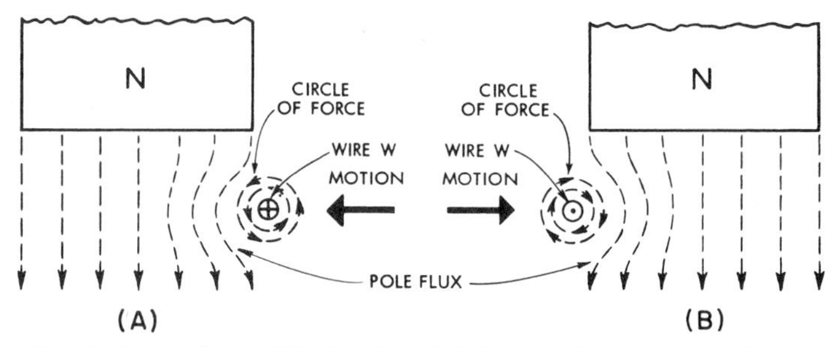

Fig. 1. A–Conductor Moving from Right to Left Across N Pole; B–Conductor Moving from Left to Right Across N Pole

Two facts should be noted here. First, the direction of the magnetic circles of force is downward on the left of the conductor, the arrows indicating the same direction as the lines of force established by pole N. These magnetic circles, therefore, tend to crowd into space already occupied by the lines from N. The second point to note is that mutual repulsion exists between magnetic lines which flow in the same direction, just as repulsion exists between like static charges of electricity.

The N lines thus resist intrusion of lines circling the conductor, trying to repel them, and in consequence conductor W, toward the right, physical force being required to overcome this magnetic resistance so long as the conductor is in motion. When *W* comes to rest, the opposing force will die out because electrons will no longer be freed in *W*, and circles of force will cease to exist.

The direction of current in conductor *W* may be determined by means of the left-hand rule already learned. It will be seen that current in *W* tends to flow downward, or "into the paper."

Reversing Direction of Motion. If conductor *W* is moved across the N pole from left to right, as in Fig. 1B, current will be established in the opposite direction. The circles of force will be clockwise, current will flow toward the observer, or "out of the paper," and the force of repulsion will be to the left. The essential fact to notice here is that reversing direction of motion reverses direction of current.

Reversing Magnetic Polarity. Fig. 2 is similar to Fig. 1A except that magnetic polarity has been changed from N to S. It will be seen that the direction of circles of force surrounding conductor *W* is opposite from that in Fig. 1A. Current flow in *W*, according to the left-hand rule, is toward the observer, or "out of the paper." Hence, reversing the magnetic polarity, direction of motion remaining the same, reverses direction of current in a conductor.

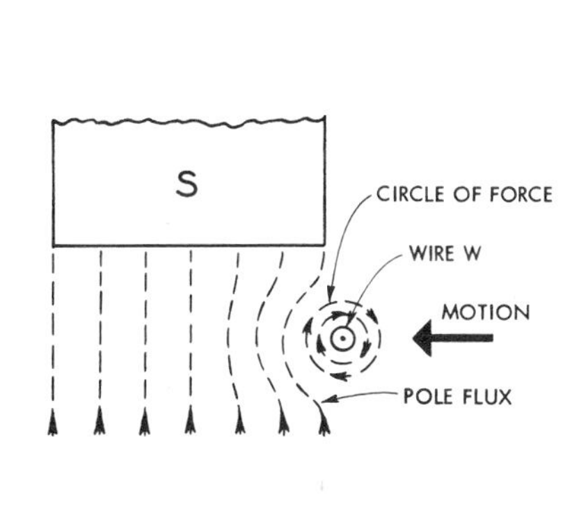

Fig. 2. Conductor Moving from Right to Left Across S Pole

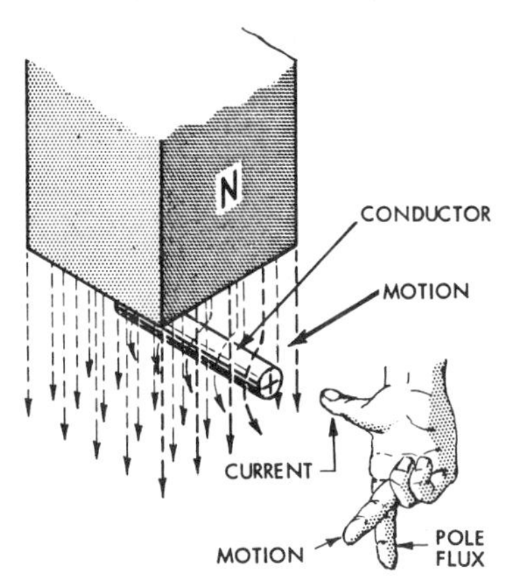

Fig. 3. Right-Hand Rule for Generators

Right-Hand Rule for Generators

A method for quickly determining direction of current is illustrated in Fig. 3. If the index finger of the right hand is extended so as to represent direction of magnetic lines, and the middle finger in the direction of conductor motion, the thumb will indicate direction of current in *W*.

Considering the present example, which is identical to Fig. 1A, the thumb shows direction of current flow to be from front to back. If direction of motion is reversed, as in Fig. 1B, the thumb indicates direction of current opposite from case A. In connection with Fig. 2, the index finger will point upward in order to represent lines flowing into an S pole, and the thumb will mark direction of current as being toward the observer, or "out of the paper."

Some generators, as will be explained later on, have stationary conductors and moving poles. To avoid confusion in applying the right-hand rule in such cases, it is advisable to picture the magnetic poles as stationary and the conductors moving across them in the proper relative direction, as illustrated here.

Elementary Generator

The elementary *electromagnetic generator* consists of a loop of wire which revolves between two magnetic poles, Fig. 4. In the figure, the

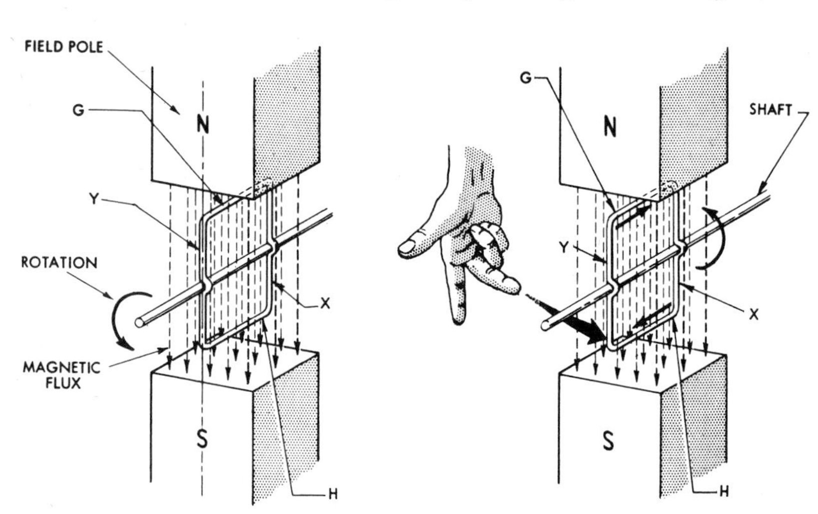

Fig. 4. Electromagnetic Generator

Fig. 5. Application of Right-Hand Generator Rule

loop is shown revolving on a central shaft. As it does so, at the instant shown, conductor G moves across lines from the upper, or N, magnetic pole of the generator, while conductor *H* moves across lines from the lower, or S, magnetic pole of the generator. Conductor *X*, at the rear of the loop, and conductor *Y*, at the front, both of which act as connecting links for conductors *G* and *H* do not cut across magnetic lines. They are parallel to, or in the same direction as, the lines.

Direction of Current. By applying the right-hand rule to conductors *G* and *H*, the direction of current in the loop may be determined. In Fig. 5, which represents the instant shown in Fig. 4, the direction of current in conductor *G* is seen to be from front to back. In conductor *H*, current tends to flow from back to front. The current then flows from conductor *G* to connection *X*, to conductor *H*, to connection *Y* and back to conductor *G*, thus completing the circuit.

A quarter of a turn later, as the loop continues to revolve, it reaches the position shown in Fig. 6A. Here, conductors of the loop are no

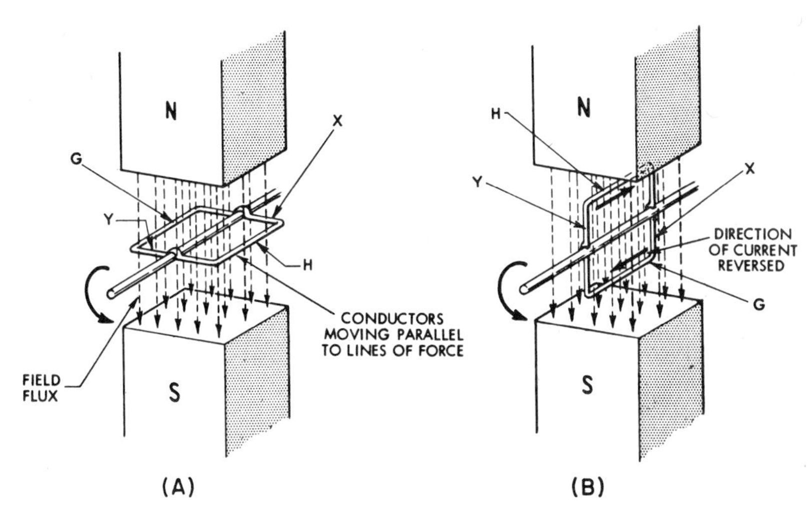

Fig. 6. A–Loop Moving Parallel to Magnetic Lines; B–Current Flow in Loop After a Half Turn

longer cutting lines of force from magnetic poles. They are moving parallel to the lines so that no voltage whatever is generated in them. The current flow in the loop at this instant, therefore, is zero. Another quarter turn, however, finds the loop in a position similar to that of Fig. 5, but with the conductors of the loop interchanged.

This position is illustrated in Fig. 6B. Conductor *G* is seen to be at the bottom where it is cutting across the flux of the S pole, while conductor *H*, at the top of the loop, is cutting across flux of the N pole. Application of the right-hand rule, Fig. 3, shows the direction of current. Comparison with Fig. 5, nevertheless, shows that direction of current flow in the individual conductors *G* and *H* is opposite from what it was in the first case. As the loop revolves, current in the two *active* conductors *G* and *H* flows first in one direction and then in the other.

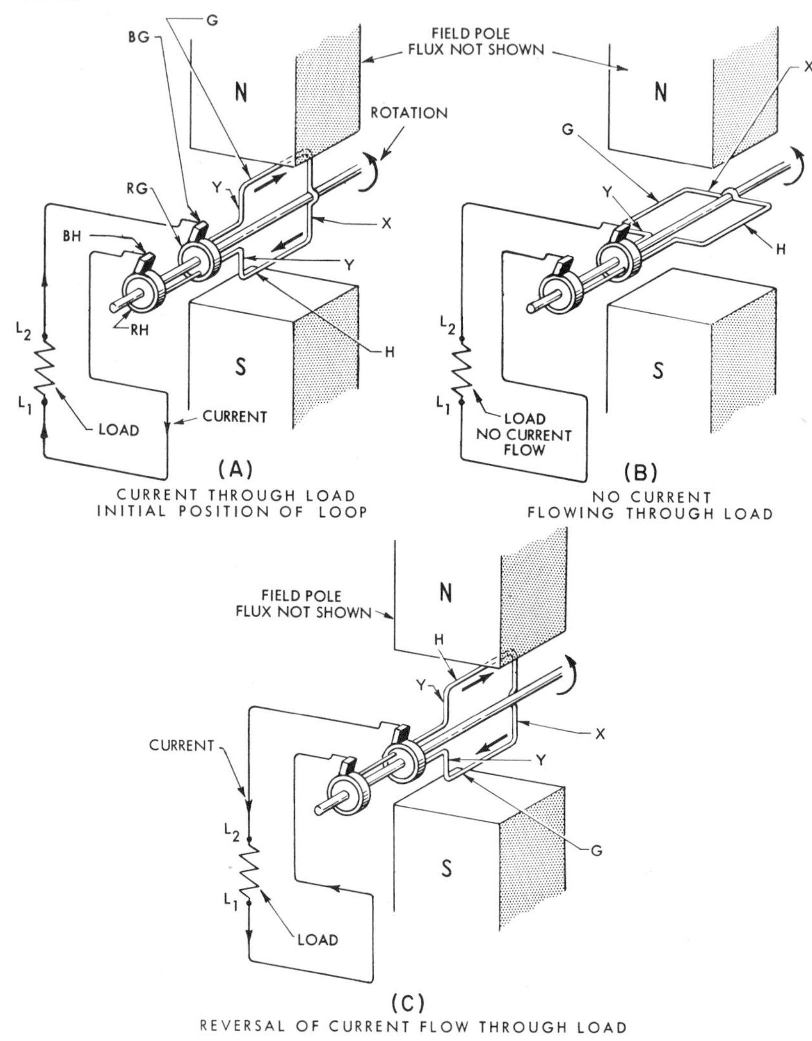

Fig. 7. Obtaining Current from Elementary Generator

Obtaining Current from the Elementary Generator. Electricity generated in a closed loop, such as shown here, would accomplish no useful purpose. Some method must be devised, therefore, of obtaining or collecting this current. Fig. 7 shows how this may be accomplished. End connection *Y* of the elementary loop has been cut. The end nearest conductor *G* is fastened to a smooth copper or brass ring, *RG,* which has been slipped over the shaft, on which the loop turns. The other end of *Y*, which is nearest to conductor *H*, is connected to a similar ring, *RH*. These rings, which now form the terminals for the conductors of the loop, are called *collector rings.*

As the loop turns, and the collector rings turn with it, they rub against two pieces of brass, *BG* and *BH*, which are termed *brushes.* Brush *BG* will press against collector ring *RG*, and brush *BH* will press against collector ring *RH* at all times, regardless of the position of the loop. The brushes are connected to the ends L_1 and L_2 of the load.

At the instant shown in Fig. 7A, current flows in conductor *H* from back to front, thence to collector ring, and to brush *BH*. The current then flows to end L_1 of the load and upward through the load to end L_2. From end L_2 of the load, current continues to flow through brush *BG*, collector ring *RG*, conductor *G*, connection *X*, and back to conductor *G*, thus completing the circuit. In this way, current generated in the loop is furnished to a load which is outside the generator.

A quarter of a turn later, when the loop has reached the position indicated in Fig. 7B, conductors will not be cutting across lines of force, and the current flow in the load will cease, but, during the next quarter turn, the conductors will be cutting lines of force. Current in conductor *G*, Fig. 7C, is back to front, and that in conductor *H* is from front to back. Following through the circuit, current flows from conductor *G* through collector-ring *RG* and brush *BG* to the L_2 end of the load. After flowing through the load, the current flows through brush *BH*, collector-ring *RH*, conductor *H*, and connection *X* to conductor *G*, completing the circuit.

Comparison of Fig. 7C with Fig. 7A shows that the direction of current flow through the load reversed while the loop made a half turn. It will reverse again as the loop continues from its present position through a second zero position similar to that of Fig. 7B, and back to its original position, which is similar to that indicated in Fig. 7A.

THE DIRECT-CURRENT ARMATURE

Alternating Current and Direct Current

With this elementary generator, current flowing in the load reverses twice with each revolution of the loop. A current which reverses in this manner is called an *alternating current.* Alternating current is satisfactory for operating an incandescent lamp load, for driving certain types of electric motors, or for performing the greater majority of tasks met with in practice. But it is not suited to other types of loads. One example is that of charging a storage battery.

As was illustrated during our discussion of the lead-acid cell, the generator must have one terminal which is permanently negative and one which is permanently positive. During the charging operation, current must flow continuously through the battery in a direction from the negative terminal to the positive terminal. A current which flows continuously in one direction through the load is called a *direct current.*

Generating Direct Current

The problem may be solved by use of the split-ring commutator, Fig. 8. A split-ring commutator might be devised by sawing a collector

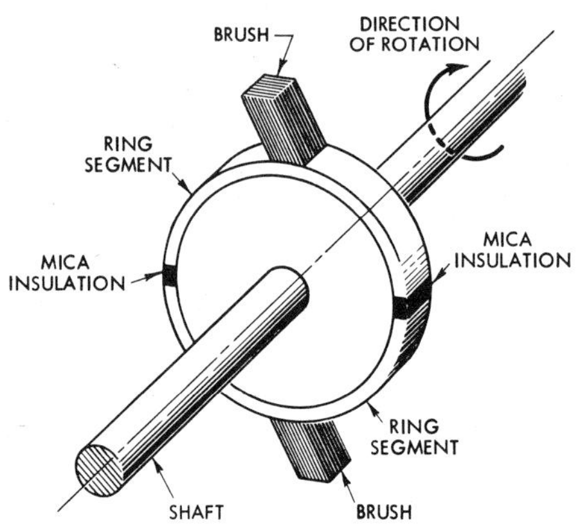

Fig. 8. Split Ring Commutator

ring in half and insulating the two halves. In Fig. 8 is illustrated a collector that has been cut in half and the halves insulated from one another with pieces of mica. The entire assembly appears quite similar to one of the rings previously used; but, electrically, it serves an entirely different purpose. Referring to the generator in Fig. 9, we will see how this unit is employed. Brush B_2 is mounted so that it touches the upper half of the ring at the instant shown in Fig. 9A, while brush B_1 is in contact with the lower half. B_2 connects to end L_2, B_1 connects to end L_1 of the load.

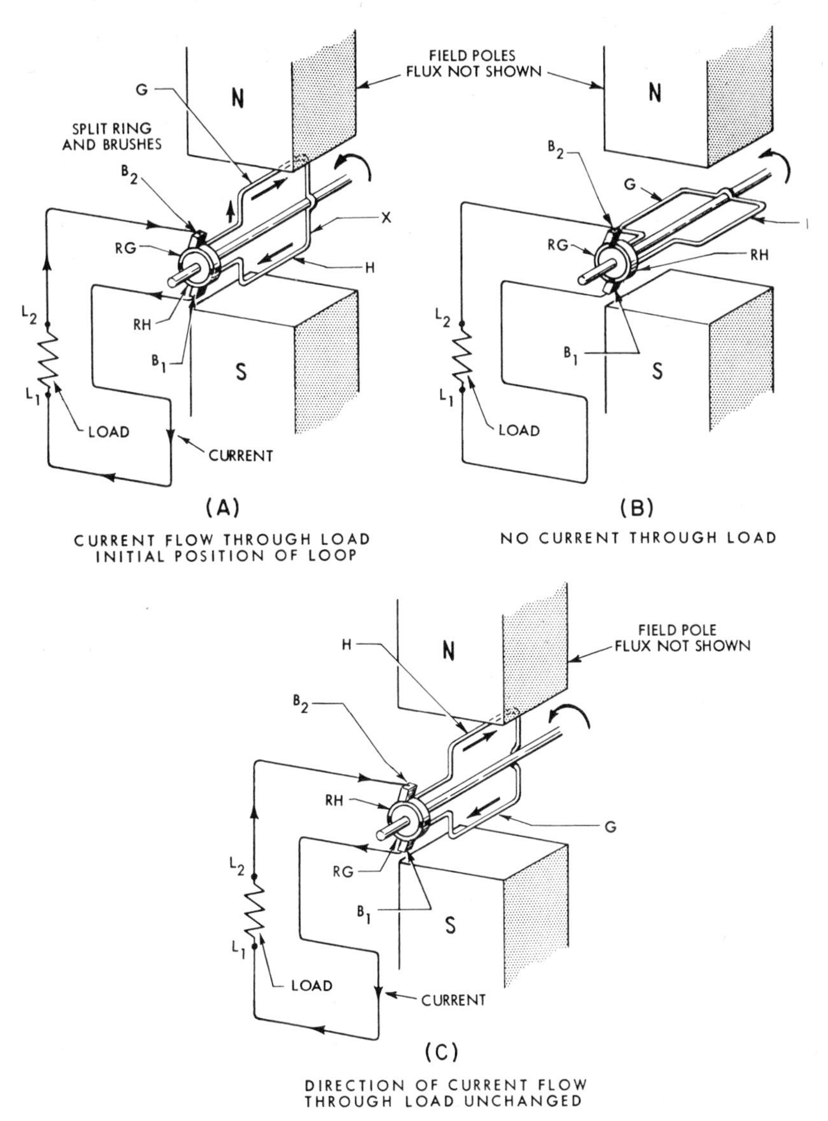

Fig. 9. Generating Direct Current

At the instant shown in Fig. 9A, the current flows from conductor H through segment RH, brush B_1, and the wire to point L_1 of the load. It flows through the load from L_1 to L_2, completing the circuit by way of brush B_2, segment RG, conductor G, and connection X. One-quarter turn later, in the position indicated in Fig. 9B, current flow through the load has ceased because the conductors of the loop are not cutting across magnetic lines. Meanwhile, brush B_2 is in contact with both halves of the ring at the top of the figure, and brush B_1 is in contact with both halves at the bottom of the figure.

When the loop continues around to the position illustrated in Fig. 9C, brush B_2 will make contact with half-ring *RH*, while brush B_1 makes contact with half-ring *RG*. If the current is again traced through the entire circuit, it will be seen that the current still flows through the load from point L_1 to point L_2.

The essential point here is that current through the load flows in the same direction at all times. In other words, it is a direct current. It is not actually a continuous flow of current, because the loop passes through two zero positions in each revolution; but the direction of current flow remains unchanged.

Making Current Flow Continuous. One way to eliminate zero current values is to add a second loop at right angles to the first one, Fig. 10A. Loop *I–J* has been placed upon the shaft at right angles to loop *G–H*, and its ends have been connected to a pair of ring segments. The ring has been sawed in four places so that each segment comprises only one-quarter of a complete ring. Brush B_2, Fig. 10A, is

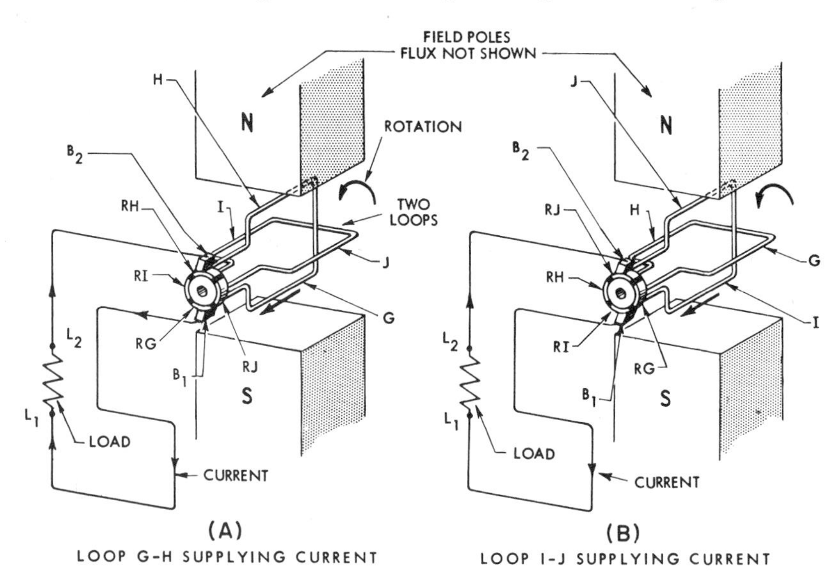

Fig. 10. Continuous Flow of Current Through Load

making contact with segment *RH*, which is connected to conductor *H*, while brush B_1 is making contact with segment *RG*, which is connected to conductor *G*. At the moment, conductors *I* and *J* of the second loop lie in the zero position midway between the two magnetic poles of the generator. As noted in connection with Fig. 9, the current in the load, under this condition, flows from end L_1 to end L_2.

A quarter-turn later, Fig. 10B, brush B_2 is making contact with segment *RJ*, which is connected to conductor *J*, and brush B_1 is making contact with segment *RI*, which is connected to conductor *I*. Following through the circuit, it will be seen that current flows through the load from end L_1 to end L_2. At this instant, conductor *G* and conductor *H* of the first loop are in the zero position.

As the rotation continues, conductors *G* and *H* will make contact with brushes B_2 and B_1, respectively; and the current will continue to flow through the load from point L_1 to L_2. Loop *I–J* is inactive at this moment because its conductors lie in the zero position. The final quarter turn brings B_2 into contact with segment *RI* and B_1 into contact with segment *RJ*. This loop sends current through the load in the same direction as before, while loop *G–H* lies inactive. Thus, a continuous flow of direct current passes through the load.

Simple Armature Winding

The arrangement shown in Fig. 10 is open to criticism because the segments are liable to burn from excessive sparking at the brushes. The reason for this sparking will be explained later. Now, the revolving member which supports the loops is called an *armature*, and the loops which carry the flow of current are called an *armature winding*. The split-ring is called a *commutator*, and the individual segments are called *commutator segments* or *commutator bars*.

In a commercial armature, the loops which compose the armature winding are connected together, and there are always more than two of them. Fig. 11 shows an armature winding which consists of four loops or *coils*. The ends of the loops are connected to the commutator bars in such a way that they form a complete, endless winding. In the figure, it is seen that two ends, or *leads* as they are called, are connected to each commutator bar. The manner in which this is done may be seen more clearly in Fig. 12.

Fig. 12 is a *developed* or flattened view of the winding. The conductors which lie upon the surface of the armature are indicated by short heavy lines, *G, N, I, H, K, J, M*, and *L*. One loop or coil includes conductors *G* and *H*, with their rear connection. Another includes conductors *I* and *J*. A third includes conductors *K* and *L*, while a fourth includes conductors *M* and *N*. The leads from coil *G–H* connect to commutator-bars *1* and *2*. Those of coil *I–J* connect to commutator-bars *2* and *3*. Those of coil *K–L* connect to commutator-bars *3* and *4*, while those of coil *M–N* connect to commutator-bars *4* and *1*.

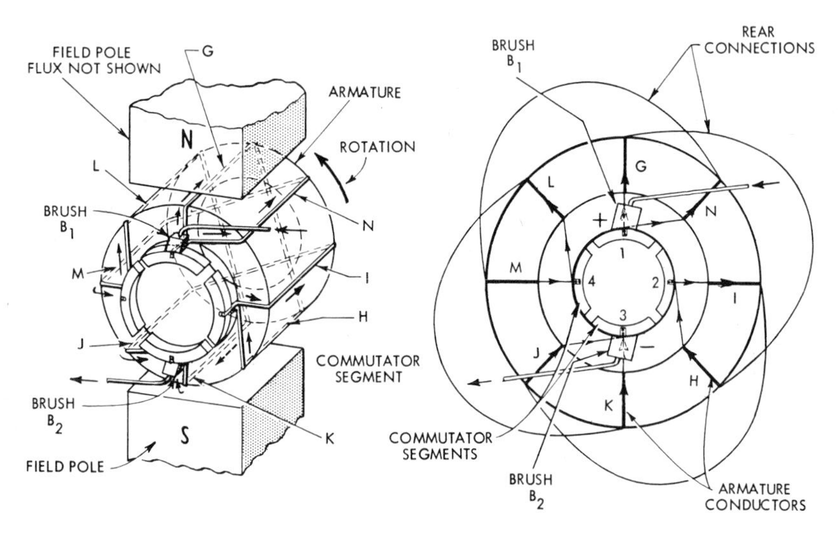

Fig. 11. Armature Winding of Four Loops

Fig. 12. Developed View of Armature Winding

Starting at commutator-bar *1*, it is possible to trace a continuous circuit which includes every conductor in the armature winding. From bar *1*, the circuit passes through conductor *G*, to the rear connection to conductor *H*, to commutator-bar *2*, to conductor *I*, to the rear connection to conductor *J*, to commutator-bar *3*, to conductor *K*, through end connection to conductor *L*, to commutator-bar *4*, to conductor *M*, through end connection to conductor *N*, to commutator-bar *1*, thus ending the complete circuit.

Current Flow in the Winding. When the armature is in the position shown in Fig. 11, conductors *L*, *G*, and *N* are cutting across the flux of the N magnetic pole. Conductors *I* and *M* lie in the zero, or neutral, zone. Conductors *H*, *K*, and *J* are cutting across the flux of the S magnetic pole. Application of the right-hand rule proves that current flows in the armature conductors as indicated by the arrows. Current in conductors *L*, *G*, and *N* flows in a direction away from the commutator.

Current in conductors *J*, *K*, and *H* flows toward the commutator. Although no voltage is generated in conductors *I* and *M*, because they are not cutting magnetic flux, current flows through them from conductors to which they are connected. Thus, conductor *I* takes current from commutator-bar *2* to conductor *J*, and conductor *M* takes current from conductor *N* to commutator-bar *4*.

From the arrows marked on the leads near the commutator bars, it is seen that two arrows meet, or oppose, one another at bar 3 and that two arrows draw away from one another at bar *1*. If a brush, B_1, makes contact with bar *1*, and a second brush, B_2, make contact with bar 3, current will flow to the load from brush B_2 and will return from the load by way of brush B_1. Thus, brush B_1 is the positive brush and B_2 is the negative brush. When the armature turns a short distance so that conductors *L* and *M* occupy the locations held by *G* and *N*, the arrows from *L* and *M* will separate at bar *4*, which at that time will occupy the location now held by bar *1*. At the same time, conductors *I* and *H* will replace *J* and *K*, while bar *2* will take the place of bar 3. Thus, brush B_1 will remain as the negative brush and B_2 will continue as the positive brush.

One more fact should be noted before leaving this subject: the number of paths in the armature winding. Start at commutator-bar 3 and pass through coils *K–L* and *M–N* to commutator-bar *1*. Start again at commutator-bar 3 and pass through coil *J–I* and *H–G* around the other half of the armature to bar *1*. Here, it is seen that there are two paths

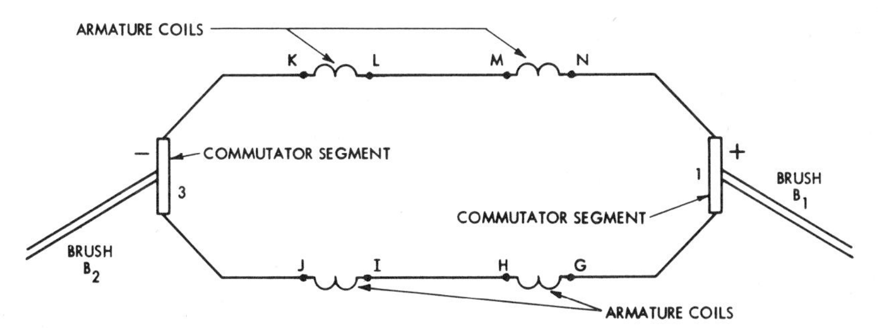

Fig. 13. Schematic Diagram of Paths in Armature Winding

from negative brush to positive brush, as indicated in Fig. 13. The arrangement is exactly the same as when two dry cells are connected in parallel, the two positive terminals being connected at one point, and the two negative terminals being connected at the other. In other words, there are two paths in the winding which are connected in parallel.

Commercial Armatures. The simple winding illustrated here serves very well for purposes of illustration. Indeed, with a few minor changes, it might be successfully employed in low-voltage applications. Commercial armatures, however, usually have a great number of coils and commutator bars. The armature is assembled from pieces of sheet steel, and the winding is contained in slots cut into the outer circumference of this steel cylinder. The commutator is mounted upon a central core from which the bars are insulated by means of *mica* or some

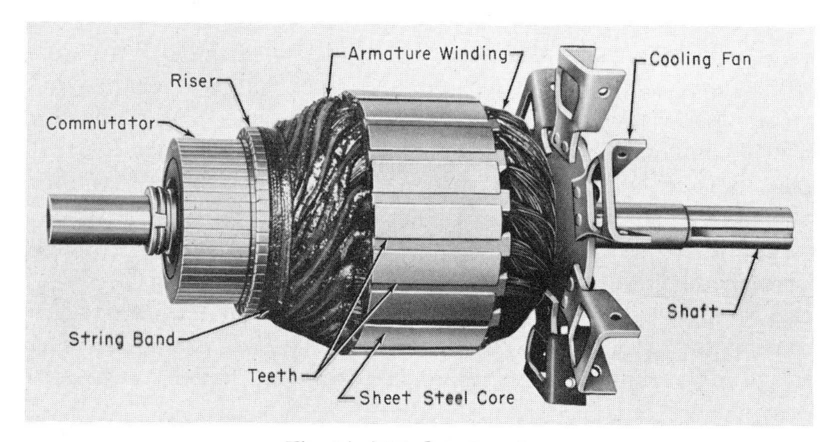

Fig. 14. A Modern Armature

other suitable nonconducting substance. The bars are separated from one another by this same material. Fig. 14 is an illustration of a modern armature. Its parts are indicated upon the figure.

DIRECT-CURRENT FIELD STRUCTURE

Permanent Magnetic Field

The armature of the commercial generator is completely surrounded by a field structure. The purpose of the field structure is to provide magnetic flux for armature conductors to cut. The flux provided by the magnetic poles is called the *field* of the generator. The term *field flux* is often used in this regard. A complete and balanced field structure might be formed of two permanent magnets bent and fastened together as in Fig. 15. The two N magnetic poles, together, form the N field pole of the generator, while the two S magnetic poles form the

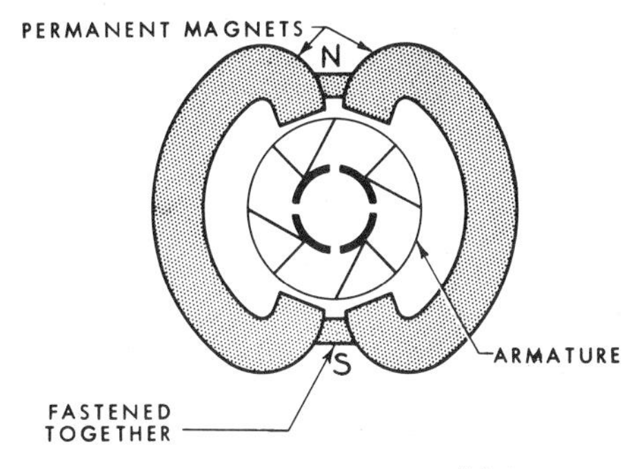

Fig. 15. Permanent-Magnet Field Structure

S field pole. When the armature is turned within this field structure, voltages are generated in the conductors, and current flows in them as shown in Fig. 12.

Electromagnetic Field Structure

In practice, the permanent magnet type of field excitation is seldom found in generators. *Magnetos* are sometimes used for gas engine ignition, a magneto being a small generator which has a permanent magnetic field. Generators used in speed-regulating devices sometimes

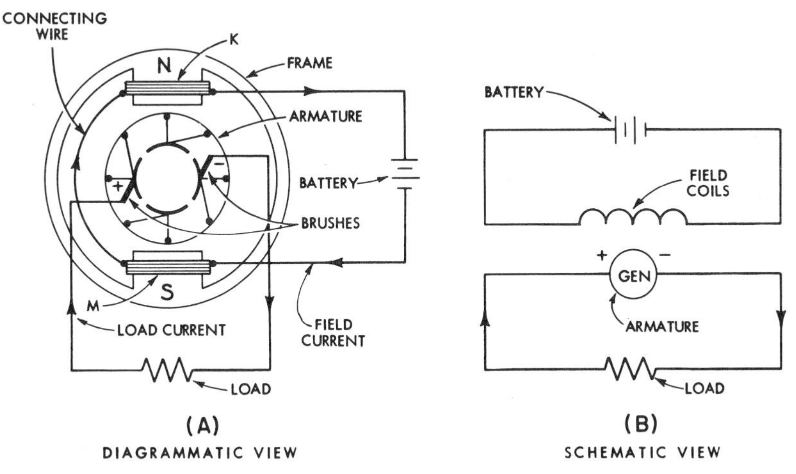

Fig. 16. Separately-Excited Generator

make use of this principle. Generally, however, the field excitation is obtained by means of electromagnets, Fig. 16.

In Fig. 16, the frame, or yoke, of the field structure is made of cast iron or of soft steel. N and S are the magnetic poles. Coil *K*, termed a field coil, surrounds the N pole, while coil *M* surrounds the S pole. When the battery is connected to the terminals of the field coil circuit, current flows from the negative battery terminal through coil *K*, then to coil *K*, and returns to the positive terminal of the battery.

Field coil *M* is wound around the lower pole in such a direction that an S pole is formed when current flows through it, this direction being determined with the aid of the left-hand rule. Field coil *K* is wound so as to produce an N pole when current flows through its turns. The flux established with the flow of current will continue to exist only so long as current is supplied by the battery. Since the material of the field structure is made of soft iron, it becomes only a temporary magnet and loses its magnetism when the flow of current ceases.

Separately Excited Generator. The unit shown in Fig. 16 is known as a *separately excited generator*, because its field coils are excited by some means outside the generator. Here, the separate source of excitation is the battery. Quite often, however, the separate source is another, but smaller, generator. When the field coils are excited by current from the battery, a voltage will be generated by the armature as it turns, and current will be supplied to the load by way of brushes and connecting wires. It may be noted in the figure that the brushes bear upon the commutator at points which are in the zero, or neutral zone, rather than directly upon the poles, as in Fig. 11. The method shown here is that usually found in practice where armatures have a great number of coils and a great number of commutator bars.

Separately excited, direct-current generators are not frequently met with in practice. It is the custom to excite field coils with current taken from the armature of the generator itself. There are three general types of such self-excited generators.

Shunt Generator

A *shunt generator*, also termed a *shunt-wound generator*, is illustrated in Fig. 17. The field coils are connected together, as before. The two lead wires which connected to the battery in Fig. 16, now connect to the brushes so that part of the current from the generator flows through these coils. When the generator is operating, current from the negative brush, passes through field-coil *K* then to field-coil *M*, and back to the positive brush. Current is supplied to the field coils so long as the armature continues to revolve. If the armature ceases to turn, current ceases to flow through the coils, and their flux ceases.

A small amount of magnetism still remains in the field structure after the current flow is discontinued. It is called *residual magnetism*

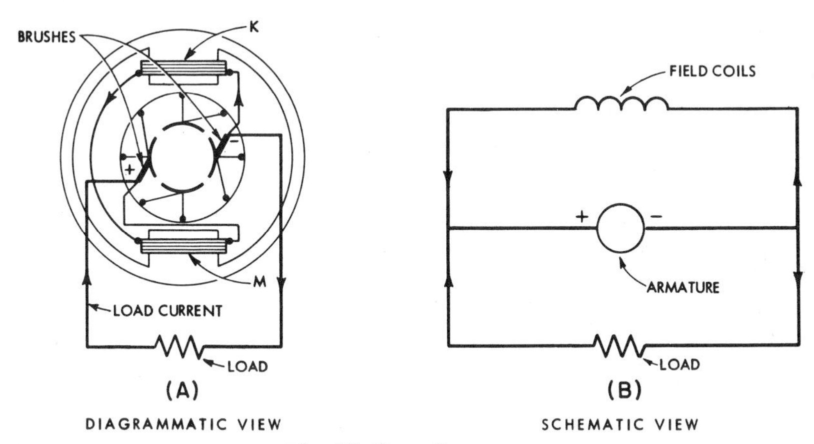

Fig. 17. Shunt Generator

because it remains or resides there for some time, gradually decreasing. The reason for the existence of residual magnetism is that some of the particles of iron or steel take up permanent positions when the exciting current flows. This residual magnetism is exceedingly weak, for not many of the iron particles will retain their magnetic force. But it is sufficient to produce some voltage in the armature winding when the armature is caused to turn. This small voltage, however weak it may be, supplies some current to the field coils. The excitation established by this weak current adds to the flux of residual magnetism to produce a somewhat greater voltage in the armature winding. The current in the field coils increases again so that an even greater amount of flux is produced. This process, which is called *building up,* continues until the generator is producing its full rated voltage. It is usually best to disconnect the load from the brushes before attempting to excite the generator. This enables the voltage to build up faster.

Strength of Generated Voltage. The voltage generated in a conductor is measured by the number of magnetic lines of force which the conductor cuts in one second. One volt of electrical pressure is generated when 100,000,000 magnetic lines are cut by a conductor in the space of one second, as illustrated in Fig. 18. In the figure, the magnetic flux from pole N is made up of 100,000,000 magnetic lines. The conductor moves across this flux in the space of one second. The voltage gen-

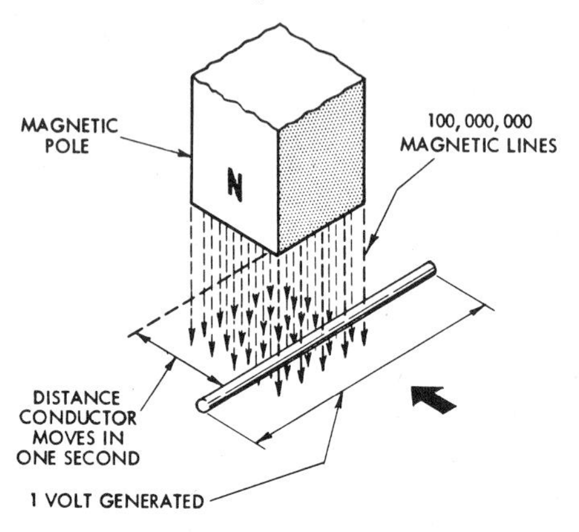

Fig. 18. Generation of One Volt

erated in the conductor amounts to 1 v, and this pressure is generated for a period of one second.

Increasing the value of the field flux to 200,000,000 lines will result in the voltage being increased to 2 v. Decreasing the value of field flux to 50,000,000 lines will result in the voltage being decreased from its original value of 1 v to ½ v. In other words, increasing the flux increases the voltage. And decreasing the flux results in a decrease in

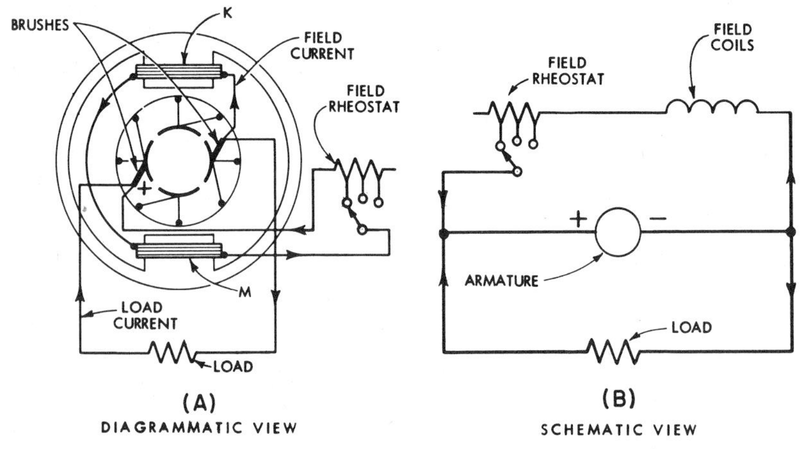

Fig. 19. Shunt Generator With Field Rheostat

voltage. It may be stated in the form of a rule: *Generator voltage varies directly as the field flux.*

Field Resistor. In practice, an adjustable resistance which is called a *field rheostat* is connected in circuit between one of the field leads and one of the brushes. In Fig. 19, the field rheostat is connected between field-coil M and brush B_1. By turning a knob, the value of the resistor may be increased or decreased at will. The usual way of indicating a field rheostat in a schematic diagram is as shown in Fig. 19. Ohm's law provides that when the resistance in a circuit is increased, while the voltage remains at certain value, the current flowing in the circuit is decreased. And when the resistance in a circuit is decreased, the current flowing in the circuit is increased.

Here, when the current flowing in the field circuit decreases, the flux decreases because the strength of the flux depends upon the amount of current flowing in the turns of the field coils. When the flux decreases, the voltage generated in the armature loops decreases. On the other hand, when the current flowing in the field circuit increases, the flux increases, and the voltage generated increases. Thus, a field resistor may be used to control the voltage generated in the armature of the shunt unit.

Compound Generator

A *compound generator,* also termed a *compound-wound* generator, has two field coils on each pole, Fig. 20. K and M are the usual type of

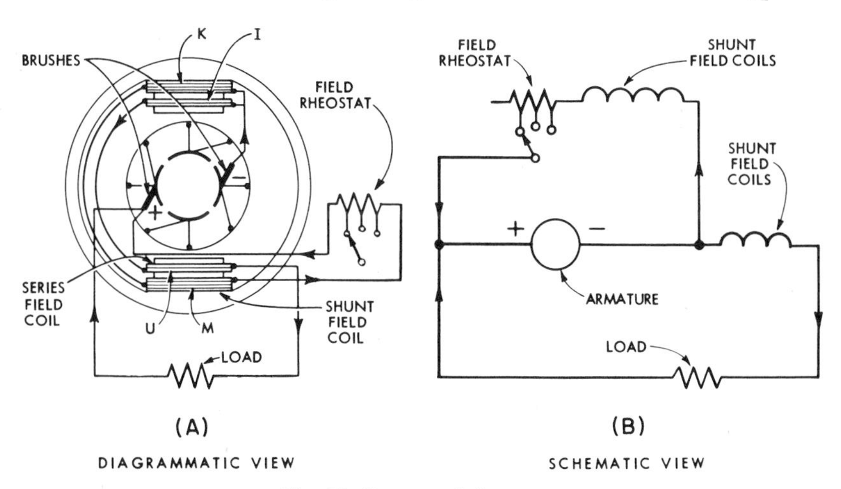

Fig. 20. Compound Generator

shunt field coils and are connected in circuit with a field resistor. *I* and *U* are called *series coils* or *series field coils.* One of the two remaining leads is connected to a brush and the second to the load. The other terminal of the load is connected to the remaining armature terminal. The series field coils are connected in series with armature and load.

The flux created by the series coils is added to that created by the shunt coils, so that the voltage of the armature is increased. If the load is disconnected, the field flux will be only that established by the shunt coils. In other words, the flux will decrease, and the voltage generated by the armature will decrease. But when the load is again connected, the voltage will rise once more.

The increase in voltage, which thus occurs automatically in the compound generator when the load comes on, supplies the voltage lost in the resistance of connecting wires between the generator and the load. If the load draws but little current, the voltage lost in the wires will be of a low value but, if the load draws considerable current, the voltage loss may be quite high. If the series field windings are accurately proportioned, the voltage at the load may be kept fairly constant in spite of the fact that the load may vary from moment to moment.

Series Generator

A *series,* or *series-wound,* generator has but one set of field coils which are much like the series coils of the compound generator. These coils are connected in circuit between armature and load, Fig. 21. This

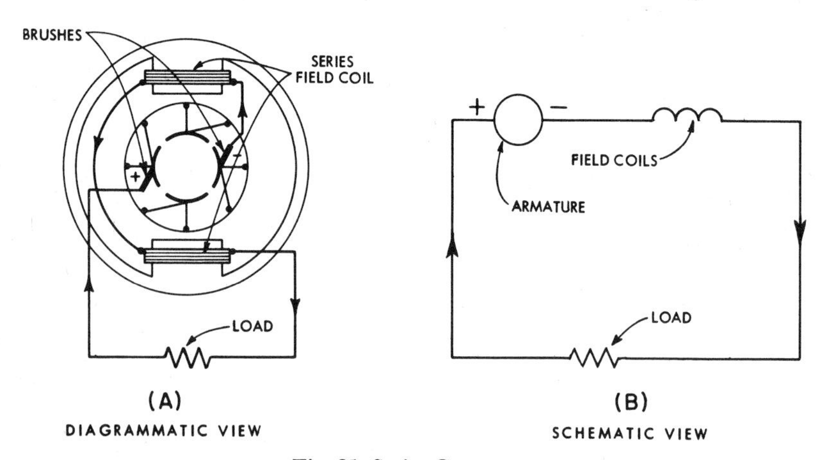

Fig. 21. Series Generator

generator resembles the compound generator of Fig. 20 except that the shunt coils are omitted. The voltage generated by the series unit depends upon the amount of current taken by the load. If the resistance of the load increases, the current through the field coils decreases. This decrease in field current results in a decrease in field flux and the decrease in field flux brings about a decrease in armature voltage, which causes a still smaller current to flow to the load.

This process of decreasing current and decreasing voltage continues until certain factors prevent current and voltage from decreasing further. If the resistance of the load is now decreased, a greater current flows through it. Since this same current flows in the series field coils, the flux is increased. The armature voltage rises, and the current through the load becomes even greater. This process, which is the reverse of the previous case, continues until certain factors prevent further change in current and voltage.

The decrease in voltage with increase in load resistance was considerable, and the increase in voltage with decrease in resistance was equally great. Therefore, the voltage of a series generator is said to be *unstable*. For this reason, the series direct-current generator is seldom met with in practice. In Europe, it is used to some extent in special circuits which are equipped with complicated regulating apparatus. Once they were used in America for street-lighting arc lamps. Today they are practically obsolete. The shunt generator was widely used, and the compound unit was looked upon with considerable favor. Alternating-current units, however, have made the large direct-current generator a rather scarce piece of apparatus.

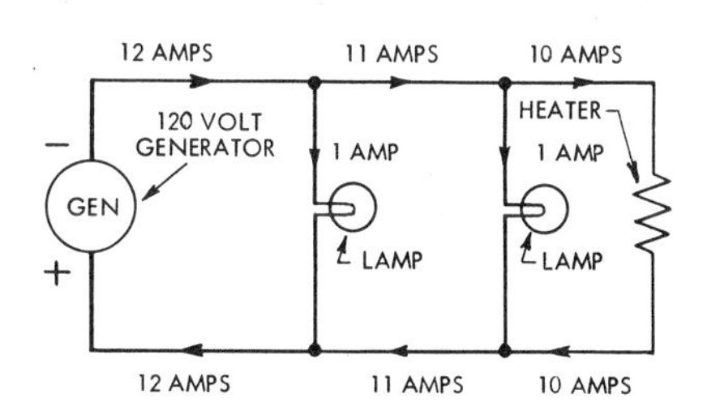

Fig. 22. Two-Wire Circuit

Two- and Three-Wire Direct-Current Circuits

For supplying commercial electrical devices, both two- and three-wire circuits are employed. Fig. 22 illustrates the familiar two-wire circuit in which current for two incandescent lamps and an electric heater is obtained from a 120-v generator. Here, 12 amps flow from the generator through the devices, and back to the generator.

In Fig. 23, two 120-v generators are connected in series. The voltage across the two outer wires is 240 v, while that between each of the outer wires and the middle one is 120 v. This middle wire is termed the *common,* or *neutral,* conductor. Between the upper and the neutral wire are connected the same devices as in Fig. 22. Across the lower wire and the neutral wire three lamps are connected, each requiring 1 amp. In this arrangement of devices, 12 amps flow from the negative

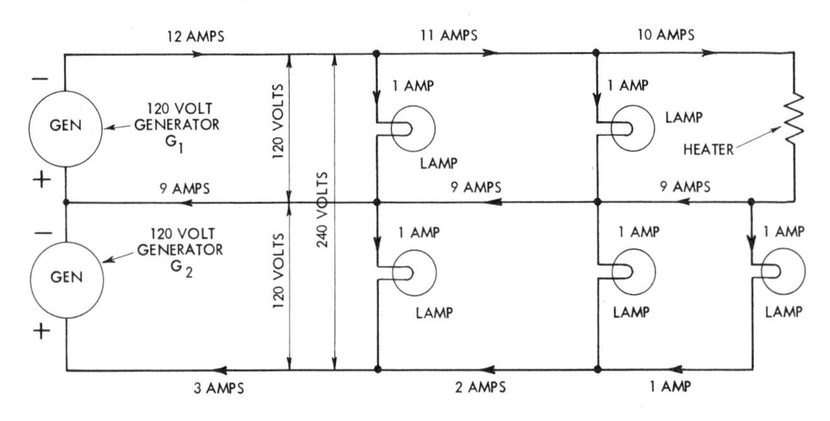

Fig. 23. Three-Wire Circuit, Unbalanced Load

terminal of generator G_1 to the two lamps and the heater. At the neutral conductor, however, 3 amps flow down through the lower lamps to the positive terminal of generator G_2. The remainder of the current, which is 9 amps, flows along the common wire to the point where the negative terminal of the generator G_2 connects with the positive terminal of generator G_1.

In the three-wire circuit of Fig. 24 five lamps are connected between the upper and the neutral wire, and five lamps between the lower wire and the neutral wire. Since each of the lamps requires 1 amp, a current of 5 amps flows along the upper wire to the upper group of lamps. A certain current must also pass from this wire down through the lower group to the other circuit wire. But, since the lower group of lamps requires 5 amps, all the current from the upper group passes down through the lower group, and the current in the common wire is zero. When current required by one side of the three-wire cir-

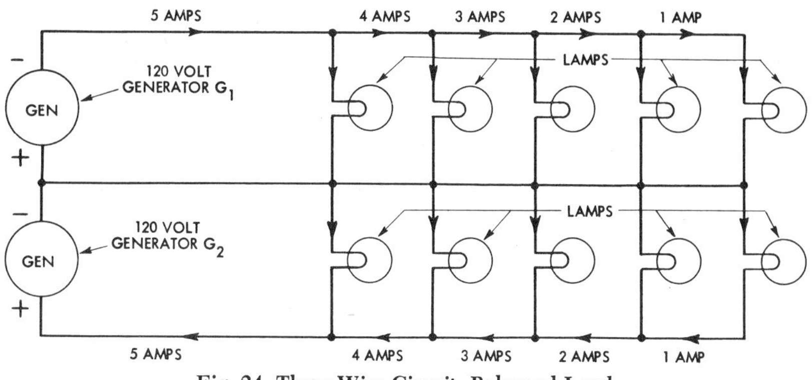

Fig. 24. Three-Wire Circuit, Balanced Load

cuit is the same as that required by the other side, the circuit is said to be balanced. In a balanced three-wire circuit, the current flowing in the neutral wire is zero; and in an unbalanced circuit, as in the first instance, current will flow in the neutral wire.

THE ALTERNATING-CURRENT ARMATURE

Single-Phase Unit

During our discussion of the elementary generator, Fig. 7, it was noted that the current flowed through the load first in one direction and then in the other direction. At that time it was mentioned that such a current is termed alternating current, because it alternates, or changes direction, continually. The type of current generated by the unit in Fig. 7 is designated not only as alternating current but also as *single-phase* current. The meaning of the term *phase* will become apparent shortly.

At the moment, it is important to understand the general nature of the unit. Current flows first in one direction; then it becomes zero when the loop is in the neutral position, and finally it flows in the opposite direction.

Variation of Generated Single-Phase Voltage. The circle in Fig. 25 represents the path of a conductor rotating between poles N and S. Since the conductor is assumed to be rotating at a constant speed of 15 times per minute, and the successive positions are equally spaced around the circumference of the circular path, the conductor will pass between adjacent points such as *a-b* or *c-d* in equal intervals of time. At a speed of 15 revolutions per minute, the conductor will make a single revolution in a period of 4 seconds, a quarter of a revolution from 0_1 to *f* in the figure, in 1 second, and the distance between any two positions, such as *c* and *d*, in 1/6 second.

Now, when a conductor moves parallel to the direction of lines of force, it does not cut them, and no voltage is generated. This condition exists only at points 0_1 and 0_2 in the figure. As the conductor moves upward from 0_1 to *a*, its direction of motion is primarily vertical, and parallel to the magnetic lines from the N pole, but it does move slightly in the horizontal direction, and therefore cuts across lines of force.

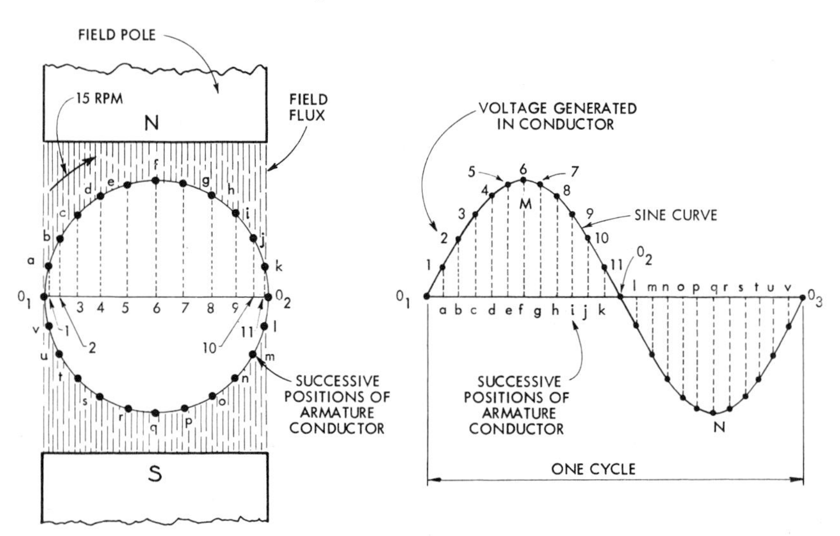

Fig. 25. Variation of Generated Single-Phase Voltage

Fig. 26. Sine Curve

Let us assume that 4400 magnetic lines are supplied by the N pole so that 2200 of them will be cut in the space of a quarter revolution. In this case, it may be determined mathematically that the conductor cuts across 130 magnetic lines in passing from 0_1 to point *a*. From *a* to *b*, the horizontal movement is somewhat greater, 250 lines are cut. In passing from *b* to *c*, a still greater portion of travel is horizontal so that 380 lines are cut. The conductor cuts across 450 lines from *c* to *d*, 480 lines from *d* to *e*, and 510 lines from *e* to *f*.

It will be recalled that the strength of the voltage generated by a moving conductor at any particular instant depends upon the rate at which it is cutting magnetic lines. Since 125 magnetic lines are cut while the conductor moves from 0_1 to *a* in the space of 1/6 second, and

250 lines are cut between *a* and *b* in the same period of time, the instantaneous voltage generated between *a* and *b* will be almost twice that from 0_1 to *a*. In a like manner, the generated voltage increases as the conductor continues moving, that generated between *c* and *d* being approximately 3.5 times that between 0_1 and *a*, and that between *e* and *f* about 4 times the 0_1 to *a*, value.

In practice, the number of lines emerging from a magnetic pole would be on the order of many thousand, and the speed of rotation several hundred per minute. Greatly reduced values were employed here to simplify explanation of principles involved.

The Sine Curve. Referring again to Fig. 25, it may be noted that relative maximum voltages generated in particular spaces can be measured by the height of vertical lines drawn from the horizontal diameter to the point in question. Thus, the maximum voltage generated in the space *a*-*b* is represented by the vertical line *b*-2, that from *c* to *d* by line *d*-4, the longest being *f*-6.

This fact is employed in constructing Fig. 26. Equal spaces have been marked off, between 0_1 and 0_2 to indicate the equally-spaced positions of the conductor around the upper half of the circular path. Vertical lines, each equal in height to corresponding lines in Fig. 25 are drawn at each marked division. Fig. 26 continues from 0_2 to 0_3, in the same way, to represent revolution of the conductor, in Fig. 25, through the lower half of its circular path. A continuous line is drawn through the ends of the vertical risers from 0_1 to maximum value *M*, to 0_2, to *N*, and to point 0_3 which is really point 0_1 again.

The curve so drawn is known as a "sine curve," and represents variation in voltage as a conductor revolves at a constant rate of speed between two magnetic poles. The sine curve applies as well to a pair of conductors connected in series to form a loop, or to any number of conductors connected in series and properly spaced around the circumference of a circular path. That portion of the figure between 0_1 and 0_2 is termed the "above-the-line," or positive, half of the curve; that from 0_2 to 0_3 is termed the "below-the-line," or negative, half.

The Cycle. When the conductor in Fig. 25 makes a full revolution, having cut across the lines of an N and an S pole, it is said to have completed two alternations, or one cycle. Each positive and each negative half of a sine curve represents an alternation, and the combination of a positive alternation and a negative alternation constitutes a cycle. In Fig. 26, therefore, the whole curve drawn between points 0_1 and 0_3

shows a full cycle of generated voltage. The number of cycles completed in one second, as the conductor rotates at high speed, is termed the *frequency* of the voltage.

Alternating current has been generated commercially, at various frequencies, some of the more common being 25 cycles, 50 cycles, and 60 cycles. Today, the frequency usually employed for lighting homes is 60 cycles.

Single-Phase Current

We have seen how the voltage varies from instant to instant. Now we will examine the current flowing in a circuit supplied by this type of voltage. Fig. 27A is a schematic of such a circuit. The load is a resistor of 1.5 ohms.

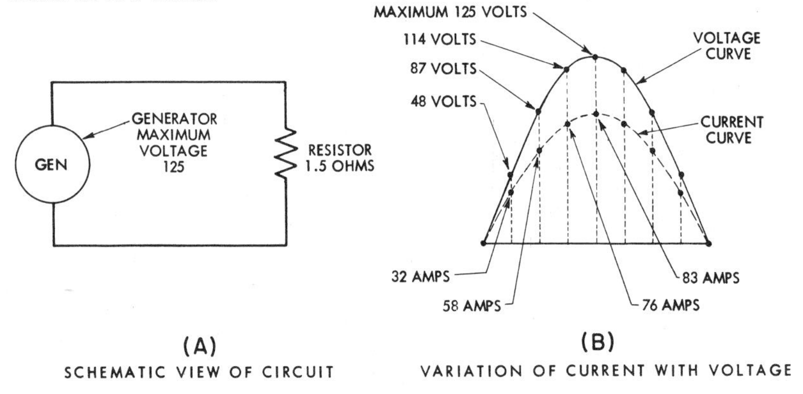

Fig. 27. Value of Single-Phase Current

We can apply Ohm's law here in the same way as in direct-current circuit. There is one difference, however. When voltage is changing from instant to instant; the current flowing, as determined by Ohm's law, is only true for the moment.

An example of the application of the law will help explain this. We will take different values of voltage as shown in Fig. 27B and determine the current in each case. First, when the voltage is zero, the current is zero, when the voltage is 48, the current

$$I = \frac{E}{R}$$

$$= \frac{48}{1.5}$$

$$= 32 \text{ amps}$$

At 87 volts, the current

$$I = \frac{87}{1.5}$$
$$= 58 \text{ amps}$$

If we go through this same process for the instants when the voltage is 114 and 125 we will find the current values to be 76 amps and 83 amps, respectively. Close inspection of this current curve shows it to be a sine wave, which rises and falls with the applied voltage.

Two-Phase Generator

Fig. 28A represents a generator with two armature loops. One of

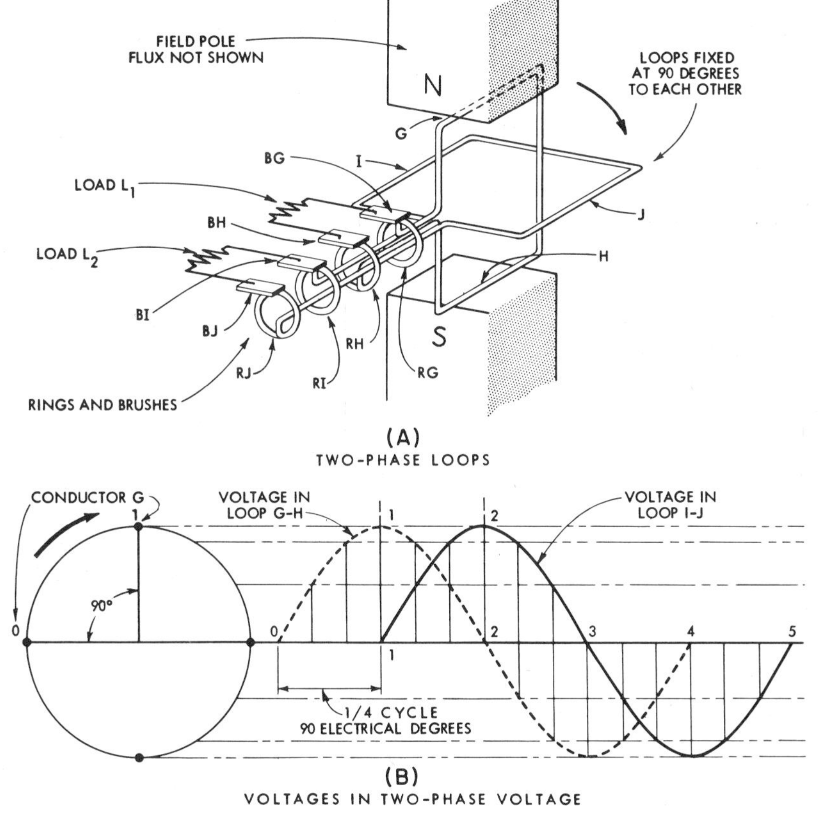

Fig. 28. Two-Phase Generator

the loops, *G–H,* is connected to the two collector rings, *RG* and *RH.* The other loop, *I–J,* is connected to collector rings *RI* and *RJ.* One set of brushes, *BG* and *BH,* supply current to load L_1. The other set of brushes, *BI* and *BJ,* supply current to load L_2. The load may be a motor with two sets of windings, each winding in a separate loop circuit. Now, each of these loop circuits is termed a *phase.* We will learn the meaning of the term *phase* and why it is used to describe this unit in a moment.

It is possible at this point to understand the difference between single-phase and two-phase units and to understand the difference between single-phase and two-phase current. A single-phase generator has but a single loop, or set of loops, all of which are in the same circuit. All of the load is connected in this circuit. A *two-phase generator* has two sets of loops which are connected in two separate circuits. That is, the load on the two-phase generator is divided into two parts, some in one phase or circuit, and the remainder in the other. There is one point of difference between single-phase and two-phase current which requires further explanation.

Phase Relation. In the two-phase generator, voltage in one loop may be at the highest value, while in the other loop it is zero. At a particular instant, point *1,* Fig. 28B, the *G–H* loop is at maximum value, and the *I–J* loop is at zero. A moment later, point *2* (the length of time that it takes the loops to rotate one-quarter of a cycle), the voltage in the *G–H* loop will have fallen to zero, for the loop will then be in the null zone. At this time the voltage in the *I–J* loop will have increased to its maximum value.

When these occurrences take place at different times, particularly when they happen one after the other in a recurring pattern, they are said to be out of phase. Voltages and currents in these two circuits are said to be 90° out of phase with one another. Referring to Fig. 28B, it is evident that when conductor *G* of loop *G–H* has turned from point *0* to point *1,* it has traveled one-quarter of the way around the circle, or 90°. At point *1,* where the voltage in loop *G–H* is at its highest value, the voltage in loop *I–J* is at zero value. It is the same state as loop *G–H* when it was starting to turn from position *0.* As noted above, loop *G–H* has traveled 90° before loop *I–J* starts to become active. The voltages generated in the two loops are separated by 90°. Two-phase current was quite popular a few years ago in commercial and industrial applications. It will be noted that two wires are required to carry current from the single-phase generator to its load and that four wires are required in the case of two-phase current. In practice, two of the two-phase collector rings are sometimes connected together, one from each phase, so that current may be transmitted over three wires instead of four. Basically, however, two-phase current requires four wires.

Three-Phase Generator

Fig. 29A represents a *three-phase armature.* It has three equally spaced loops, *G–H, I–J,* and *K–L.* The leads from these coils fasten to six collector rings, *RG, RH, RI, RJ, RK,* and *RL.* Each set of rings is

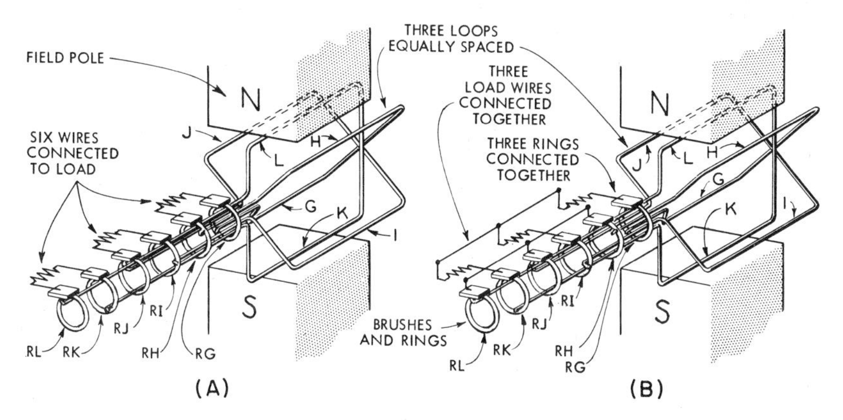

Fig. 29. Three-Phase Generator

connected to a separate circuit. It is seen, therefore, that a three-phase unit has three generating circuits, the current being supplied to the load by means of six circuit wires. In practice, however, six wires are never used. The relationship between the three generated voltages is such that rings *RH, RJ,* and *RL* may be connected and the current transmitted over the remaining three wires, Fig. 29B. Note that three load wires are connected together. Usually, the three leads which ordinarily fasten to these three rings are connected inside the unit, and only three collector rings are needed. Thus, three wires are usually associated with the transmission of *three-phase current.* Sometimes, for certain purposes, a fourth wire is added, this wire being connected to the three leads which are fastened together inside the armature.

Three-Phase Current. The relationships between voltages generated in the three loops is illustrated in Fig. 30. The voltage generated in *G–H* is represented by curve E_1, that in *I–J* is represented by curve E_2, and that in *K–L* is represented by curve E_3. The loops generate voltages which are separated by 120° because they are spaced 120° apart around the armature. *G–H,* represented by curve E_1, has passed through 120° in the positive direction before *I–J,* represented by curve E_2, starts to generate in the positive direction. *I–J* has passed through 120° before *K–L,* represented by curve E_3, begins to generate in the positive direction. By this time, *G–H* has completed its path in the negative direction.

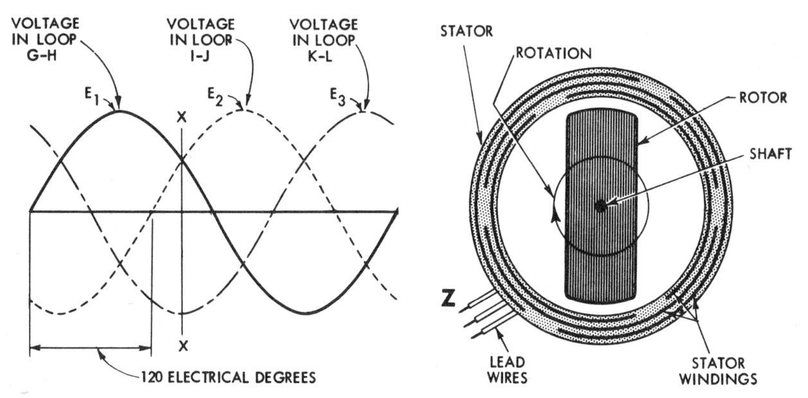

Fig. 30. Voltages in Three-Phase Circuit

Fig. 31. Revolving Field Magnets

Interesting relationships may be observed by glancing at the figure. For example, it becomes apparent why three of the circuit wires may be omitted. This is illustrated at point *X,* where curves E_1 and E_2 are both at one-half maximum positive value. At this instant, curve E_3 is at maximum value in the negative direction. Thus, the circuit represented by curve E_3 may act as a *return* for the other two circuits represented by E_1 and E_2. By carefully measuring respective values at any instant, it will be found that one of the three circuits acts as the return for the other two at all times.

The 120° relationship is characteristic of three-phase alternating current. This form of current has largely replaced two-phase. It may be distributed more economically than single-phase or two-phase because of the saving in circuit wires permitted by the omission of three out of six. Three-phase current has many other advantages which cause it to be preferred over other forms of alternating current. It has also taken over many tasks once firmly within the direct-current field of application.

FIELD STRUCTURE OF ALTERNATING-CURRENT GENERATORS

Method of Exciting Field Magnets

Alternating-current generators are often classed under the general name of *alternators.* The field coils of alternators are usually separately excited. It would be possible to mount a commutator upon the armature shaft and so change some of the output into direct current for purposes of exciting the field coils. In the early days, this method was followed to some extent. Today, alternators are magnetized by current from a small direct-current generator, which is called an *exciter.*

Revolving Field Magnets. In the elementary single-phase generator, field poles remain fixed in position while the armature and its winding revolve. The same results could be accomplished by having the armature remain in a fixed position while the field poles revolve about it. Mechanical complications would be introduced by this method, however, but these may be avoided if the field poles, which revolve, are placed inside the armature, which now surrounds the field poles, Fig. 31. Here the field magnets are placed upon the revolving member, which is termed the *rotor.* The field coils are supplied with direct current, which is carried to them by means of collector rings and brushes. These are not shown in the figure.

The armature winding is placed in slots cut into the inner circumference of the stationary portion of the unit. The stationary member is not called an armature here but is termed a *stator.* Since the stator winding does not turn, collector rings are not required to make connection to it. Current for the load is taken directly from three lead wires which are brought out of the stator at point Z.

It should be noted that the field structure of the alternator is the same for any type of unit. That is, the stator might be wound for single-phase, for two-phase, or for three-phase without altering the rotor.

Practical Considerations

The armature windings of generators illustrated here were quite simple, usually having but a single loop. Commercial armatures have many loops and make use of more or less complicated schemes for connecting them. The basic principles, however, are exactly as outlined here. All of the illustrative units were of the two-pole type. In practice, many direct-current machines of moderate and small size have two-pole field structures. Alternators, aside from those used in connection with high-speed steam turbines, seldom use this form of construction but employ field systems that have several poles.

It should be mentioned that the number of electrical degrees in an alternator which has more than two poles is greater than 360°. There are 180° between the center of an N pole and the next S pole. And there are 180° between the center of this S pole and that of the next N pole. That is, there are 360° between the center of one N pole and the center of the next N pole. These are termed *electrical degrees* to distinguish them from those of a circle in which a complete revolution is necessary to cover 360°. When dealing with multipolar alternators, that is, those having more than two poles, the difference between mechanical and electrical degrees should be kept in mind.

The voltage generated by a single loop is quite low, even if the field strength is large. In practice, direct-current machines put forth voltages on the order of 115 v, 230 v, or perhaps 600 v. Alternators generate voltages of 115 v, 230 v, or 460 v. In large power stations, the alternating-current generators may produce voltages of perhaps 13,800 v. In this case, the voltage is reduced, by means which will be explained later, to one of the three voltages listed above for use in home or in commercial or industrial applications. In the home, the usual voltage is 115 v.

Eddy Currents

The iron core on which the armature coils are wound cuts a magnetic field as it rotates; since it rotates in the same field as the armature. Because it is a conductor, a current is induced in it. This current is not confined to the surface of the iron but also develops inside the core. The current generated cannot be utilized in any way and is wasted in the form of heat. In extreme cases it can damage coil insulation. This current is called an *eddy current*. The path of eddy currents in a solid armature is shown in Fig. 32A. Efficiency is also reduced by eddy currents since an extra turning effort is required to generate them.

Eddy currents are reduced by *laminating* the armature core; that is, building it up of thin iron sheets insulated from each other with lacquer. This does not seriously affect the magnetic properties of the core but reduces the induced currents by breaking up and shortening the current paths. The paths of eddy currents in a laminated armature core are shown in Fig. 32B.

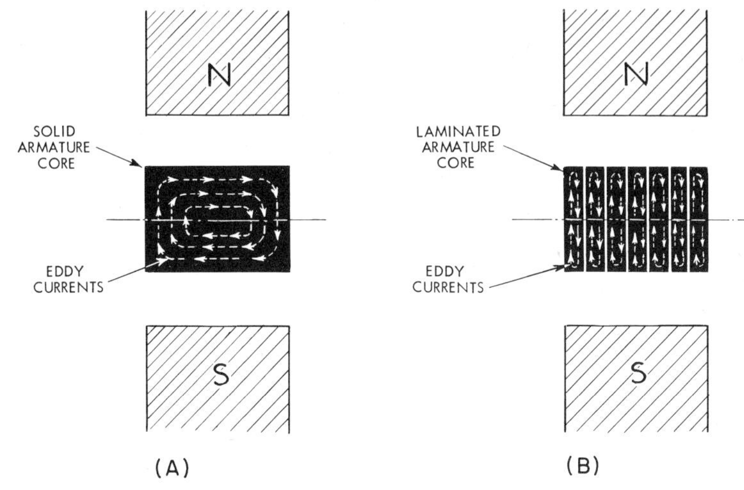

Fig. 32. Eddy Currents in Armature Defeated by Lamination of Core

REVIEW QUESTIONS

1. State the right-hand generator rule.
2. Why is an alternating voltage generated by the elementary loop?
3. How is the alternating current in the loop conductors changed to direct current?
4. What is the effect of adding more loops?
5. What factors determine the strength of generated voltage?
6. Make sketches of shunt, series, and compound generator circuits.
7. State briefly the manner in which the voltage of a series generator varies.
8. If the series coils of a compound generator are connected, accidentally, so as to oppose the shunt excitation, what effect will this have on the generator load voltage?
9. If the series coils of this generator are connected in parallel with each other instead of series, what effect will this have on the generator load voltage?
10. How many electrical degrees separate loops of a simple two-phase generator?
11. How many electrical degrees separate adjacent loops of a simple three-phase generator?
12. Tell how three of the six wires from the simple three-phase generator may be eliminated.
13. Discuss methods of exciting alternator field coils.
14. Would it be possible to have more than three phases in an alternator?
15. What are eddy currents?

CHAPTER 8

CIRCUIT ELEMENTS

INDUCTANCE IN DIRECT-CURRENT CIRCUITS

Expansion of Circles of Force

It was mentioned earlier that circles of force surround a conductor in which a current flows. And it was explained that these lines spread out farther from the conductor as the value of current is increased. Fig. 1A shows a conductor in which current flows as indicated by the arrow. From the application of the left-hand rule, it is found that circles of force will have directions indicated by small arrows in the figure.

When the current is of small value, circles of force surround the wire at a distance shown by circle *1*. As the current increases slightly, circles spread out as far as position *2*. Further increase causes them to spread out to position *3*, and still greater increase causes them to reach position *4*. While current is increasing in this way, the spreading of circles of force on the right side of the conductor is similar to the movement of an N magnetic pole in a direction marked by arrow D_1. When

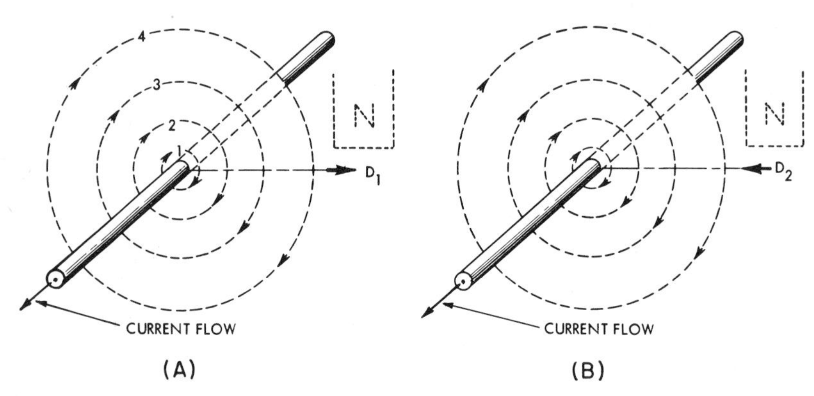

Fig. 1. A–Circles of Force—Current Increasing; B–Circles of Force—Current Decreasing

the current decreases, the circles of force shrink, or collapse, toward the conductor, as in Fig. 1B, this movement being similar to that of an N magnetic pole which is moved in the reverse direction as indicated by arrow D_2.

Effect of Current Change upon Adjacent Circuit

Fig. 2A shows two wire loops, L_1 and L_2. Loop L_1 contains a battery and a switch. L_2 is a closed loop. When the contacts of the switch are touched together, current begins to flow around loop L_1 in a counterclockwise direction so that in wire *M* it is upward. Now, as will be

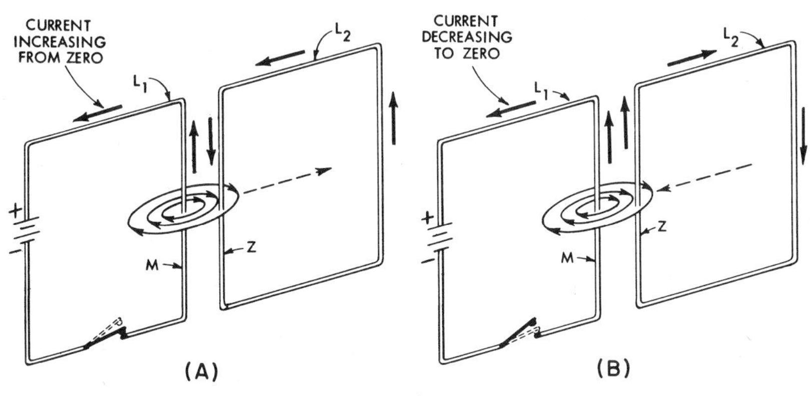

Fig. 2. Induction

seen shortly, the value of the current does not reach its highest point immediately, but it must build up gradually from zero. While current is building up, circles of force spread out from conductor *M* toward conductor Z of loop L_2.

Application of the left-hand rule shows that the direction of the circles of force about conductor *M* is clockwise. As they continue to spread out and to cut across conductor Z, the effect will be the same as if an N magnetic pole were moved across the conductor. By applying the right-hand rule, it is seen that the voltage induced in Z forces current to flow in a downward direction in the wire and to circulate in the loop in a counterclockwise direction. As the current in conductor *M* rises to maximum value, circles of force stop spreading and remain at their respective distances from conductor *M*.

Since the circles have stopped spreading, magnetic flux no longer cuts across conductor Z, and the voltage and current in loop L_2 die away to zero value. There will be no further current flow in loop L_2 so long as the switch in loop L_1 is held closed. If the switch is now opened, the current flowing in L_1 will cease. But it cannot do so upon the instant, for it takes time for the current flow to die out in much the same way as it took time for it to build up.

While current in conductor M dies out, the magnetic circles of force shrink toward the conductor, Fig. 2B. Those which have passed beyond conductor Z of loop L_2 now cut across it. The effect is equivalent to moving an N magnetic pole in the opposite direction from when current in loop L_1 was increasing. The left-hand rule shows that the direction of current in conductor Z, and in loop L_2, is opposite from before, or in a clockwise direction.

After the shrinking circles of force have passed conductor Z as they withdraw, the voltage in loop L_2 is zero, and current no longer flows. The process by which current in one conductor creates a voltage in another is called *induction.* Here, current flowing in conductor M is said to *induce* a voltage in conductor Z.

Self-Induction—Current Increasing

Fig. 3 illustrates the effect of induction upon the circuit, itself. The wires in the single-turn coil are marked W_1, W_2, and W_3. When current

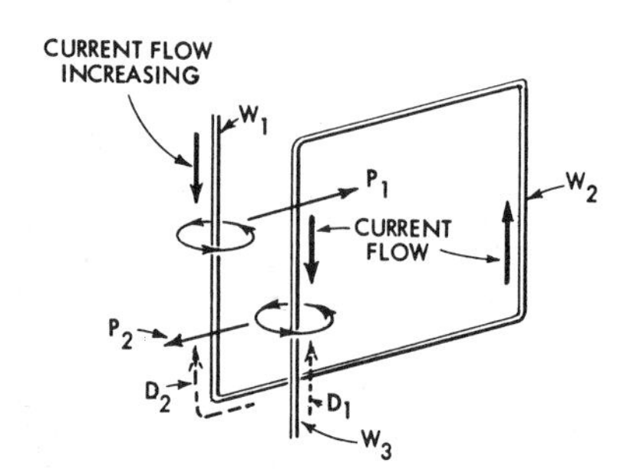

Fig. 3. Self Induction—Current Increasing

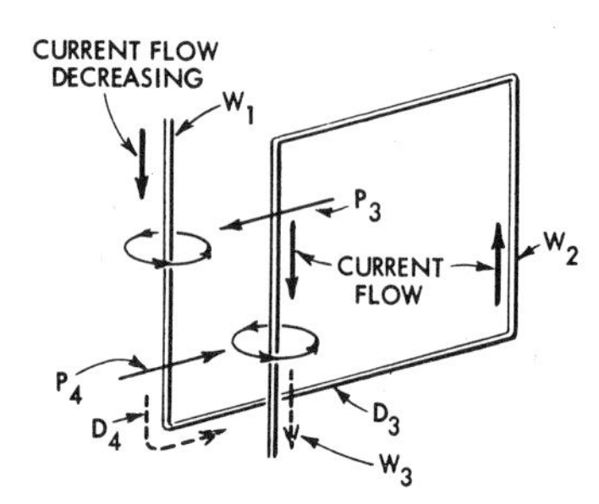

Fig. 4. Self Induction—Current Decreasing

begins to flow downward in conductor W_1, magnetic circles of force spread out from the wire, their direction being determined by the left-hand, "current," rule. In the vicinity of conductor W_3, the arrows on the circles are inward, the effect upon W_3 being the same as if an N pole were moved across W_3 as indicated by arrow P_1. Under this condition, the voltage generated in W_3, as determined by the right-hand "generator," rule, will be such as to oppose the flow of current. Dotted arrow D_1 indicates this fact.

At the same time, current starting to flow in W_3 will create circles of force which cut across conductor W_1, as shown by arrow P_2. The voltage thus induced in conductor W_1 will oppose flow of current, as indicated by dotted arrow D_2. The flow of current in each conductor, therefore, induces in any adjacent conductor, a voltage opposing flow of current in the circuit. This induced force continues so long as current is increasing, until it reaches a steady value. Conductor W_2 is assumed to be so far away that its circles do not affect the other conductors, and the horizontal conductors are subject to a like assumption.

Self-Induction—Current Decreasing

Fig. 4 shows the effect of self-induction with decreasing current. Under this condition, magnetic circles of force connected with W_1 start to shrink. In doing so, they cut across W_3 as indicated by arrow P_3. The direction of voltage induced in W_3, according to the right-hand rule, is such as to assist, or to continue, the flow of current in W_3, this fact being shown by dotted arrow D_3. In the same way, the shrinking circles of W_3 induce a similar voltage in W_1, as shown by dotted arrow D_4. This induced force will continue, so long as current is decreasing in value, until the current falls to zero.

Cause of Spark at Switch Contacts

The force of self-induction, which induces a voltage in the circuit as current begins to decrease, is the cause of sparking at switch contacts. In Fig. 5 a battery is connected to a coil. When the switch is

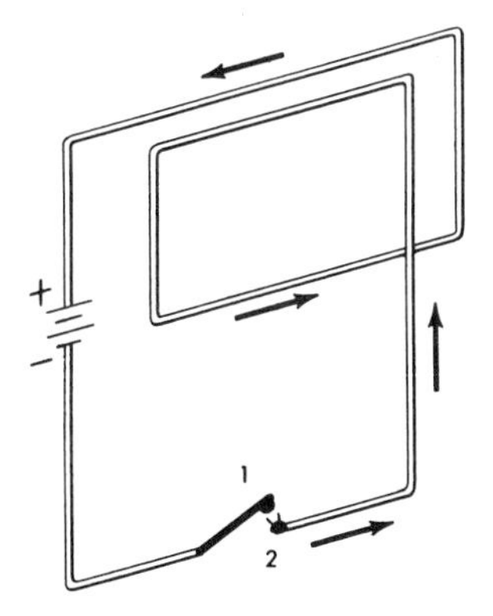

Fig. 5. Effect of Spark at Switch Contacts

closed so that contact *1* is connected to contact *2*, current flows through the coil from the negative battery terminal, through the switch and to the positive terminal. As the switch contacts are opened, the force of self-induction in the coil tries to continue the flow of current. The voltage of self-induction sends a current across the short air space between the separating contacts, this current appearing as a spark. The spark indicated in the figure jumps from the negative switch contact (contact 1) to the positive switch contact (contact 2).

Value of Induced Voltage. The value of induced pressure in a circuit depends upon its physical construction. The term used to express this quality of the circuit is called *inductance*. The inductance of a particular circuit depends upon the number and the spacing of the turns of wire in it and its nearness to iron objects. The principal factor, insofar as the present discussion is concerned, is the number of turns of wire. A coil with two turns has more inductance than one of a single turn. And one of four turns has more inductance than another of two turns. Inductance is expressed by a term called a *henry*.

Inductance will be considered at greater length in the next section. At this point, however, it may be stated that inductance in a direct-current circuit is active only during a short space of time. When the circuit switch is first closed, the effect of inductance prevents the current from rising immediately to the value it must have under Ohm's law but, as the current gradually rises to this steady value and the circles of force cease to cut across turns of wire, the induced voltage becomes zero and inductance is of no further concern until the circuit switch is opened. As the switch is opened, the force of self-induction becomes active again so that destructive sparking sometimes takes place at switch contacts.

INDUCTANCE IN ALTERNATING-CURRENT CIRCUITS

Normal Voltage and Current Curves

Curve *E*, Fig. 6, is a sine curve of voltage. *I* is the current curve. The value of current at any instant is determined by Ohm's law, the current depending upon the voltage and the resistance of the circuit. Here, at zero point on the voltage curve, the current is also zero. At maximum on the voltage curve, point *1*, the current is maximum. The two curves are in agreement at the next zero point, which is marked *2*. In the next half-cycle the two curves carry on together, being maximum at point *3* and zero at point *4*. The cycle, or *wave*, of voltage and of current shown here represents the condition in a circuit which has no inductance. In such cases, the voltage and current are said to be *in phase* with one another. Usually, circuits do have some inductance so that the relationship of current and voltage curves will be altered from that of Fig. 6.

Current Lag in Inductive Circuit. Fig. 7 illustrates the relationship between voltage and current curves in an alternating-current circuit in

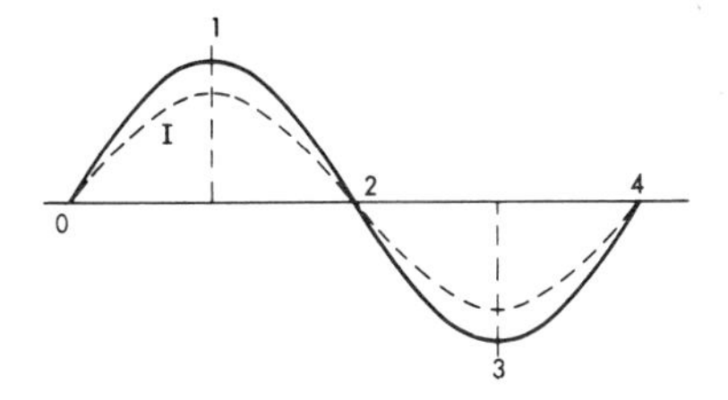

Fig. 6. Relation of Current and Voltage in a Non-Inductive Circuit

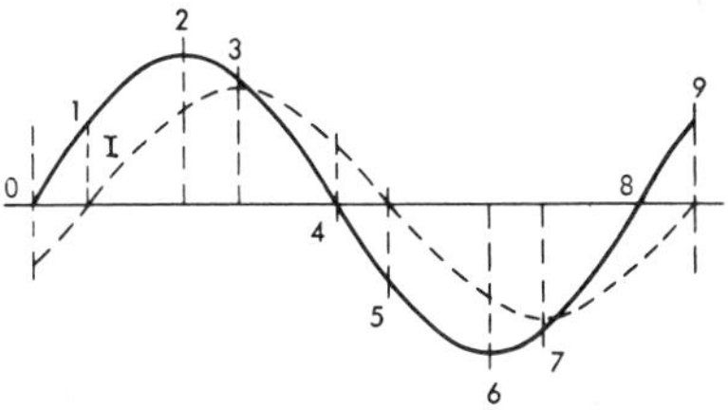

Fig. 7. Relation of Current and Voltage in an Inductive Circuit

which inductance is present. As the voltage, curve *E*, rises from zero, it tends to force current to flow in the circuit in exactly the same manner as in Fig. 6. The voltage of self-induction, however, opposes the circuit voltage, for it is trying to maintain current flow in the former direction. At point *1*, the circuit voltage and the voltage of self-induction are equal to one another, and the value of current represented by *I* is zero.

From point *1* the circuit voltage is greater than the voltage of self-induction so that current flows in the circuit. The circuit voltage reaches maximum value at point *2*, but the current does not reach maximum until point *3*. When the voltage passes through zero, point *4* in the figure, the value of current is yet some distance from zero, which is at point *5*. From point *4* to point *5*, the circuit voltage is trying to force current to flow in the negative direction but the voltage of self-induction is so great that it maintains flow in the positive direction in spite of opposition from the circuit voltage.

The circuit voltage reaches its maximum value in the negative direction at point *6*. The current, however, does not reach its maximum value until point *7*, and the voltage reaches its zero value again at point *8*, while the current does not reach zero until point *9*. It should be noted that the normal shape of sine wave, *I*, which represents current, is not altered by the effect of self-induction. The only effect is to shift the current curve some distance to the right of the voltage curve. This result is similar to the phase difference in a two-phase or three-phase armature with which we are already familiar. Therefore, it is said that the current lags behind the voltage in an inductive circuit. The amount of this lag depends upon the inductance of the particular circuit.

Reactance of Inductive Circuit. In some respects, inductance acts like ordinary resistance. For this reason, *inductive resistance,* or *inductive reactance* as it is called, is always expressed in ohms. In other words, the inductive reactance of a certain coil which has an inductance of 1/100 henry offers as much opposition to the flow of 60-cycle current as does a resistance of 3.77 ohms.

We will take a moment to examine the method of arriving at this value. The inductive reactance of a circuit is indicated by the term X_L, and its value is determined by the following formula.

$$X_L = 2\pi fL$$

X_L = inductive reactance in ohms.
π = a constant which is 3.14
f = frequency of the supply current in cycles per second.
L = value of the inductance in henries

In determining the inductive reactance of the coil which has an inductance of 1/100 henry when placed in a 60-cycle alternating-current circuit, we will substitute these values in the formula.

$$X_L = 2\pi fL$$
$$X_L = 2 \times 3.14 \times 60 \times \frac{1}{100}$$

Multiplying $2 \times 3.14 \times 60$, we have 376.8 (377 approximately), so

$$X_L = 377 \times \frac{1}{100}$$
$$X_L = 3.77 \text{ ohms}$$

We should take note of the fact that the frequency of the supply voltage is an important factor in determining this reactance; therefore, the reactance varies with the frequency. For example, this coil with an inductance of 1/100 henry offers only 3.14 ohms to the flow of 50-cycle current, which is determined as follows:

$$X_L = 2\pi fL$$
$$X_L = 2 \times 3.14 \times 50 \times \frac{1}{100}$$

$$X_L = 314 \times \frac{1}{100}$$
$$X_L = 3.14 \text{ ohms}$$

If the circuit contained nothing but inductance, the current flowing in the circuit would be determined simply with the aid of Ohm's law. There is no such thing, however, as a pure inductance, for all circuits contain at least some resistance. For this reason it becomes necessary to combine the resistance value with the inductive reactance value in order to obtain the total resistance of the circuit. This total resistance, which is the combination of both resistance and inductive reactance, is called the *impedance.*

A specific symbol has been given to the term impedance, and this symbol is the letter Z. We will see that this indicates the total opposition to current flow in a circuit.

Determining Impedance

The ohmic resistance of a circuit can not be added directly to the ohmic reactance in order to determine circuit impedance, but must be

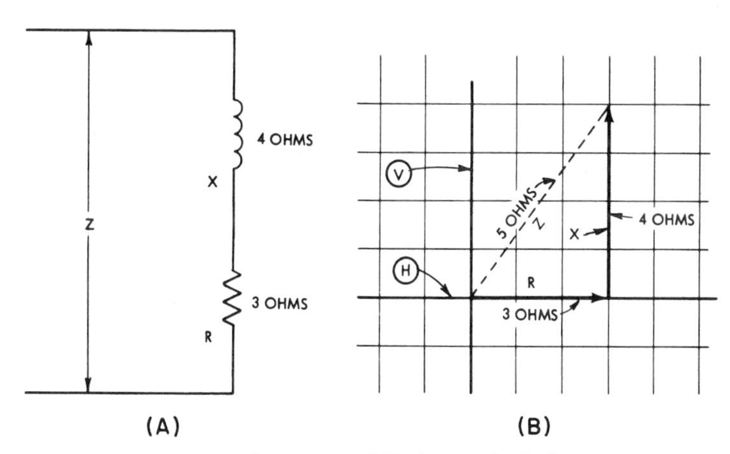

Fig. 8. Inductance and Resistance in Series

added in a particular way. This special way may be termed the right-angle method of addition, and can be performed easily with the help of graph paper. On this paper, which may be obtained at stationery stores, lines are drawn horizontally and vertically to form small squares. The ¼-inch square size used here, is a common variety.

In Fig. 8A, the value of inductive reactance in the circuit is 4 ohms, the resistance 3 ohms. It is desired to find the impedance of the circuit. Select a piece of squared paper. Draw two lines, *H* horizontal, and *V* vertical as in Fig. 8B. From the point of their intersection, draw a line to the right to indicate resistance of the circuit, this line being 3 squares in length. At the end of this line, draw another line vertically upward, and 4 squares long, to represent inductive reactance of 4 ohms.

Next, draw line Z, which is shown dotted in Fig. 8B, from the left end of the resistance line to the upper end of the reactance line, thus forming a triangle. If Z is now measured with a ruler, it will be found to be 1¼ inches long, this distance being equal to 5 of the ¼-inch squares, and thus indicating an impedance of 5 ohms.

Another Example of Impedance Calculation. A second example may be worked out with the aid of Fig. 9. The resistance of a circuit

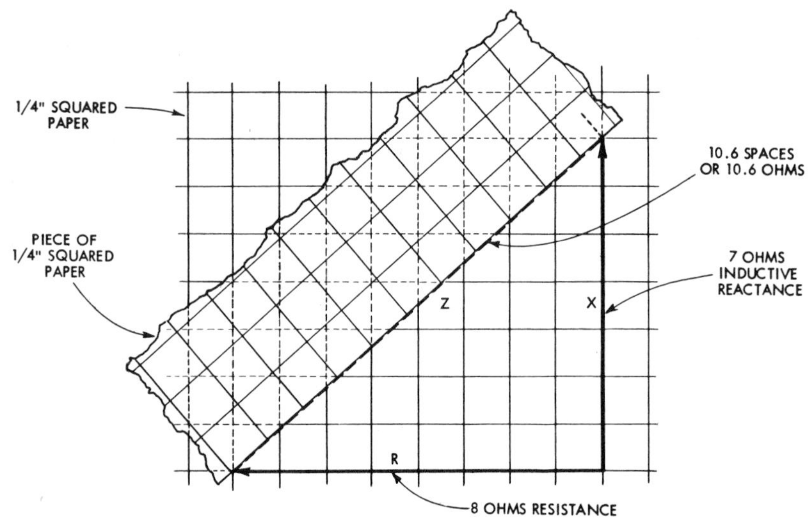

Fig. 9. Measuring Impedance with Edge of Squared Paper

is assumed to be 8 ohms, its inductive reactance 7 ohms, and its voltage 105. We desire to learn the current flowing in the circuit. Before this can be ascertained, it is necessary to find the impedance of the circuit.

Two lines are drawn on ¼-inch squared paper at right angles to one another. Resistance is always marked off on the horizontal line, while inductive reactance is marked upon the vertical line extending upward from the right-hand end of the resistance line. Here, 8 spaces are counted off to represent 8 ohms on the horizontal line, and 7 spaces are counted upward from this point to represent 7 ohms on the vertical line.

A ruler shows the length of the Z-line as somewhat over 2½ inches, or between 10 and 11 quarters of an inch. A simple method for measuring the impedance line, especially where, as in the present case, fractions of a quarter are encountered, is illustrated in the figure. A piece of the squared paper, itself, is used as the measure, an edge of the paper being laid along the Z-line. It will be noted that there are 10 full spaces, and slightly more than another half space, so that the length is approximately 10.6 spaces, or 10.6 ohms.

Since the voltage is 105 and the impedance approximately 10.6 ohms, the current flowing in the circuit may be determined by Ohm's law to be 9.9 amperes.

Where there are a number of parallel circuits, each having a different value of inductance and of resistance, the impedance of each branch may be obtained separately, and the current determined for each branch with the aid of Ohm's law.

CAPACITANCE IN ALTERNATING-CURRENT CIRCUITS

Capacitor

A *capacitor,* or a *condenser* as it is sometimes called, is primarily a device for storing electricity. It does not store electricity by chemical action, as does the secondary battery, nor does it store it in such a way that a small steady current may be taken from it over a long period of time; yet the action of capacitors in alternating-current circuits is as important as that of inductances.

The manner in which a capacitor acts may be learned with the help of Fig. 10A. The capacitor consists of two metal plates, S_1 and S_2,

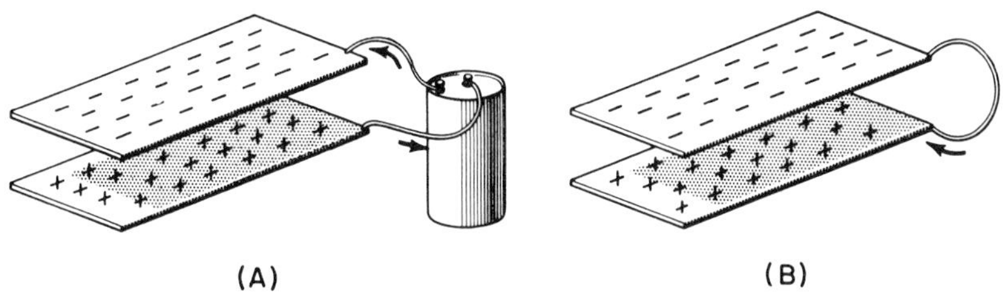

Fig. 10. Charge and Discharge of Capacitor

which are separated by a small air space or by a piece of insulating material. When a dry cell is attached to the plates of the capacitor unit by small connecting wires, current flows to the positive plate of the capacitor. That is, the *electron flow* is from the negative plate of the capacitor into the dry cell, resulting in a shortage of electrons on this plate. The negative plate, on the other hand, has a surplus of electrons.

If the dry cell is now removed, one plate of the capacitor having a positive charge and the other plate a negative charge, the unit will store these charges for a considerable length of time. But if a wire makes connection between the two plates, Fig. 10B, the excess electrons on S_2 rush through the connecting wire as a current of electricity to neutralize the positive charge on plate S_1.

Unit of Capacitance. The amount of charge which a capacitor will hold depends upon its physical dimensions as well as upon the insulating material between the plates. This quality of a capacitor is termed

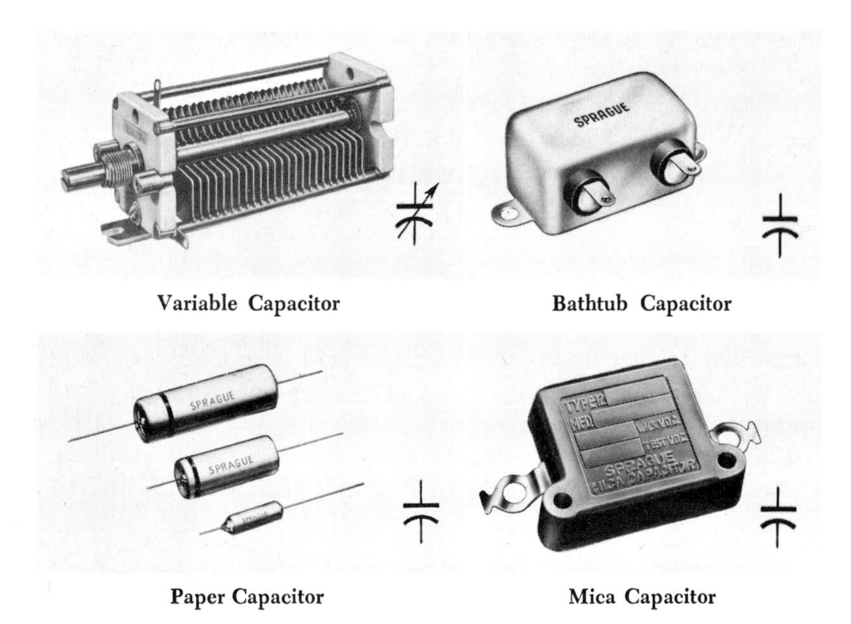

Variable Capacitor **Bathtub Capacitor**

Paper Capacitor **Mica Capacitor**

Fig. 11. Types of Capacitors and Their Schematic Symbols

its *capacitance* or its *capacity*. The latter term, though not exactly a correct one, is often used. The unit of capacitance is the *farad*. This unit is much too large for expressing the quantity of capacitance ordinarily found in electric circuits. Therefore, the term *microfarad* is more common. A microfarad is simply one-millionth ($1/_{1,000,000}$) part of a farad. These terms need not be dwelt upon at this point, however, because the effect of capacitance, like that of inductance, is always expressed in ohms. Several types of capacitors are shown in Fig. 11.

Effect of Capacitance in Circuit

In Fig. 12A *G*, an alternating-current generator, is connected in series with resistor *R* and capacitor *C*, the upper terminal of *G* being

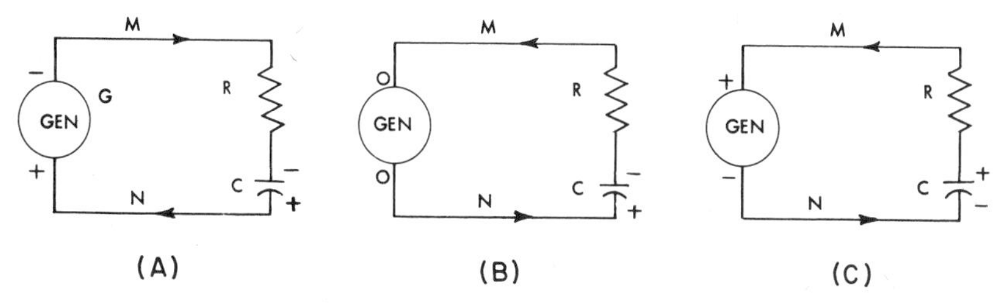

Fig. 12. Alternating Current in a Capacitive Circuit

negative and the lower terminal positive at the moment. Electrons are attracted from the lower plate of *C* to the positive terminal of *G*, the passage of these electrons through wire *N* forming a current of electricity. At the same time, electrons pass from the negative terminal of *G* to the upper plate of *C* to supply atoms whose electrons have been drawn out of orbits by attraction of the now positively-charged lower plate of *C*. This flow of electrons from the negative terminal of *G* to the upper plate of *C* constitutes a flow of electric current in wire *M*.

It should be observed that no current flows directly from the upper plate of *C* through intervening space to the lower plate. The only flow of current in the circuit is from *G* to *C* or from *C* to *G*.

Now, as a positive charge grows on the lower plate of *C*, and a negative charge increases on the upper plate of *C*, electrical pressure (voltage) is built up in *C*. This voltage tries to force electrons from the upper plate of *C* through the generator in a counterclockwise direction to the lower plate of *C*. The generator voltage opposes this force, since *G* is trying to send current in the opposite, or clockwise, direction. But, as *G*'s voltage decreases along a sine curve of pressure, the voltage of the capacitor finally exceeds that of the generator, and manages to force current in the counterclockwise direction.

At the instant shown in Fig. 12B, when *G*'s voltage is passing through zero, the flow of current established by *C*'s voltage is quite high. When the generator pressure starts to increase again, but in the below-the-line direction, it tends to establish a current which flows in a counterclockwise direction, as in Fig. 12C. The capacitor has already started a flow of current in this direction. A capacitor is said, therefore, to force current to lead the voltage of a circuit. This effect is directly opposite to that of circuit inductance which, it may be recalled, forces current to lag behind the voltage.

Relationship of Voltage and Current Curves. Fig. 13 shows the sine curves of voltage and current in a circuit which contains capacitance.

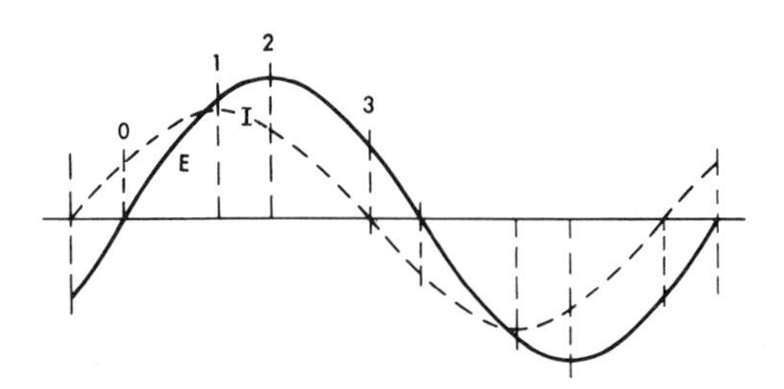

Fig. 13. Relation of Current and Voltage in Capacitive Circuit

At point *O*, when voltage *E* of the generator is zero, current *I* in the circuit is already at a considerable value. The current reaches its maximum value at point *1*, but the voltage does not do so until point *2*. At point *3*, although the generator voltage is still active and is trying to force current through the circuit, the voltage of the capacitor exactly equals that of the generator so that the current in the circuit is zero.

The negative relationship is exactly the same as the positive relationship, the current reaching its maximum and zero values ahead of the voltage. Thus, while current lags behind the voltage in an inductive circuit, it leads the voltage in a capacitive circuit.

Determining the Reactance of a Capacitor

The capacitor, like the inductor, offers opposition to the flow of alternating current. This opposition to alternating current is known as capacitive reactance and it is measured also in ohms. The symbol used to indicate capacitive reactance is X_c. The value of capacitive reactance is determined by means of a formula, which is somewhat similar to formula for finding inductive reactance. This formula is written

$$X_c = \frac{1}{2\pi fC}$$

X_c = capacitive reactance in ohms
π = 3.14
f = frequency of the alternating current in cycles per second
C = capacity of the unit in farads

We have already mentioned that the farad is a unit much larger than found in normal use, but the formula calls for the value of the capacitance in farads. Therefore, we will have to write the value of the capacitor in farads. This is done by dividing the value as given in microfarads by 1,000,000. An example will show how this is done.

Let us place a 665-microfarad capacitor in a 60-cycle alternating-current circuit. To express the value of this capacitor in farads, we must divide by 1,000,000. This is easily done by moving the decimal point 6 places to the left. Therefore, $665.00 \div 1{,}000{,}000 = 0.000665$. Substituting in the formula we have

$$X_c = \frac{1}{2\pi fC}$$

$$X_c = \frac{1}{2 \times 3.14 \times 60 \times 0.000665}$$

Multiplying the numbers in the denominator, we have

$$X_c = \frac{1}{0.250572}$$

For our purposes, it is sufficiently accurate to write the denominator as 0.25, which gives

$$X_c = \frac{1}{0.25}$$

$$X_c = 4 \text{ ohms}$$

Let us make note of one change that can be made in this formula, namely, we can write the value of the capacitor in microfarads if the denominator is divided into 1,000,000 instead of one. Therefore, using the value of the capacitor in microfarads, the formula is written:

$$X_c = \frac{1{,}000{,}000}{2\pi fC}$$

Now that we have determined the capacitive reactance of this 665-

microfarad capacitor, we will place it and a resistor in a 105-volt, 60-cycle circuit.

Determining Impedance of Circuit Having Resistance and Capacitance

Fig. 14A shows a circuit which contains a resistor whose value is 3 ohms and a capacitor whose reactance is 4 ohms. The impedance of the group may be obtained by the use of squared paper in a manner quite

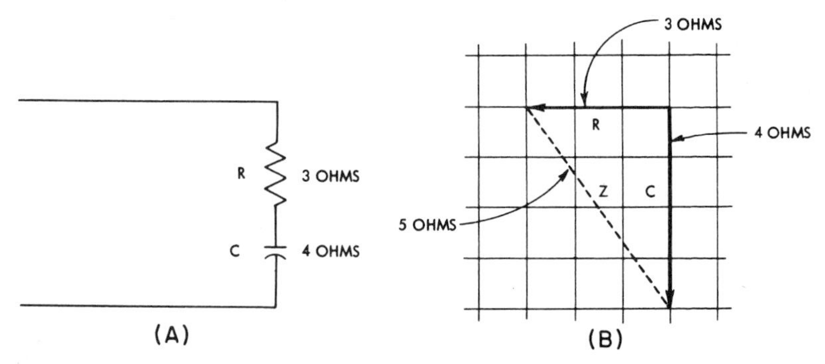

Fig. 14. Resistance and Capacitance in Series

similar to that for determining impedance in the inductive circuit. Two lines are drawn at right angles, Fig. 14B. As before, the horizontal line represents resistance in the circuit. The vertical line represents reactance due to capacitance. It should be noted that the vertical line is drawn downward from the corner instead of upward, as in the case of inductance. This relationship must be followed at all times: *inductive reactance upward* and *capacitive reactance downward.*

Mark off three spaces to the left of the corner to indicate 3 ohms resistance and 4 spaces downward to indicate 4 ohms capacitive reactance. The length of the Z line, which is drawn from the point where the vertical and horizontal lines cross to the tip of the arrow indicating capacitive reactance, is measured in the same way as in Fig. 8. This measurement indicates that the impedance is 5 ohms, which is the same as a similar circuit containing inductance rather than capacitance.

Circuit Containing Resistance, Inductance, and Capacitance

Fig. 15A illustrates a circuit which contains a resistance of 5 ohms, an inductance of 4 ohms, and a capacitance of 3 ohms. The impedance of this group may be determined as shown in Fig. 15B. A horizontal line is drawn to represent circuit resistance. A vertical line which extends both above and below the resistance line is drawn at right angles to it to represent inductance and capacitance. Resistance is marked off on the horizontal line to represent 5 ohms. Inductive reactance amounting to 4 ohms is marked off, upward, on the vertical line. Capacitive reactance amounting to 3 ohms is marked off downward on the vertical line.

Now, transfer the shorter of the two vertical lines, which is the capacitive reactance, and place it by the longer line, which is the inductive reactance. The shorter line is marked off from the tip of the longer. In Fig. 15B, the capacitive-reactance arrow is indicated with a broken arrow pointing downward. This measurement brings us to

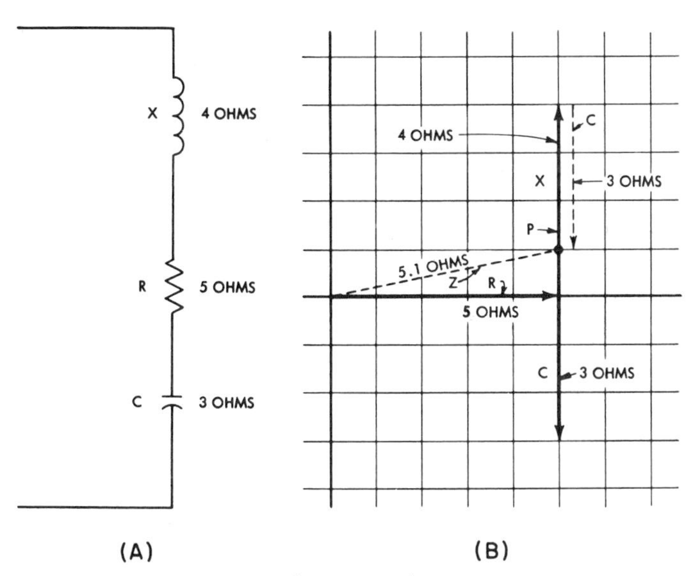

Fig. 15. Resistance, Inductance and Capacitance in Series

point *P*. By this means, the value of capacitive reactance is subtracted from the inductive reactance. A moment's reflection will show why this procedure is followed. Since inductive reactance forces the current to lag behind the voltage and, since capacitive reactance forces current to lead the voltage, the two forces are in opposition. And, since the value of the reactance in ohms represents the effectiveness of inductance or of capacitance in the circuit, the resultant effect upon the circuit is equal to the difference between the two values. If inductive reactance is greater than capacitive reactance, the second quantity would be subtracted from the first. If capacitive reactance were greater, the inductive reactance would be subtracted from it.

Drawing the Z line from the origin (the point where the horizontal and vertical lines cross) to the point *P*, we find that the impedance is about 5.1 ohms. Current in the circuit is determined by dividing circuit voltage by this value of impedance. It is well to mention that the impedance would lie below the resistance line if the value of capacitive reactance were 4 ohms and the inductive reactance 3 ohms. The impedance would have the same value, for the impedance line would be equally long in either case. Where the inductive reactance is greater, the current lags the voltage, which is represented by the fact that point *P* lies above the resistance line. If the capacitive reactance is greater, the current leads the voltage, which fact is indicated by point *P* lying below the resistance line.

Resonance. Fig. 16A shows a circuit containing a resistance of 5 ohms, an inductance of 4 ohms, and a capacitance of 4 ohms. It is seen

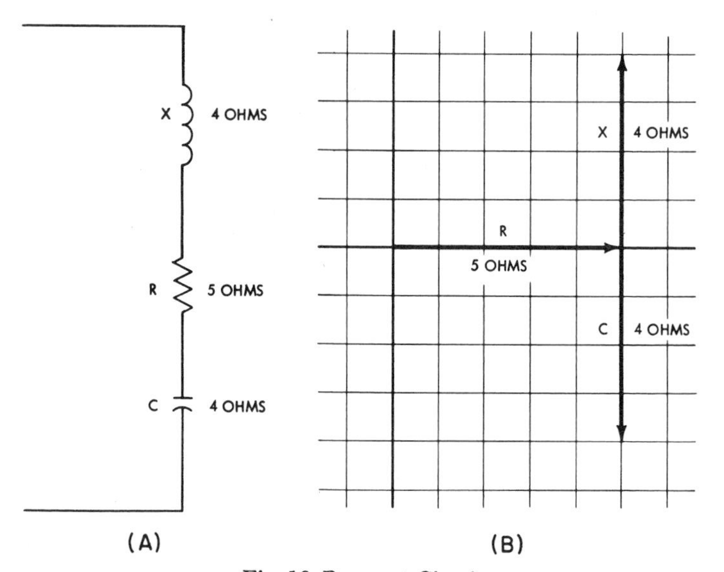

Fig. 16. Resonant Circuit

that the value of inductive reactance is exactly equal to capacitive reactance. Fig. 16B illustrates how these quantities may be represented on graph paper. The arrows for resistance, inductive reactance, and capacitive reactance are indicated, but if either capacitive or inductive reactance is subtracted from the other the result is zero.

That is, the effect of capacitance is neutralized by that of inductance. Under this condition, the circuit is said to be *resonant*, and the quality of being resonant is expressed by the term *resonance*. The current in a resonant circuit may be obtained by dividing circuit voltage by circuit resistance.

Power Factor

A term which is quite important in connection with alternating current is "power factor." The meaning of the expression may be clarified by referring back to Fig. 15B. It is simply the numerical relationship between the line representing resistance and that representing impedance. The resistance line, here, is 5 units long, which means 5 ohms. The impedance line is 5.1 units in length. The power factor of the circuit is equal to 5 divided by 5.1, or approximately 0.98.

Inductance and Capacitance in Two-Phase and Three-Phase Circuits. Facts and principles brought out here with regard to single-phase circuits are directly applicable to two-phase and three-phase circuits. Inductance and capacitance affect the relationship between current and voltage in exactly the same way as in the single-phase circuit. The fact that impedance calculations may prove somewhat more involved is of no great concern at the moment.

REVIEW QUESTIONS

1. When do circles of force cease to expand as they move out from the center of the wire?
2. What effect has the voltage of self-induction as the current is increasing?
3. What effect does it have as the current begins to decrease?
4. Tell how a spark occurs at switch contacts.
5. What factors determine the strength of a voltage of self-induction?
6. Discuss current lag in the inductive circuit.
7. How is the value of inductive reactance, in a circuit, usually expressed?
8. Outline the method for determining circuit impedance by the use of squared paper.
9. Explain how capacitance affects current flow in a circuit.
10. What is the practical unit of capacitance?
11. How is capacitive reactance determined?

12. How is circuit impedance determined when both inductance and capacitance are present in the circuit?

13. If a circuit contains 10 ohms resistance, 5 ohms of inductive reactance, and 10 ohms of capacitive reactance, what is its impedance?

14. What condition makes a circuit resonant?

15. To what does the term "power factor" refer?

CHAPTER 9

POWER AND HEATING EFFECTS

DIRECT-CURRENT POWER

Heat Created by Current Flow

An earlier chapter pointed out that force or energy supplied by the generator is partially expended in forcing current through the conductor. It was pointed out, too, that electrical pressure is lost in the process. The loss of pressure is termed voltage drop. Voltage drop is only one sign of loss of energy. A more noticeable result is the production of heat, for heat is always created when a current flows through a conductor.

Rate at which Heat Is Created. The amount of heat so created depends upon the physical nature of the material of which the conductor is made. For a certain amount of current flow, the amount of energy used up in some conductors is much greater than in others. To some extent, the physical nature of the material is expressed in its resistance for a certain length; but resistance is only one of the factors which determine the quantity of heat produced. The other factor is the amount of current flowing in the conductor. In other words, the amount of heat depends upon both resistance and current.

But it does not vary simply as the product of resistance and current. It has been found that the heat created depends upon the product of resistance times the current squared. Since power is required to generate heat, we can say that the *power* varies as the resistance times the current squared.

Power Formula. This rule may be expressed by means of the formula

$$P = I^2R$$

P = power being used in the circuit.
I^2 = the value of the current in the circuit squared. $(I \times I)$
R = the resistance of the circuit.

The letter P is used to represent the term power, and P is a measure of the rate at which power is consumed. When the amount of power that is converted into heat is determined, the temperature rise of the conductor may be calculated with the aid of certain mathematical procedures. However, the actual temperature rise of the conductor is unimportant at this time. The essential requirement is to determine the amount of power expended.

Unit of Power. The unit of power is the *Watt*. The term will be more fully explained in a moment, but it is necessary to refer again to the formula for power.

Here,

$$P = I^2R$$
$$P = I \times I \times R$$

From our study of Ohm's law, we learned that

$$E = I \times R$$

therefore, we can substitute E for $I \times R$ in the power formula and write it as

$$P = E \times I$$
$$P = EI$$

And, since power is expressed in watts, it may be said that watts equals volts times amperes. The watt, then, which is the unit of power, is equal to one volt times one ampere, and the number of watts consumed in an electrical resistor is equal to the voltage drop in the resistor multiplied by the current flowing through it. The term *kilowatt* means 1,000 watts.

Examples of Power Consumption

The circuit shown in Fig. 1 will help make clear the relationship between these terms. In Fig. 1 a wire having a resistance of 5 ohms is connected across a 25-volt, direct-current generator. Employing Ohm's law, we find that 5 amps will flow through the wire.

$$I = \frac{E}{R}$$
$$I = \frac{25}{5}$$
$$I = 5 \text{ amps}$$

In order to determine the power used in sending 5 amps through the 5-ohm wire, we will use the power formula.

$$P = EI$$
$$P = 25 \times 5$$
$$P = 125 \text{ watts}$$

Another example of power consumption is illustrated by Fig. 2. A toaster and hotplate are connected to a circuit which is supplied by a 120-volt generator. The current consumption marked on the toaster

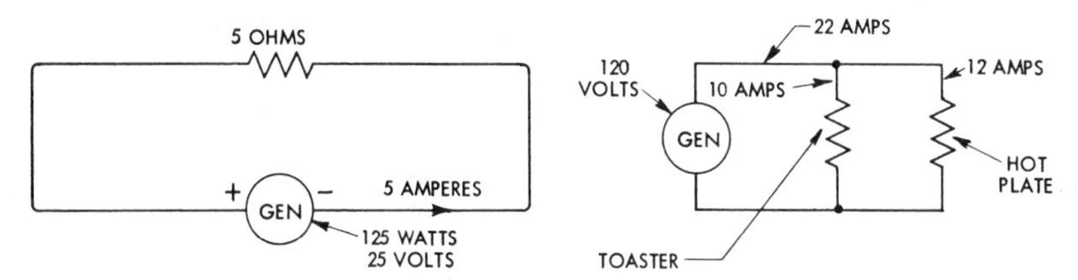

Fig. 1. Power in Simple Circuit

Fig. 2. Another Example of Power Consumption

nameplate is 10 amperes, that on the hotplate 12 amperes, the total current in the circuit being 22 amperes.

Power dissipated by the toaster is equal to $E \times I$, or 120×10, or 1200 watts. That dissipated by the hotplate is equal to 120×12, or 1440 watts. The total wattage is equal to $1200 + 1440$, or 2640 watts. The same result may be obtained by multiplying voltage and circuit current, 120×22, which equals 2640 watts, as before.

ALTERNATING-CURRENT POWER

Effective Value of Alternating Current and Voltage Waves

Before proceeding with the study of alternating-current power, it is necessary to understand just what is meant by the terms "current" and "voltage" in the alternating-current circuit. Fig. 3*A* shows a sine curve

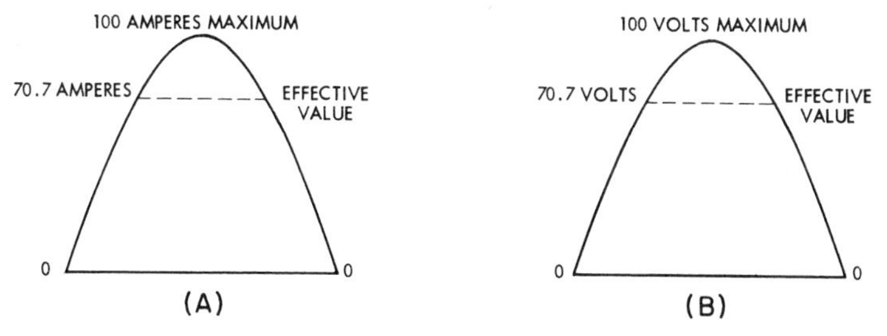

Fig. 3. A–Sine Wave of Current; B–Sine Wave of Voltage

of current with a maximum value of 100 amperes. But we know that when a current of 100 amperes flows through a resistance of 1 ohm, 10,000 watts $(100^2 \times 1)$ of heat are dissipated. The 100-ampere value cannot be used, therefore, because this maximum state holds for such a small portion of the full alternation. Some other value, then, must be chosen.

Laboratory tests show that a sine wave of current having a maximum value of 100 amperes and flowing through a 1-ohm resistor, liberates the same amount of heat as a direct current of 70.7 amperes flowing under the same conditions. For this reason, it is said that the effective value of a sine wave of alternating current is equal to 0.707 times the maximum value.

It is equally apparent that the sine curve of alternating voltage necessary to form this alternating current through a 1-ohm resistor, will be similar to the current curve. This is shown in Fig. 3B. And, since its effectiveness must be the same as that of a direct-current voltage of 70.7 volts, the effective value of the sine wave of alternating voltage is also equal to 0.707 times its maximum value.

This effective value is that which is indicated by alternating-current measuring instruments, which will be studied later. When we speak of 5 amperes of alternating current; of 100 volts of alternating current, or any such quantities as may be selected, the effective values are intended.

Power in Non-Inductive Circuit

Fig. 4A shows a 2-ohm resistor connected to a 120-volt alternating-current generator, 60 amperes flowing in the circuit $(E/R = I)$.

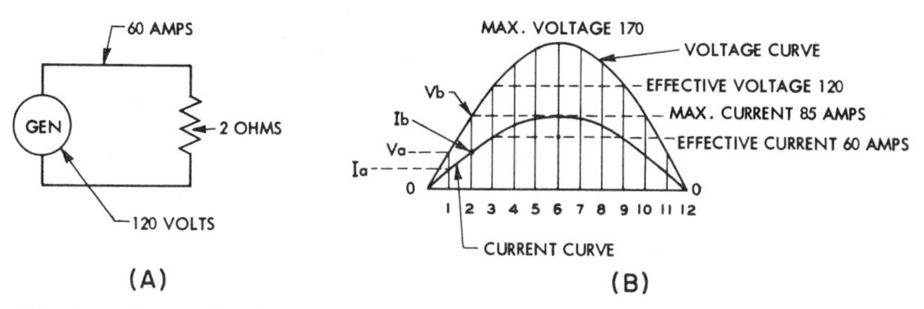

Fig. 4. A–Non-Inductive Circuit; B–Sine Waves of Voltage and Current in the Circuit

Fig. 4B illustrates the sine curves of voltage and current active in the circuit. It may be noted that the maximum voltage is approximately 170, effective 120, and the maximum current approximately 85, effective 60. It is worth noting that the effective value of alternating voltage is divided by the resistance of the circuit in order to determine the effective value of current.

In Fig. 4B, voltage and current rise from zero to maximum together, and fall to zero again at the same instant. That is, they are in phase with each other. At any particular moment, the power dissipated in the circuit is equal to the instantaneous values of voltage and current. The power at instant *1*, for example, is equal to $Va \times Ia$. That at instant *2* is $Vb \times Ib$, and so on throughout the whole alternation, following the sine-curve pattern of voltage and current. These various amounts might be added together to obtain the total quantity of power expended during the alternation, a very complicated process. But, since we know that the effective voltage is 120 and the effective current 60 amperes, we need only multiply these two amounts in order to obtain the total power.

Here, the total power is equal to 120×60, or 7200 watts. Laboratory tests prove the accuracy of this method, the heat generated in the present instance being exactly equal to that produced by a direct current of 60 amperes at 120 volts flowing through a resistance of 2 ohms.

Power in Inductive Circuit

Fig. 5A represents a circuit in which a 120-volt alternating current generator supplies an inductance of 1 ohm and a resistance of 1.73 ohms. In order to find the current flowing through the circuit, we must obtain circuit impedance as in Fig. 5B, using the right-angle method of addition. The impedance is found to be 2 ohms and the current 60 amperes. But, since inductance is present, circuit current lags circuit voltage as shown in Fig. 5C.

This illustration is similar to Fig. 4B, except that the current curve has been shifted two spaces to the right. This "shift" distance may be determined with the help of Fig. 5B, where the angle *C* represents a full revolution of a conductor in a two-pole generator, or a complete cycle of 360 degrees. Angle S represents a half-revolution of 180 degrees, or an alternation. If angle (*A*) of the impedance triangle is measured with a protractor it will be found to equal 30 degrees, which is $\frac{1}{6}$ of an alternation. In Fig. 5C, $\frac{1}{6}$ of the alternation is equal to two of the twelve spaces into which the base line is divided.

Since the voltage and current curves do not rise and fall together, the power dissipated at any particular instant will be different from that of Fig. 4. At point 2, for example, where momentary voltage is

Vb and momentary current zero, the power at that instant is $Vb \times 0$, or zero. We cannot, therefore, multiply effective voltage and effective current to find the amount of power expended over the full period of an alternation.

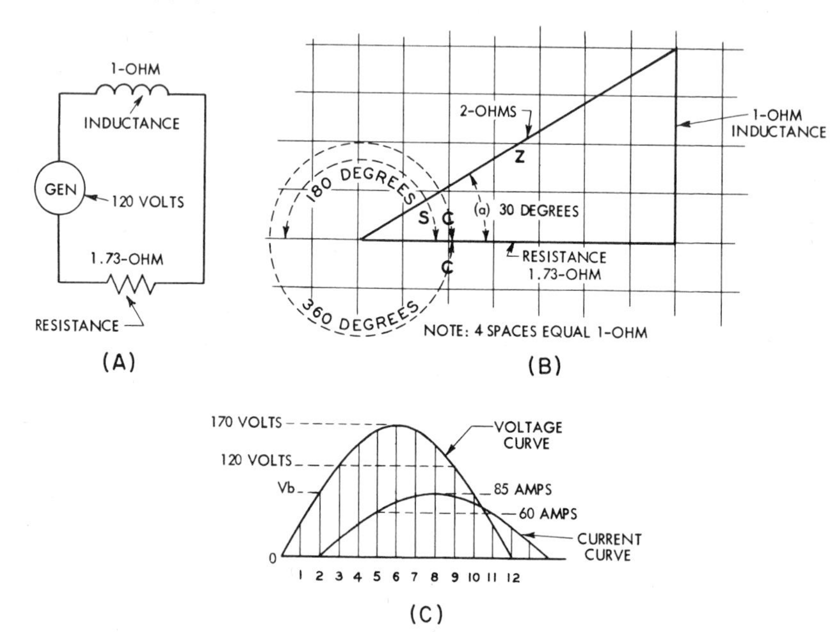

Fig. 5. A–Inductance and Resistance in Series; B–Impedance of Circuit and Angle of Lag; C–Current Leading Voltage

Tests show that power may be determined, however, by multiplying effective voltage, effective current, and power factor. It may be recalled, from the preceding chapter, that circuit power factor is a value obtained by dividing circuit resistance by circuit impedance. In the present case, where the impedance is 2 ohms and resistance 1.73 ohms, the power factor is equal to 1.73/2, or .866.

Thus, the power in the circuit illustrated here is equal to $E \times I \times .866$, which is: $.20 \times 60 \times .866$, or approximately 6235 watts.

LIMITING CURRENT IN ELECTRICAL CONDUCTORS

Carrying Capacity of Insulated Conductors

A short section of No. 14 copper wire is indicated in Fig. 6A. Since the wire has no insulating cover, it is called *bare wire*. Now, as current flows through this wire, a certain amount of heat is generated per foot of conductor. When 5 amps flow, heat is generated at a certain rate. When 10 amps flow, heat is generated four times as fast. This is because the heat generated varies as the current squared, as in $P = I^2R$. Taking the square of the current in each case, we have

$$I_1^2 = 5 \times 5 = 25$$
$$I_2^2 = 10 \times 10 = 100$$

and

$$\frac{25}{100} = \frac{1}{4}$$

This shows that the heating effect with 10 amps flowing is four times that when 5 amps is flowing.

If the wire is placed upon a substance which will not burn, this wire could transmit a current of perhaps 50 amps without damage to itself, but, if the wire is insulated as in Fig. 6B, its current must be restricted to a value where the amount of heat which is generated will not raise the temperature high enough to damage the insulating material. The insulation upon the wire in Fig. 6B is largely rubber, this material being next to the copper. The rubber coating is 3⁄64 of an inch thick, and it has a cotton braid around it. The braid affords mechanical protection to the rubber, and the rubber provides insulation of high quality to prevent leakage of current to surrounding objects.

By means of careful laboratory tests, it has been determined that this No. 14 copper wire may carry 15 amps continuously without gen-

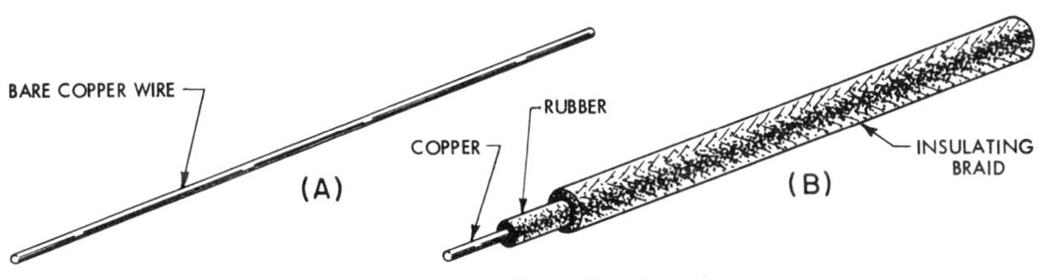

Fig. 6. Bare and Insulated Wire

erating sufficient heat to damage the rubber insulating material. If the current is permitted to rise above this value, the material will be overheated so that it will lose its insulating properties. For this reason, it is said that the *carrying capacity* of No. 14 rubber-covered copper wire is 15 amps. Larger sizes have larger carrying capacities. Smaller wires have less carrying capacity.

Overcurrent Protection

It is now possible to explain the purpose and the operation of overcurrent devices commonly found at electrical panelboards. Overcurrent protective units are connected in series with the supply wires, and they are constructed to limit the current flowing in the conductors to a safe value. The methods for limiting the current flow, both through conducting wires and the various pieces of electrical equipment, can be broadly divided into two classifications. These are *fuses* and *circuit breakers.* Although both units are built to serve the same purpose, namely, prevent the flow of excessive current, the construction and operation of these units differ widely. Therefore, we will consider them individually.

Construction of Fuses. In its basic form, a fuse is a section of metal inserted in the supply line, Fig. 7, that will fuse (melt) when

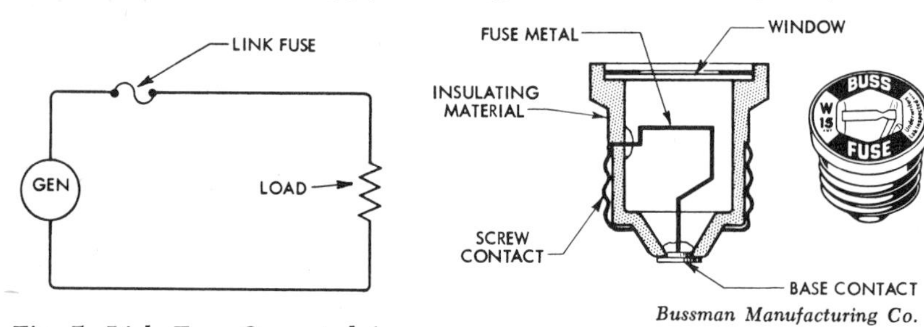

Fig. 7. Link Fuse Connected in Circuit

Bussman Manufacturing Co.

Fig. 8. Plug Fuse

an excess of current flows and open the circuit. The section of metal that makes up the fuse proper is called the *link,* and the cross-sectional area of this metallic link is such that it will carry its rated current without melting. Fuses are built in two general forms, cartridge and plug fuses.

A modern plug fuse is shown in Fig. 8. The outer portion of the fuse has a threaded brass shell which fits into a socket. When placed in the socket, the outside shell of the fuse makes contact with the screw shell of the socket, and the center contact of the fuse touches a center contact in the socket. The fusible link is connected between the center contact and the fuse shell. With the fuse in place, current flows through the socket to the fuse shell. It then flows through the fusible link to the center contact and on through the socket to the connecting lead.

The fuse link is visible through a mica or glass window of the fuse. The metal of the link is often made somewhat narrower at this point so it will blow there. In this case, it may be determined whether or not the fuse is blown by glancing at the window.

The other commonly employed type is the cartridge fuse, Fig. 9.

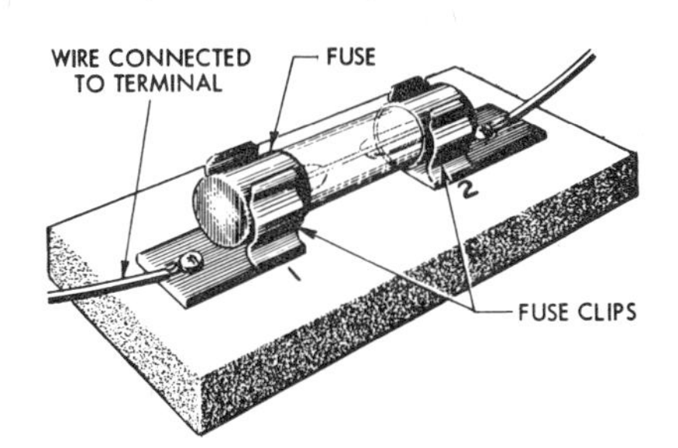

Fig. 9. Cartridge Fuse

The fuse is held in place by means of two clips at each end. Connection is made to the fusible link by means of the clips and the ferrules. When the fuse is pressed into the clips, current passes from the terminal to *clip 1,* to the ferrule of the fuse, through the fuse link, to the other ferrule, to *clip* 2 and its terminal, to the second circuit wire.

The link of the cartridge fuse may be embedded in an earthen material to prevent air from coming in contact with it. This helps extinguish the arc which forms when the fuse blows. This type is more accurate than either the open type or the plug type, for the material which surrounds the link tends to make its temperature rise quickly to the melting point when the normal current is exceeded. A fuse of this type rated at 15 amps would carry perhaps 16.5 amps continuously but it would blow before the current reached 20 amps.

Some cartridge fuses are so constructed that the link may be replaced when they have blown, and these are known as *renewable* fuses. The other cartridge fuses and the plug fuses must be replaced after they have opened the circuit.

An additional feature has been incorporated in the design of certain modern fuses which is known as *time lag.* This means the fuse will not immediately melt when more than rated current flows through the circuit. Let us examine where this is employed to advantage. Consider the case where fifteen 100-watt lamps are connected to one supply source that is fused for 15 amps. During normal operation these lamps draw about 13 amps, which is well within the limit of the fuse. Should all these lamps be switched on at once, the inrush of current would be about 170 amps. This inrush of current lasts only for about $\frac{1}{20}$ of a second, but fuses without the time delay feature will blow before the filaments of the lamps heat up, and the current falls to normal. The duration of this high current flow is for too short a time to injure the circuit wiring. If the duration of this current flow is extended, however, the fuse with time lag will blow in less than a second, and prevent damage to the insulation on the conductors.

Although a fuse serves a very useful purpose in protecting wires and equipment from excessive continuous loads, it also serves as a guard against fire hazards in case of a short circuit. A short circuit,

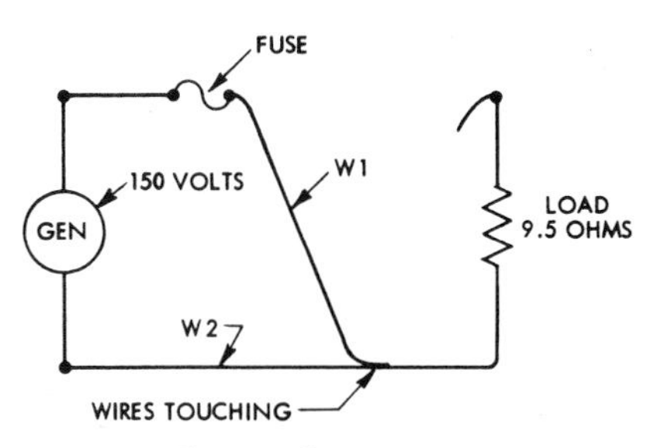

Fig. 10. Short Circuit

as the term states, is a shortening of the normal circuit. This fact may be explained by referring to Fig. 10. Here, the generator has been supplying current to the load which has a resistance of 9.5 ohms. The resistance of connecting wires W_1 and W_2 is 0.5 ohm. Thus, the total resistance in the circuit is 10 ohms, and the current is 15 amps, but wire W_1 has broken loose from the load and fallen upon wire W_2 so that the two copper conductors make contact with one another.

The total resistance of the circuit has now decreased from 10 ohms to approximately 0.5 ohm. Under this condition, Ohm's law shows that the current in the circuit is

$$I = \frac{E}{R}$$

$$I = \frac{150}{0.5}$$

$$I = 300 \text{ amps}$$

This current would be sufficient to burn up the insulation on the wire and to melt the conductor, perhaps causing a fire; but at the instant of short circuit, when the current begins to soar from its normal level of 15 amps, the fuse will melt and open the circuit.

Circuit Breakers

Overcurrent protection is also obtainable with the aid of circuit breakers, one of which is shown in Fig. 11. When excessive current

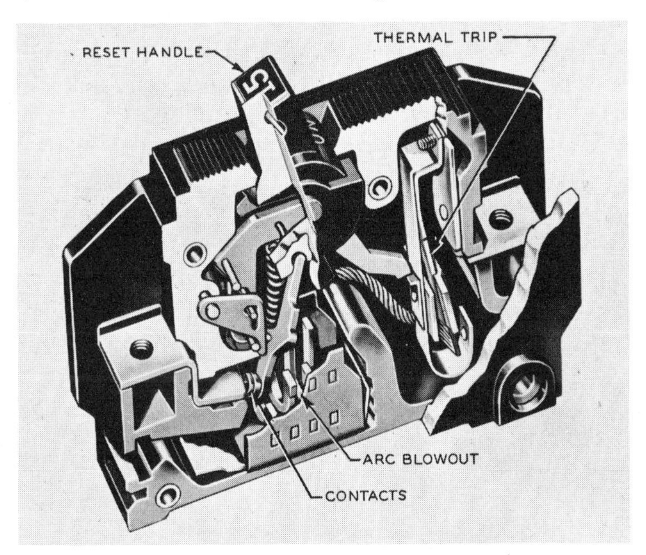

Federal Electric Products Co.

Fig. 11. Circuit Breaker

flows through the device, an electromagnet or a thermal arm trips a latch which opens the contacts.

Circuit Protection. Fuses and circuit breakers have both advantages and disadvantages. The initial cost of a fuse is usually less than a circuit breaker, but the fuse or the link must be replaced each time the fuse opens the circuit. The circuit breaker, although having a higher initial cost, merely needs to be reset, and the circuit is back in operation. We must remember, however, that the circuit breaker is a mechanical device, and all mechanical devices are subject to failure. These failures are almost nonexistent in this field, for a great amount of research has gone into the building of circuit breakers.

There is one point to be born in mind, regardless of whether circuit breakers or fuses are used for circuit protection, namely, clear the fault before supplying power. Overcurrent devices do not open without reason; therefore, we must find the cause for the overcurrent device opening before renewing service.

HEATING DEVICES

Heating Elements

The units which create heat in domestic and industrial heating devices are called *heating elements.* Fig. 12 shows a simple heating element. The wire used to form the element is a special material which has a resistance several times that of copper. If this unit were wound

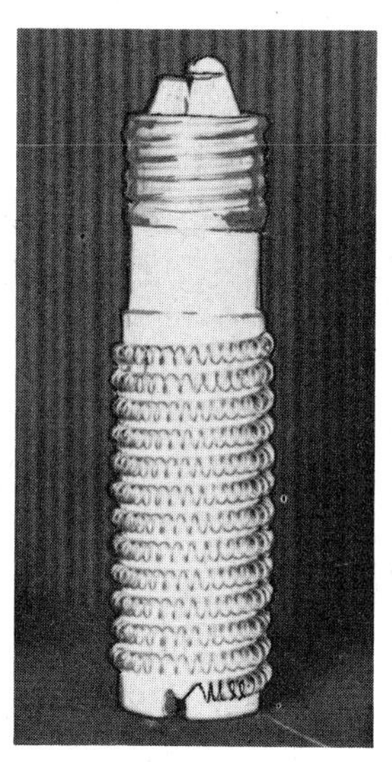

Fig. 12. Heating Element

Fig. 13. Electric Toaster Heating Element

of copper and the current were 6 amps, the voltage drop across the unit would be 2 volts. The wattage available for producing heat would be 6×2, or 12 watts. When wound with this special resistance wire, the voltage necessary to force 6 amperes through the unit is 120. In this case, the wattage available for purposes of heating is equal to 6×120, or 720 watts. A sufficient number of copper units to produce this much heat would require 60 times as much space for copper wire as for resistance wire. In other words, it would be impractical to use copper heating elements.

Electric Toaster. There are many kinds of resistance wire. They are marketed under various trade names, such as Nichrome and Climax. These wires are formed into elements of every conceivable shape and size for performing special tasks. Fig. 13 shows the element of an electric toaster. A flat resistance wire is used for this application and is usually called *ribbon nichrome.* A device such as an iron or toaster whose operation depends upon heat, is called a heating appliance.

Thermostat

The temperature of electrical heating devices is controlled usually by some form of heat-operated switch which is called a *thermostat.* An electric iron usually uses a thermostat which is adjusted to some extent by turning the temperature-control dial. The principle which governs operation of thermostats is illustrated in Fig. 14. The view

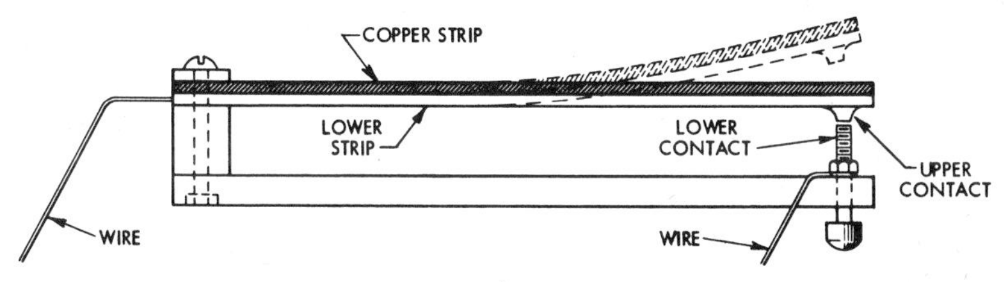

Fig. 14. Thermostat

shows a metal strip, which is actually made up of two strips of different types of metal which are welded together. The metal on the bottom expands much more than does the strip on top, when they are heated.

When the two strips are straight, which is before the temperature increases, there is a closed circuit through the thermostat. Current can flow from the lead wire connected to the strip, through the strip to its contact. When the strips are straight, upper and lower contacts are touching, so that current may flow through them to complete the circuit from one wire to the other.

As the temperature of the strip is increased, the two metals begin expanding, the upper expanding at a greater rate than the lower. This causes the strips to bend, the upper contact moving away from the lower, opening the circuit through the thermostat and stopping the current flow.

The control dial varies the position of the lower contact and this, in turn, determines the amount of temperature increase needed to cause sufficient bending for the contacts to open. In the electric iron, the temperature is adjusted by setting the dial for various types of material. When the iron is first put into operation, it is cold and, therefore, the contacts are closed. Current flows through the contacts and the heating element until the iron reaches the desired temperature. Then the contacts open, and the heating element is no longer in operation. When the heat decreases to a certain point, after the current flow has ceased for some time, the strip returns to its original shape, and the contacts touch once more. Current flow is again established, and the heating element is put into operation. This cycle of operation occurs continually while the device is connected to the supply wires.

Other Appliances. The principles brought out in connection with the electric iron are applicable to a great number of domestic and commercial heating appliances, such as toasters, ranges, hot plates, ironing machines, and waffle irons. There are minor variations, of course. For example, the toaster, the hot plate, and the domestic waffle iron would not contain thermostats. In other respects, they would all resemble the electric iron. Thermostats would certainly be found in the range, the ironing machine, and the commercial waffle iron. Most industrial applications, such as ovens, would usually have some form of thermostat to regulate the heat.

Early Type of Heating Element

The open-coil element shown in Fig. 12 was once used in the majority of heating applications. Today, however, it has been largely displaced by certain other types.

The core of the heating unit, which is made of porcelain or similar material, is fastened to the screw shell. The resistance wire is wound spirally in slots which circle the core. The wire may be a single straight conductor, or it may be wound into small tight coils. In either case, its two ends are fastened to the shell which screws into the socket.

Modern Heating Elements. Aside from purely domestic units, heating elements are of the fully enclosed variety. Fig. 15A shows one that is known as a strip, or space, heater. The heating coil is wound around a flat piece of mica, and the ends are brought out to terminals. A metal covering is pressed tightly around the heating element. Outwardly, the strip heater is a metallic object which will stand fairly rough usage. It is employed in many different types of ovens and is sometimes employed in a convection type of room heater.

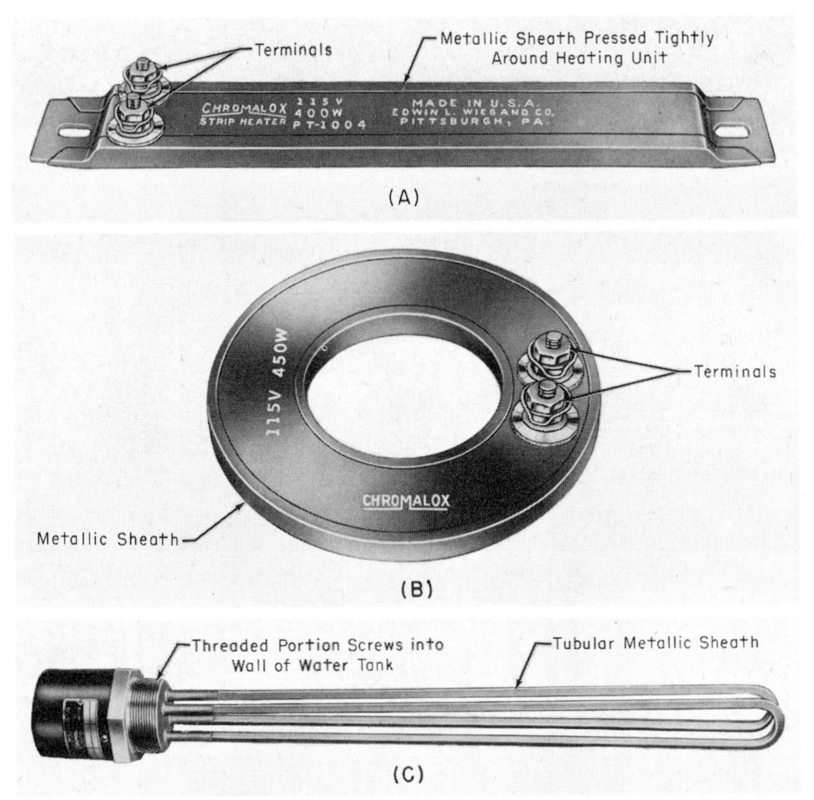

Edwin L. Wiegand Co.

Fig. 15. Modern Heating Elements

These units are made in many shapes. Fig. 15B shows a circular space heater which is used in certain types of electric ranges and similar equipment. Fig. 15C illustrates a slender U-shape heating unit that is employed in water heaters, the threaded portion of the device being screwed into the wall of the tank. In this unit, water comes directly into contact with the metal sheathing of the element.

ELECTRIC LAMPS

Edison's Experiments

About 1880, Thomas A. Edison produced the first successful incandescent lamp. He had observed that considerable light was produced by an electrical conductor which became white-hot or *incandescent.* This heat was produced, of course, by forcing a great deal of current through a very small conductor which possessed considerable resistance because of its small cross section. The light obtained

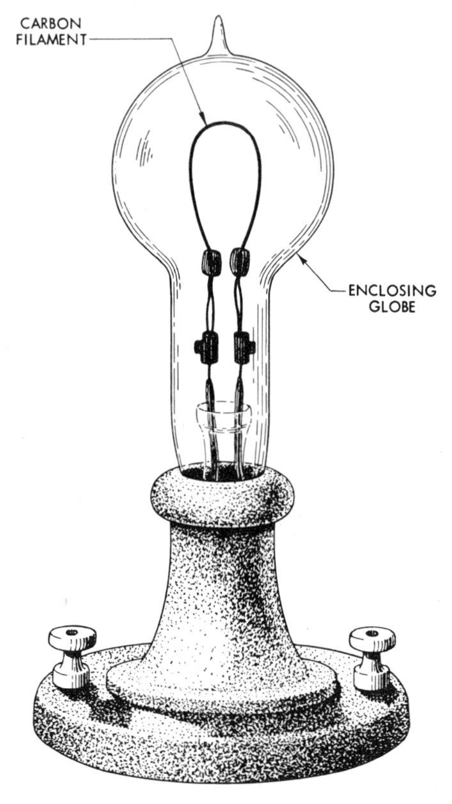

Fig. 16. Elementary Incandescent Lamp

from such a conductor proved to be quite intense, but it did not last more than a few seconds because the conductor literally burned itself up. A metallic conductor usually melted, but other conductors, such as thin strips of carbon, simply flamed and disappeared as smoke.

From his experiments, Edison concluded that the reason for burning up of the carbon conductor lay in the fact that oxygen from the air combined with the carbon and thus led to its destruction. It occurred to him that the light obtained from an incandescent strip of carbon might be enjoyed indefinitely if air were prevented from coming into contact with it. Therefore, he formed a coiled filament of bamboo fiber and converted it into carbon by means of heat and chemicals. He inserted the filament into a glass enclosing globe, as in Fig. 16, two lead wires from the filament being brought out through the base of the unit. The base was made of heat-resisting material which was sealed into the enclosing globe with cement. After inserting the filament and the stopper, air was removed from the interior of the globe by means of a pump which drew the air out through a small hole in the base. When the air had been largely removed, the small hole was sealed up.

The filament was now surrounded by a vacuum, which is a space without air and, since there was no air to furnish oxygen for the material of the filament to combine with, Edison reasoned that it would last as long as he desired. When an electric battery was connected to the lead wires from the filament, the coiled fiber glowed brightly and remained undamaged. The first successful incandescent lamp had been developed. Certain difficulties arose, for air leaked in and the filament quickly burned out.

Development of the Modern Incandescent Lamp. Further experiments overcame initial difficulties, and a rather sturdy unit was brought into existence. It was realized that a simple method was needed for connecting the lamp to the electric circuit, and so a bi-pin base was devised. This type, shown in Fig. 17A, had two pins on the

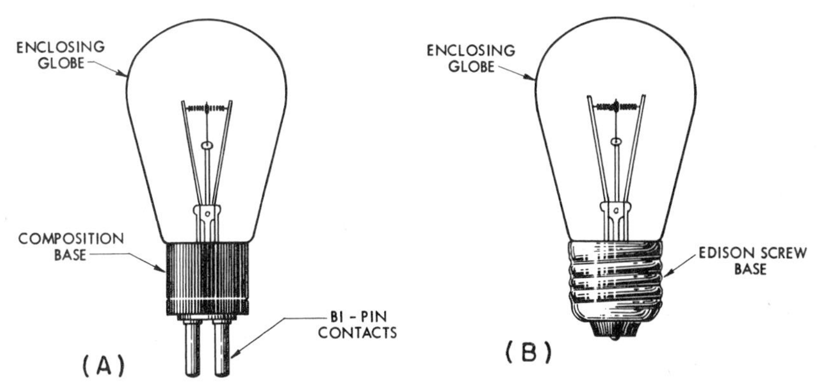

Fig. 17. Bi-Pin Base and Edison Screw Base

end of filament wires, the pins being inserted into socket type terminals which were attached to the circuit wires. The lamp could be attached to or removed from the circuit simply by inserting the pins into the sockets or by removing them. Though the method was later discarded, it has been revived as a means of connecting very large incandescent lamps.

Edison invented the base which bears his name and which has proved the most practical of all. It is the Edison screw base, Fig. 17B, which is exactly the same as the screw shell base studied in connection with the plug fuse. The lamp socket into which the lamp screws is precisely like that of the fuse socket. The lamp base is cemented to the glass bulb which contains the filament.

Metallic filaments, which would stand much greater heat, took the place of the original carbon filament. Several metals were tried, among them tantalum and tungsten. Tungsten filaments proved the most successful, and are used today. The original single-coil filament was replaced by a tightly coiled unit of small diameter. This is supported on stiff rods which are molded into the lower portion of the glass-enclosing globe. Filaments are made in a great variety of shapes, depending upon the field of application of the particular lamp.

Ratings of Incandescent Lamps. Large incandescent lamps are sometimes filled with an inactive gas such as nitrogen, which tends to slow down the rate at which the filament is destroyed by continuous heat. All filaments are eventually destroyed, of course, the lamps being rated in hours of life. The average life of the more common lamps is about 1,000 hours.

Incandescent lamps are designated according to the number of watts the lamp consumes and the voltage upon which it may be safely used. The more common wattages are 50, 100, 200, and 300. The most common voltage is 120, although many lamps are rated at 110 volts and at 115 volts. The voltage rating of lamps obtainable in neighborhood stores is usually that of the particular area where the lamps are sold. If the lamp is used on a circuit where the voltage is higher than that at which it is rated, its life will be shortened. If used on a circuit whose voltage is too low, the light output will be reduced, as we have already noted.

Though the common types of lamp use the Edison screw base, there are some variations in size of bases. Small lamps, such as used on Christmas trees, have a very small screw base, which is known as the *candelabra* base. The next size is known as the *intermediate* base. A slightly larger base is used for the lamps in our homes, and is known as the *medium,* or Edison, base. The large lamps used in floodlighting oil stations have a larger screw base, known as a *Mogul* base.

Fluorescent Lamps

A special tubular lamp has been developed in recent years, which operates on a principle different from the incandescent lamp. A sectioned view of this lamp, which is known as a *fluorescent lamp*, is

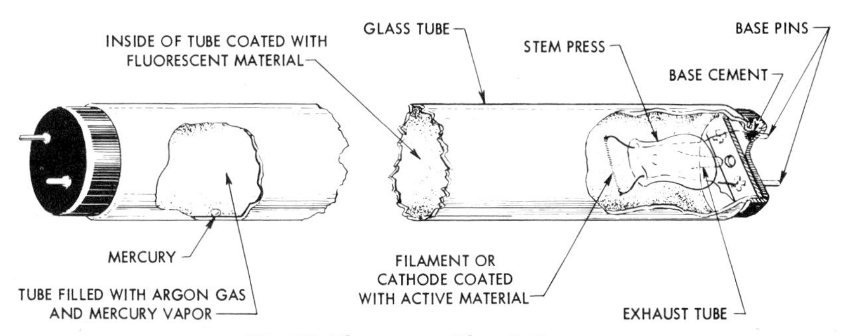

Fig. 18. Fluorescent Electric Lamp

illustrated in Fig. 18. The long glass tube has bases, with connection pins, fitted at each end. The interior of the tube is coated with a fluorescent material. Fluorescent means that this material will give off visible light while being struck or bombarded by invisible light waves or by particles (electrons or atoms). The tube is filled with a colorless gas called *argon* and a small amount of *mercury*. Mercury is a metallic substance that is liquid at ordinary temperature.

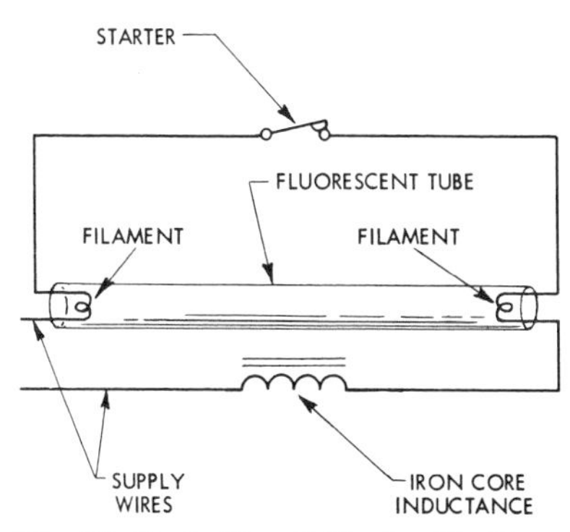

Fig. 19. Basic Circuit Used with Fluorescent Lamps

Operation of the Fluorescent Lamp. Fig. 19 illustrates a method for connecting the fluorescent tube in circuit. Current from a supply wire enters the filament in the left end of tube, then passes through the starter to the filament at the opposite end. From here, current flows through iron-core inductance to the other supply wire, completing the circuit. As the filaments heat, raising temperature inside the tube, mercury evaporates and mingles with the argon gas, the combination of these two elements forming a very good conductor of electricity. The starter, which is an automatic switch, now opens the circuit between the filaments, suddenly interrupting current flow through the inductance. The sudden decrease of current in the inductance creates a high voltage of self-induction which sends a spark, or burst of electrons, through the conducting gas from one filament to the other, establishing a flow of current. This current, once started, is readily maintained by the normal voltage of the supply circuit.

A more recent type of fluorescent lamp does not require heated filaments. Instead, a transformer device is used to send a high voltage impulse from one end to the other at starting, the spark so established being sufficiently hot to vaporize the mercury. This type is known as the "cold cathode" tube.

Although fluorescent units are designed primarily for operation on alternating-current circuits, special types have been designed for use on direct current.

Other Types of Lamps

The tubular mercury lamp once popular in photographic work, has been superseded by newer types of mercury lamps which resemble incandescents. One of these is shown in Fig. 20. When a starting electrode vaporizes the liquid mercury, an arc drawn between two main electrodes supplies the greater part of its light.

A lamp similar in construction to the mercury unit employs a gas known as *neon* and metallic *sodium*. Sodium is normally solid in form, but heat caused by current flowing through the neon gas turns it into vapor. When the metallic sodium has been vaporized, the mixture provides a low-resistance path for the arc. The sodium-vapor lamp, as it is called, produces a golden light. It has been widely used for highway lighting.

Mercury-type lamps are used for many purposes other than lighting. It was mentioned above that such units are employed in photography. They are also used to produce healing rays for treatment of skin ailments and beneficial rays in the so-called *sun lamp*. Some of the light rays sent forth by a mercury arc stream are useful in exterminating bacteria and molds. The surface of meat which is kept in large commercial refrigerating boxes often darkens because of bacteria which attack the meat. Placed in the refrigerator, the small mercury

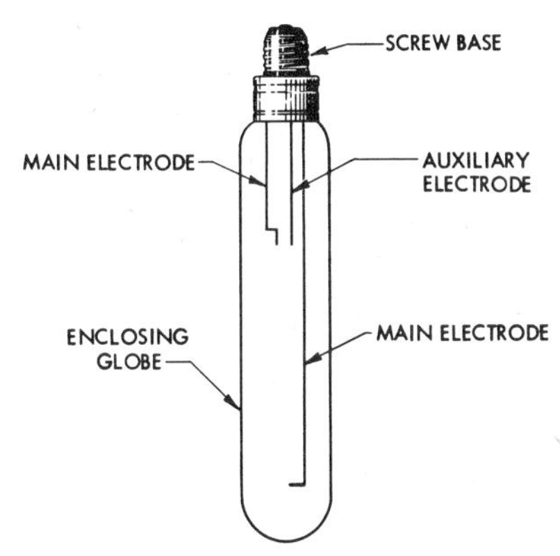

Fig. 20. Mercury Vapor Lamp

lamps called *germicidal lamps* kill these germs, and keep the meat fresh.

Heat Lamps. When the filament of a lamp is operated at temperatures below incandescence, it gives off considerably more heat than light. The heat rays are invisible, but they may be detected at some distance from the lamp. Such units are called *infrared lamps,* because the heat waves given off are called *infrared rays.* These lamps are widely used in the drying of painted parts and similar industrial processes. It is interesting to note that reflectors which are used to concentrate the heat rays given off by the lamp must be gold plated for best results. The reason is that gold does not absorb infra-red rays but reflects them.

REVIEW QUESTIONS

1. What factors determine the rate at which heat is generated?
2. Discuss carrying capacity of wires.
3. Explain how a fuse protects a circuit.
4. What is the essential difference between a fuse and a circuit breaker?
5. Why isn't copper wire used in the heating element?
6. Describe a simple thermostat.
7. What effective current, in amperes, flows through a 5-ohm resistor when maximum supply voltage is 170?

8. What maximum value of current flows in this case?
9. How is the amount of power determined in a non-inductive circuit?
10. What additional factor must be taken into account when dealing with an inductive circuit?
11. Sketch a simple fluorescent lamp circuit.
12. What is the purpose of the ballast used in connection with the fluorescent lamp?
13. Can fluorescent lamps be used on direct current circuits?
14. Which creates the greater amount of heat, a 50-watt incandescent lamp or a 50-watt fluorescent lamp?
15. Do you think that ordinary incadescent lamps produce any infrared rays?

CHAPTER 10

ELECTRIC MOTORS

SIMPLE METHODS OF PRODUCING MOTION WITH ELECTRICITY

Coil and Plunger

The simplest way to produce motion electrically is with an electromagnet. Fig. 1 represents a coil of several turns and an iron rod or plunger. If the plunger is brought close to one end of the coil, while

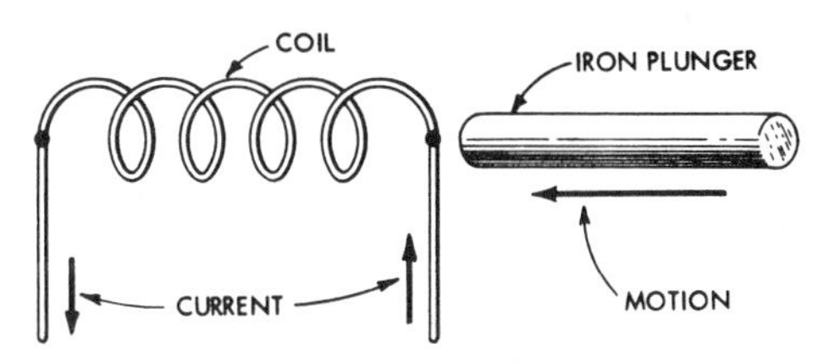

Fig. 1. Coil and Plunger

the coil is excited by electric current, the plunger will be drawn into the coil. Once this has occurred, however, motion ceases, regardless of how long current flow is maintained.

Barlow's Wheel

One of the earlier methods of accomplishing rotary motion was *Barlow's wheel,* Fig. 2. Here, a metallic wheel is mounted upon a shaft. The wheel is arranged so that its lower edge dips into a small metal receptacle which contains mercury. A brush of spring brass or bronze touches the upper edge of the wheel. A horseshoe magnet is placed so that the disk is between its poles.

With the metal receptacle connected to the negative supply terminal, current flows upward across the diameter of the wheel from the mercury, which is a good conductor. The brush is attached to the positive supply wire. The diameter of the wheel becomes a simple electrical conductor which is carrying electricity. Circles of force about the conductor react with magnetic lines of the magnet so that motion is produced. The wheel turns, in a counterclockwise direction, as indicated by the arrow. In this unit, motion continues so long as current flows. A light mechanical load may be attached to the shaft, and work may be performed. The output of such a unit is rather small; therefore, another, more efficient type of motor was developed. Before turning to it, however, it would be well to pay some attention to the direction of rotation resulting from a given direction of flux and of current.

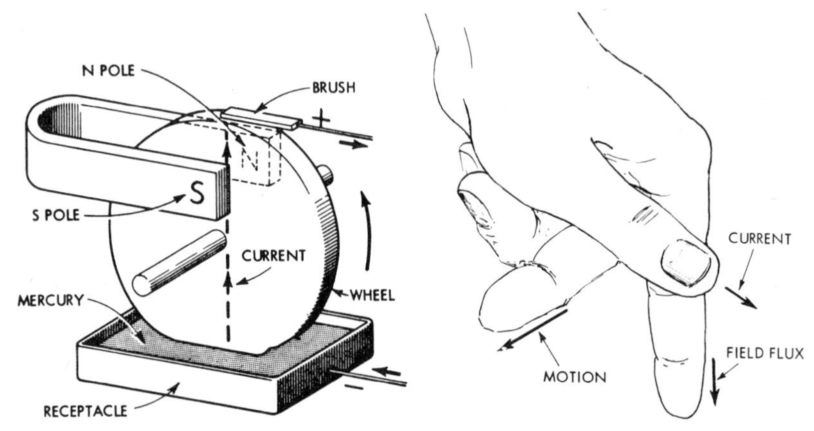

Fig. 2. Barlow's Wheel **Fig. 3. Left-Hand Rule for Motors**

Left-Hand Rule for Motors. If the right-hand rule is applied to the device shown in Fig. 2, it is seen that direction of rotation appears to be opposite from what it should be. In other words, the direction of rotation in a motor is opposite from what it would have been in a generator for the same direction of current flow.

It is possible, however, to use the left hand in a manner similar to the right, Fig. 3, the thumb indicating direction of current, the forefinger indicating direction of flux, and the other fingers indicating direction of motion. Using the left hand in this way, the direction of rotation indicated by the second finger is the correct one for the motor, Fig. 2.

DIRECT-CURRENT MOTOR WITH WOUND ARMATURE

Single-Loop Armature with Collector Rings

Fig. 4 illustrates a simple unit in which loop L_1–L_2 is in position to rotate between magnetic poles N and S. Current is furnished to the loop by means of brushes and collector rings, Fig. 4A. With current flowing as indicated by arrows, an N pole is created in the upper face

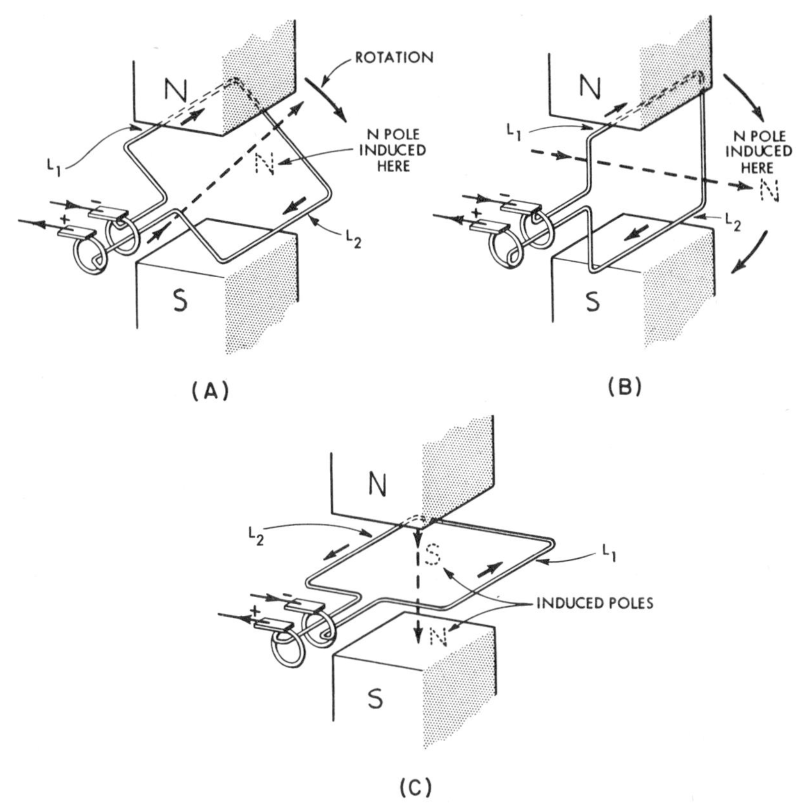

Fig. 4. Single Loop with Collector Rings

of the loop, the direction of its flux being indicated by the dotted arrow.

Because of repulsion between like N poles, the loop will be repelled until it is in a vertical position, Fig. 4B. Then the attraction between unlike poles will cause rotation to continue, the S field pole attracting the N pole of the loop and the N field pole attracting the S pole of the loop. Rotation will proceed until the coil lies in position indicated by Fig. 4C, where the N pole of the loop faces the S pole of the field, and the S pole of the loop faces the N pole of the field. The loop will be held in this position because of the tendency of magnetic lines to become as short as possible.

Single-Loop Armature with Split Ring. A split ring may be used to help solve the difficulty here, just as in the direct-current generator. Fig. 5 shows how this is done. The wires of the loop are lettered L_1

and L_2 as before. Wire L_1 is connected to that half of the split ring marked R_1, and wire L_2 is connected to R_2. At the instant shown in Fig. 5A, negative brush B_1 is in contact with R_1 and positive brush B_2 with R_2. These contacts are maintained while the loop rotates from its position in Fig. 5A until just before reaching the position indicated in Fig. 5B.

The direction of current in the loop is such as to create an N pole in that face of the loop which is uppermost in Fig. 5A. When the brushes change rings, Fig. 5B, so that B_1 touches R_2 and B_2 touches R_1,

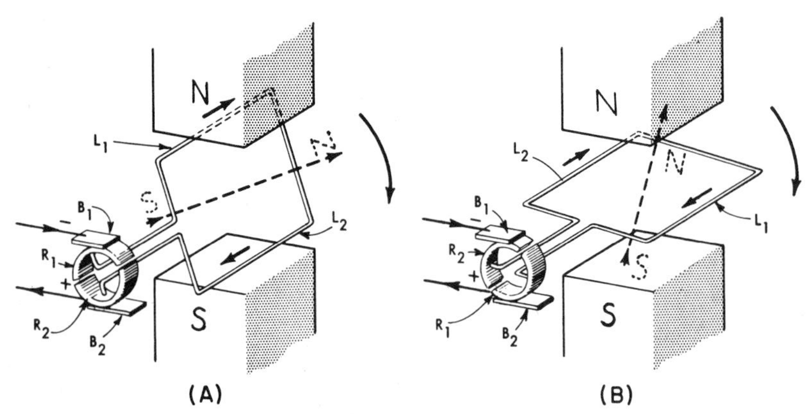

Fig. 5. Single Loop with Split Rings

the direction of current flow in the loop is reversed, and the face of the loop nearest the S pole is now of S polarity. Repulsion takes place between this face of the loop and the S pole so that rotation continues.

Now, it may be asked how the loop got into the position shown in Fig. 5B. In other words, why did it not lock into position when directly in line with the magnetic pole as in the case of the simple loop with collector rings in Fig. 4. The answer to the question is that the loop must first be spun rapidly before the circuit wires are connected. In this way, it has sufficient momentum, or tendency to continue in motion, to rotate past the locking point, but this sort of procedure is impractical except in an experimental unit.

Armature with Multiple Loops

The unit is made practical in the same way that the armature of the generator was made practical, namely, by introducing a number of additional loops and ring segments. Fig. 6 shows a motor which has an armature similar to that of the generator which was considered in a preceding chapter. There are four loops and four commutator bars, the loops being connected to the bars so as to obtain a closed-circuit winding.

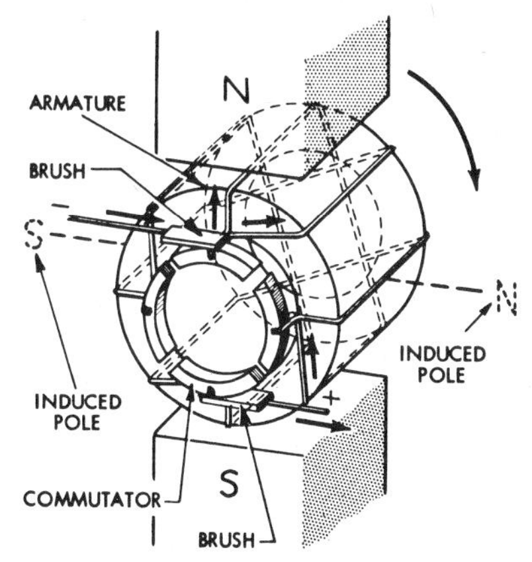

Fig. 6. Armature with Multiple Loops

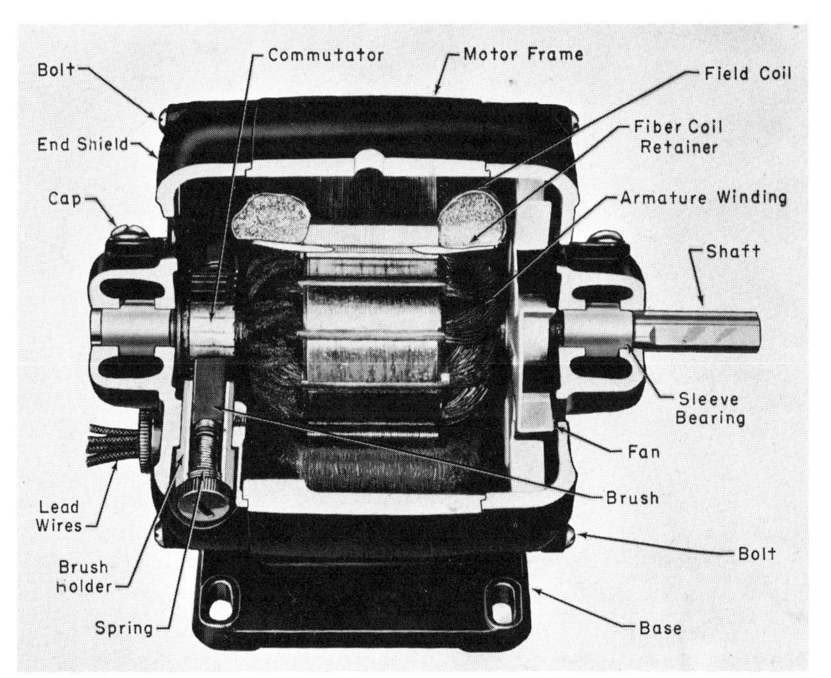

Fig. 7. Cut-away View of Direct-Current Motor

When current is supplied to the brushes so that it enters at the upper brush and leaves the winding at the lower one, N and S poles are formed on the armature. The location of these magnetic poles is such that an N pole is formed at the right as indicated in the figure, and an S pole at the left. These poles are located midway between the field poles, and they maintain this position in space as the armature continues to turn. The upper, or N, field pole repels the N armature pole and attracts the S armature pole so that the armature tends to rotate in a clockwise direction, and the S field pole attracts the N armature pole and repels the S armature pole. As a result, continuous rotation is brought about. Fig. 7 shows a cutaway view of a commercial direct-current motor. The armature with its windings, the field coils, the commutator, and the brushes can be seen. This view also illustrates certain of the mechanical features of a commercial motor, such as the armature bearings, the cooling fan, and the motor mountings.

Counter-Electromotive Force

As the motor armature turns under the influence of current furnished to its windings, the wires cut magnetic flux and a voltage is generated in them. Fig. 8 will help explain this condition. Consider wire

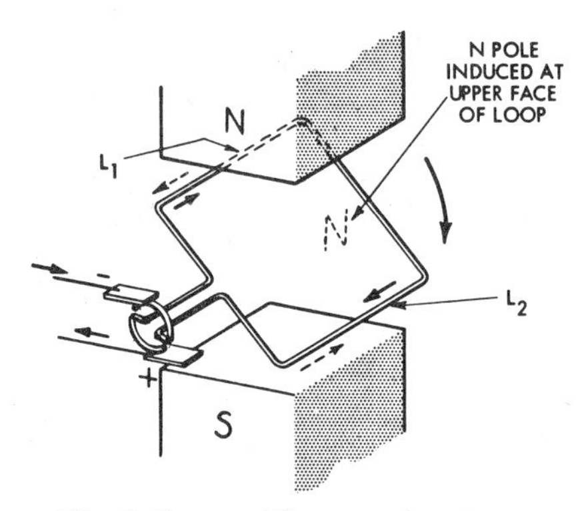

Fig. 8. Counter Electromotive Force

L_1 of loop L_1–L_2. Current flows from the negative brush through wire L_1 as indicated by the solid arrow marked upon it. An N pole is formed at the upper surface of the loop, and rotation takes place as indicated. By applying the right-hand rule, it is found that voltage generated in the wire through the cutting of magnetic flux from an N pole is in the direction indicated by the dotted arrow marked on the wire. In other words, the generated voltage opposes the supply voltage in a manner quite similar to the opposition offered to flow of current by an inductance. Such voltages are generated in each of the conductors in the armature winding, the generated voltage opposing the supply voltage in each case.

Voltage so generated is called a *counter voltage*, or *counter-electromotive force*. The common abbreviation for this term is *counter-emf*. The counter-emf can never be greater than the supply voltage because, in this case, it would furnish current to the supply wires. This is impossible, for it would amount to producing something with no effort, and it is never exactly equal to the supply voltage because, in this case, no current will flow from the supply wires. This, of course, would cause rotation to cease. The counter-emf is always just enough less than the supply voltage that sufficient current flows to carry the load which the motor is driving.

Sufficient current, here, means that the current must produce armature poles of such strength that the attraction between them and the field poles is great enough to maintain rotation against the physical resistance of the load.

SPEED CHARACTERISTICS OF DIRECT-CURRENT MOTORS

Motor Speed

The speed of a motor is usually determined by the number of times it rotates or revolves in a period of one minute. This is known as the r.p.m. (revolutions per minute) of the motor.

The *load* applied to the motor is that device that the motor is turning or operating. It may be something easy to turn or it may be difficult to turn. If the device is easy to turn, it is known as a *light load;* and if it is difficult to turn it is known as a *heavy load.* Now, in most cases, a motor will turn more slowly under a heavy load than it will under a light load, but the amount of difference in speed of a motor between turning a light load and a heavy load depends upon the individual type of motor. As we will see, different types of motors will react differently to various loads, and the manner in which the motor reacts to a load is known as the *speed characteristic* of the motor.

Shunt-Motor Speed Characteristics

The manner of exciting the fields in direct-current motors is quite similar to that used in direct-current generators. Except in special devices, motor field coils are never separately excited. The various types of direct-current motors are noted by the type of field coils employed, for each field winding produces a motor which has different speed characteristics than the others. We will consider each of these arrangements separately.

The *shunt-wound* motor, which is more commonly known as a *shunt motor,* has the field coils connected in parallel with the armature, as shown in the schematic diagram of Fig. 9. Since the field coils are

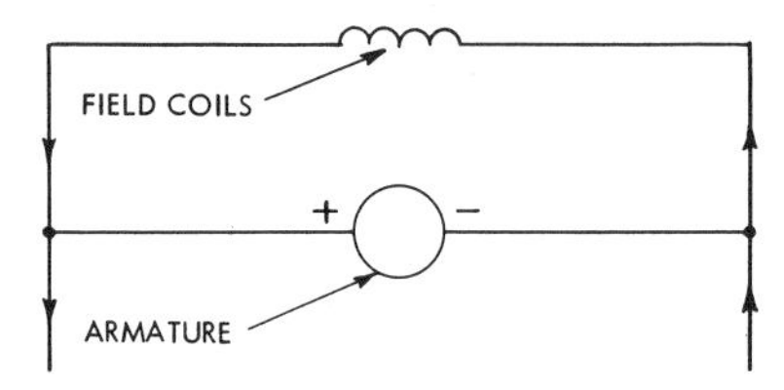

Fig. 9. Shunt Motor

connected directly to the supply lines, the current flowing through the coils is constant (with a constant supply voltage) and, accordingly, the field excitation in the shunt motor remains practically the same regardless of the nature of the load on the motor. With a constant field flux, the counter-emf is directly proportional to the speed of the armature, for the faster the armature revolves the more counter-emf will be developed. In a like manner, the slower the armature rotates, the less counter-emf is generated.

Suppose the supply voltage is 115, armature resistance .2 ohm, no-load armature current 5 amperes, and no-load speed 1500 r.p.m. (revolutions per minute). Since the armature draws a current of 5 amperes in order to rotate with no load connected to its shaft, the counter-emf cannot be greater than the difference between the supply voltage and the voltage drop in the armature. Here, 5 amperes flowing through an armature resistance of .2 ohm causes a voltage drop of 1 volt ($5 \times .2 = 1$). The counter-emf developed in the armature must be the difference between 115 volts and 1 volt, or 114 volts.

When full load is applied to the armature shaft, it is found that the armature draws a current of 25 amperes in order that it may continue to revolve. The voltage drop in this case, is equal to: $25 \times .2$, or 5 volts. The counter-emf, under this condition, must be equal to 115 minus 5, or 110 volts. And, since the armature speed at no-load is 1500 r.p.m. with a counter-emf of 114 volts, the armature speed must be 1447 r.p.m.

at full-load with a counter-emf of 110 volts. This result follows because the counter-emf is directly proportional to speed when the field strength remains constant, and

$$\frac{110}{114} \times 1500 = 1447.$$

Between no-load and full-load, then, the speed of the motor decreases only 53 r.p.m. (1500 minus 1447). The values obtained here apply only to the particular motor tested, but similar results will be found in connection with any other shunt motor. For this reason, the shunt motor is said to be a constant-speed unit.

Compound-Motor Speed Characteristics

Fig. 10 shows the diagram of a compound motor. The supply voltage is 115 v, as before, the armature resistance is 0.2 ohm, no-load current is 5 amps, and the speed at no load is 1,500 r.p.m. The resistance of the series field winding is so low that it may be disregarded here. This winding is designed so that it increases the field flux $\frac{1}{10}$, or 10 per cent, at full load. Suppose this armature draws 25 amps at full load. As in the case of the shunt motor, the voltage drop will be 5 v, so the counter-emf must be 110 v.

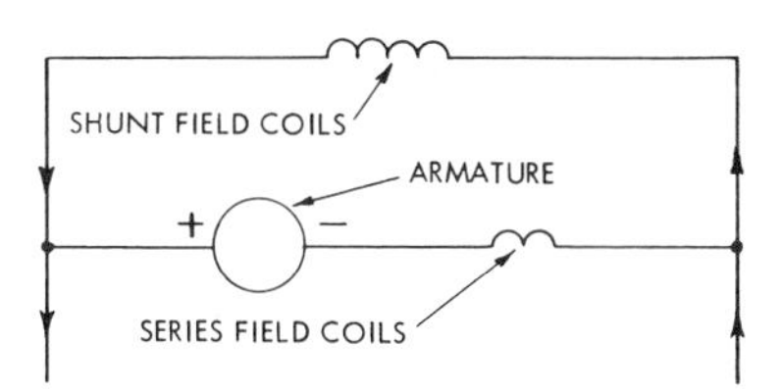

Fig. 10. Compound Motor

If the strength of the field flux were unchanged between no-load and full-load, the speed of the armature at full load would be exactly the same as that of the shunt motor, or 1,447 r.p.m., but the strength of the field flux has been increased by 10 per cent, so that for every revolution the armature will produce 10 per cent more counter-emf than before. The speed of the armature must be lower than 1,447 r.p.m. It must be $\frac{100}{110}$ times 1,447, or 1,316 r.p.m.

The drop in speed between no load and full load is equal to 1,500 minus 1,316, or 184 r.p.m. It is evident that the speed of the compound motor is not so constant as that of the shunt motor. As a matter of fact, the full-load speed of a compound motor depends upon the strength of the series field as compared to that of the shunt field. Here, the series field produces, at full load, 10 per cent of the excitation of the shunt field. If it had produced 20 per cent as much excitation, the speed at full load would have been even lower than 1,316 r.p.m. If it had produced only 5 per cent as much excitation as the shunt field, the speed at full load would have been higher than 1,316, but it would not have been equal to that of the shunt motor.

The compound motor also has good speed regulation, but it is not so good as the shunt motor.

Series-Motor Speed Characteristics

Fig. 11 is the diagram of a series motor. The supply voltage is 115 v, and the armature resistance is 0.2 ohm. Since there is no shunt field

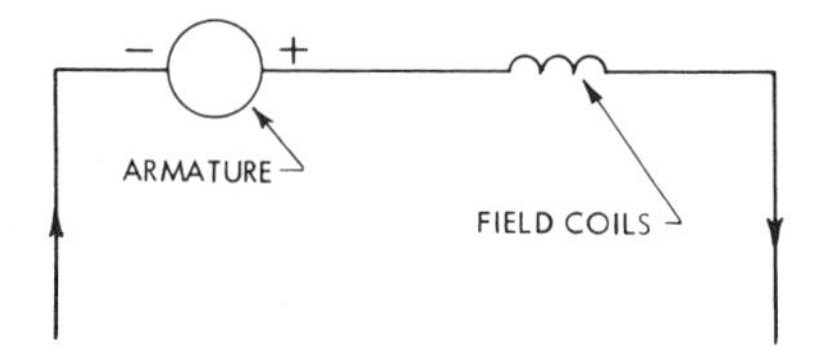

Fig. 11. Series Motor

winding, the strength of the field flux will depend upon the current flowing through the armature and the number of turns of wire in the field coils. If this winding is designed to produce the same field strength at full load as that of the corresponding shunt motor, it will have full field strength when the armature current is 25 amps. Let us suppose that the speed at this time is 1,450 r.p.m.

Now, since it requires approximately 5 amps to supply armature losses at no load, so that the armature may continue to rotate, the field strength of the motor will be only $\frac{1}{5}$ that at full load. The armature will have to run considerably faster, in this case, in order to generate a counter-emf of 114 v, which is the value necessary to limit armature current to 5 amps. As a matter of fact, the armature will require somewhat more than 5 amps to keep it rotating at the higher speed. Let us say that 10 amps are required.

The armature drop is now 10 amps times 0.2 ohm, or 2 v, so that the counter-emf must be 115 v minus 2 v, or 113 v. With full-load field strength, the speed would be $\frac{113}{114}$ times 1,500 r.p.m., or 1,487 r.p.m. but the field strength with 10 amperes flowing is only $\frac{10}{25}$ times normal value, or 40 per cent. In order to generate the required counter-emf, the armature must run at a speed $2\frac{1}{2}$ times as fast as full-load speed, or 3,717. The speed variation from no load to full load, therefore, will amount to 3,717 r.p.m. minus 1,487 r.p.m., or 2,230 r.p.m. For this reason, the series unit is said to be a varying speed motor, its speed changing drastically with change in load.

Although the maximum speed attained by the motor at no load, here, was only 3,717 r.p.m., a motor with a lower armature resistance might attain a speed of several thousand revolutions per minute. Such a speed is often sufficient to tear the windings out of armature slots. For this reason, series motors are usually applied to loads in which it is impossible for the motor to be without load. In very small motors, the pressure of the brushes on the commutator is sufficient to limit the speed to a safe value. Larger sizes are usually applied to geared loads, or direct-connected loads, so that it is unlikely for dangerous speeds to occur.

Torque of Motor

The term *torque* means *turning effort.* It is usually expressed as the turning effort in pounds at a distance of 1 foot from the center of the armature shaft. Fig. 12 illustrates this term. Now, the torque of a motor armature depends upon two factors: the strength of the magnetic flux in the field poles, and the strength of the armature poles. The strength of the armature poles depends upon the value of the current flowing in the armature winding. It may be said, therefore, that torque depends upon field strength and armature current.

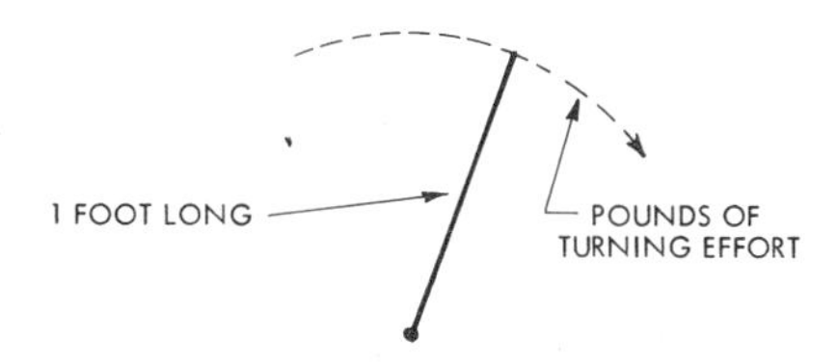

Fig. 12. Torque

The torque developed by a motor at the instant of starting is called its *starting torque.* In direct-current motors, it is usual to limit starting current to 150 per cent, or $1\frac{1}{2}$ times, its full-load running current. The manner in which the current is limited will be considered shortly. In a shunt motor, whose field strength is the same at all times, the field strength may be said to be 100 per cent, or 1. With a current of $1\frac{1}{2}$ times normal full-load value, and a field strength of 1, the starting torque of the motor will be $1\frac{1}{2} \times 1$, or $1\frac{1}{2}$ times normal full-load, or running torque.

Now, the torque required at starting is usually greater than required after the driven machine has started to rotate. In some cases it is several times running torque. Therefore, it is desirable to have a motor whose starting torque is fairly high. In the compound motor, the armature current flows through the series field winding. If this winding is so proportioned that it provides 10 per cent, or $\frac{1}{10}$, more field flux at full load, it will provide 15 per cent, or $\frac{3}{20}$, more field strength at starting when $1\frac{1}{2}$ times normal current flows. Here, the starting torque will be approximately $1\frac{3}{4}$ that of the running value. If the series field coils are wound with a greater number of turns, the starting torque will be correspondingly greater. Because the compound motor has the higher torque, it is often preferred to the shunt motor even though its speed will vary more during operation.

The series motor provides the greatest starting torque of the three, for, if normal running current provides a field strength which is 100 per cent, a field current which is equal to $1\frac{1}{2}$ times the normal value will provide a field strength of $1\frac{1}{2}$ times the normal value. This follows from the fact that the same current flows through the series field coils as flows through the armature. The starting torque of the series motor, under this condition, is $1\frac{1}{2}$ times $1\frac{1}{2}$, or $2\frac{1}{4}$ times normal running torque. Thus, the starting torque of the series unit is much greater than that of the other types for the same amount of current.

Horsepower. Electric motors are rated in horsepower (abbreviated h.p.). A motor of 1 h.p. which runs at a speed of 1,000 r.p.m. will exert a force of 11.5 pounds at the outer surface of a pulley 12 inches in diameter. The electrical equivalent of 1 horsepower is 746 watts.

Limiting Starting Current

The armature conductors are not cutting across the field flux before the armature begins to rotate. The counter-emf of the armature at this instant is, therefore, zero, and the current which flows in the armature circuit may be determined by Ohm's law. Fig. 13 shows the *starting rheostat* connected in series with the armature of a shunt motor. It will be noted that the field coils are connected directly to the supply wires. The rheostat consists of a resistor and a movable contact arm. The resistor is connected to three contact-buttons, *1, 2,* and *3*. Contact-button *3* is connected to one brush of the armature. The contact arm is also connected to a supply wire.

At starting, the arm makes contact with button *1* at the end of the starting resistor. The value of the resistor is approximately 2.8 ohms. This resistance added to that of the armature, which is 0.2 ohm, totals approximately 3 ohms. With a supply voltage of 115 v, the current is

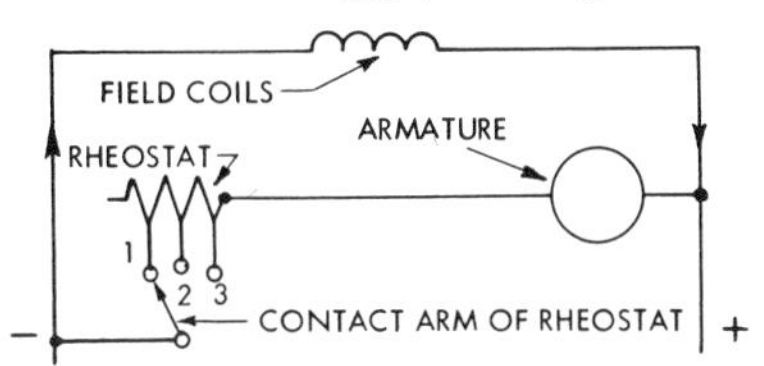

Fig. 13. Starting Rheostat Connected to Shunt Motor

about 37.5 amps, which is 1½ times running value. As the armature starts to rotate and to generate a counter-emf, the current decreases; and the arm is moved to button *2*. The current increases once more as the resistance is thus decreased, but decreases again as the armature builds up counter-emf. Then the arm is moved to button *3* which connects the armature directly across the supply wires.

This method of starting may be used equally well in connection with the compound or the series motors. Starting rheostats are employed for motors larger than 1 h.p. In the smaller sizes, the armature resistance is large enough to limit starting current to a safe value without using a resistor.

Speed Control

If a resistor is placed in series with the armature of a direct-current motor, the voltage drop in the resistor prevents the armature from receiving full supply voltage. In this case, the counter-emf of the armature is less than when the armature is subjected to full voltage. Since the counter-emf is less than normal, the speed of the armature is less than normal. That is, the insertion of a resistor in the armature circuit reduces the full-load speed of the armature.

In Fig. 14A a resistor of 2.3 ohms is connected in series with the armature of a shunt motor, which draws 25 amps at full load. By applying Ohm's law, it is found that the voltage consumed in the resistor is 57.5 v, which is one-half the supply voltage. The armature is, therefore, subjected to but 57.5 v, and its counter-emf will be approximately ½ normal running value. Since the counter-emf is ½ normal value and since the field strength is constant, the speed of rotation must be ½ normal speed.

The speed of compound and series motors may be reduced below normal in this way. If various speeds are required, the resistor may be arranged in the form of a rheostat so that its value may be altered to suit the desired speed. It is to be noted, however, that any speed variation obtained by means of a series resistor is below normal operating value.

Some applications require that the speed be varied upward from normal. This result may be accomplished, in the case of a shunt motor,

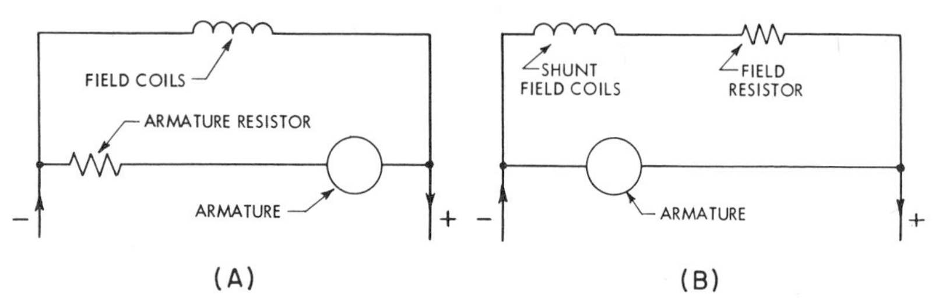

Fig. 14. Speed Control of Shunt Motor

by inserting a resistor in series with the field coils, Fig. 14B. The resistor reduces the shunt field current, which results in decreased field flux. The armature is, therefore, forced to run at a higher speed than normal in order to generate the required counter-emf. The amount of the speed increase may be adjusted by making the resistor variable. In this case, an increase in resistor value results in an increase in speed, and a decrease in resistor value results in a decrease, the speed in any case being higher than normal value.

A field resistor may be used in connection with a compound motor, but the results are not as satisfactory as with the shunt motor because of the presence of series field coils. It is impractical to use a field resistor to increase the speed of a series motor. In one special type of series motor, a resistor is connected in parallel with the field coils so that the speed may be increased somewhat; in general, this is seldom attempted.

ALTERNATING-CURRENT MOTORS

Series Motor

It is impractical to use a shunt-wound, direct-current motor on alternating current. The main reason is that the reactance of the shunt field coils is extremely high. Consequently, the current in the field circuit is considerably out of phase with the current in the armature conductors, so that the magnetism of the field poles and armature poles reach points of greatest strength at different instants. As a result, the torque developed by the unit is very low.

In the series motor, however, the field coils and the armature are in series, the same current flowing through both. The strength of the field poles and the armature poles increase and decrease together so that a good torque is developed and, even though the direction of current alternates several times per second, rotation continues in one direction. Fig. 15 shows this condition. In Fig. 15A, at the instant when the polarity of the supply line is as indicated in the figure, the upper field pole is an N pole, while the lower one is an S. At this moment, the armature has an N pole at the right side and an S pole at the left. The force of attraction and repulsion between field and armature poles is such that rotation is in a clockwise direction.

When current reverses, the upper field pole becomes S and the lower one N, Fig. 15B. The right armature pole becomes S, while the

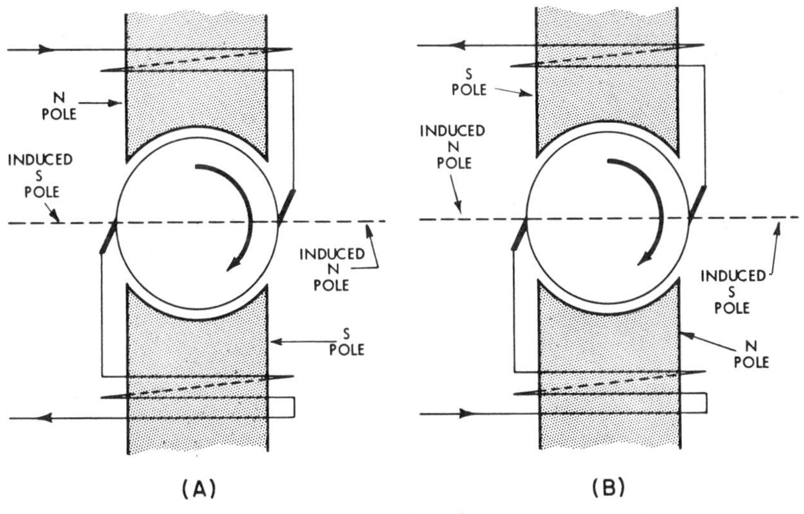

Fig. 15. Series Motor Connected to Alternating-Current Circuit

left becomes N. The attractions and repulsions, it will be noted, are such that rotation continues in a clockwise direction. The series motor, therefore, is suitable for operation on alternating current. Certain minor changes are introduced in a motor which is to operate on alternating current, and the field circuit must be laminated in order that it may not overheat from eddy currents. It may be said, then, that the series motor is capable, basically, of operating on either direct or alternating current.

Single-Phase Loop

If alternating current is supplied to the single loop of Fig. 16A, no rotation will take place. The loop, in the figure, lies midway between the field poles which are magnetized by direct-current coils so that their polarity is always the same. When current in the loop creates an N pole in the upper face, the N field pole will tend to repel it, but the force of repulsion is vertically downward so that no rotation takes place. An instant later, when current through the loop reverses, an S pole is formed in its upper face. There is a force of attraction between field pole and loop, but no rotation takes place because the force is vertically upward.

If the loop is placed in some other position, such as Fig. 16B, its N pole tends to be repelled by the N field pole at the instant the current flow makes the upper face of the loop an N pole, but before the loop can move any distance the current in it changes direction so that the

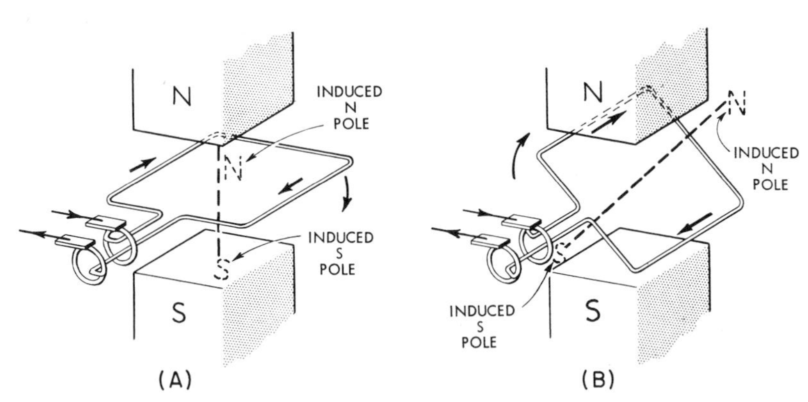

Fig. 16. Alternating Current Supplied to Single Loop

upper polarity is S. In this instant it will be attracted by the N field pole. As a consequence, the loop will gradually assume the position shown in Fig. 16A.

However, the simple loop may be made to rotate while alternating current is supplied to it. If the supply frequency is 60 cycles, there are 60 times 60, or 3,600 cycles, in one minute. When the loop is speeded up to 3,600 r.p.m. by mechanical means, and current is then furnished to it, the loop will continue to revolve at a speed of 3,600 r.p.m. as long as current flows.

The reason the loop continues to rotate may be understood by referring to Fig. 17. In Fig. 17A current flows from the negative brush to

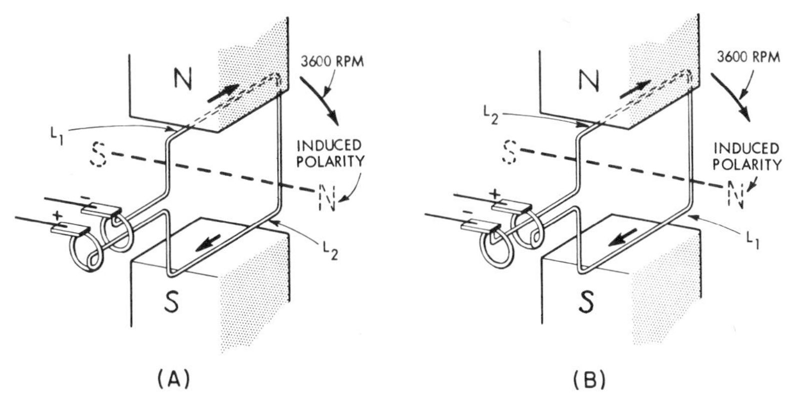

Fig. 17. Principle of the Synchronous Motor

wire L_1, around the end connection to wire L_2, and from wire L_2 to the positive brush. This direction of current flow in the loop results in an N pole forming at the right side and an S pole at the left. This polarity holds during one-half cycle of current flow. By the time the next half cycle of current flow has reached maximum value, Fig. 17B, the loop has completed a half-turn so that wire L_1 is below and wire L_2 is above. The direction of current flow has now changed so that wire L_1 is connected to the momentarily positive brush. The direction of current in the loop is such that an N pole is formed at the right and an S pole at the left, as before.

Thus, continuous motion results from a flow of alternating current in the loop. If the loop is speeded up to approximately 3,600 and current is then applied, it will *pull in* to the position in which there is maximum attraction between its poles and those of the field structure. The loop is then said to have *pulled into step,* or synchronized with the supply frequency.

The principle brought out here is used in the alternating-current synchronous motor. The term *synchronous* is used here because a 2-pole motor, whose speed in r.p.m. is equal to cycles per minute, is said to be in step with, or in synchronism with, the supply frequency.

Synchronous Speed. We may easily determine the synchronous speed of a motor by a simple formula.

$$R.P.M. = \frac{f \times 60}{\frac{P}{2}}$$

$R.P.M.$ = the speed of the motor in revolutions per minute.

f = the frequency of the supply current in cycles per second.

60 = the number of seconds in one minute.

$\frac{P}{2}$ = ½ the number of poles in the motor.

This rule can be rearranged and written in the following simplified manner:

$$R.P.M. = \frac{f \times 120}{P}$$

In our first example, let us determine the speed of a 2-pole motor that is built to operate on 25-cycle alternating current. All we need do is substitute the proper values for the f and the P in the formula.

$$R.P.M. = \frac{25 \times 120}{2}$$

Multiplying the numerator, we have

$$R.P.M. = \frac{3{,}000}{2}$$

$$R.P.M. = 1{,}500$$

The synchronous speed of a 4-pole motor is one-half that of a 2-pole motor; therefore, the speed of a 4-pole, 25-cycle motor is

$$R.P.M. = \frac{f \times 120}{4}$$

$$R.P.M. = \frac{25 \times 120}{4}$$

$$R.P.M. = \frac{3{,}000}{4}$$

$$R.P.M. = 750$$

It has just been mentioned that the synchronous speed of a 2-pole, 60-cycle motor is 3,600 r.p.m. The synchronous speed of a 4-pole, 60-

cycle motor is 1,800 r.p.m. and that of a 6-pole, 60-cycle motor is 1,200 r.p.m. Accordingly, we can determine the synchronous speed of a motor having any number of poles and built to operate on any frequency by the use of our formula.

Revolving Flux in Two-Phase Motor

Two-phase and three-phase circuits and equipment are termed *polyphase,* the term meaning *more than one phase.* Polyphase motors operate largely because of a *revolving magnetic flux* set up by flow of current in their windings. Fig. 18 will help explain the meaning of the term.

Fig. 18A shows a two-phase armature which has two loops, these two loops being connected to collector rings as shown. When two-phase current is supplied to the armature, magnetic poles are created

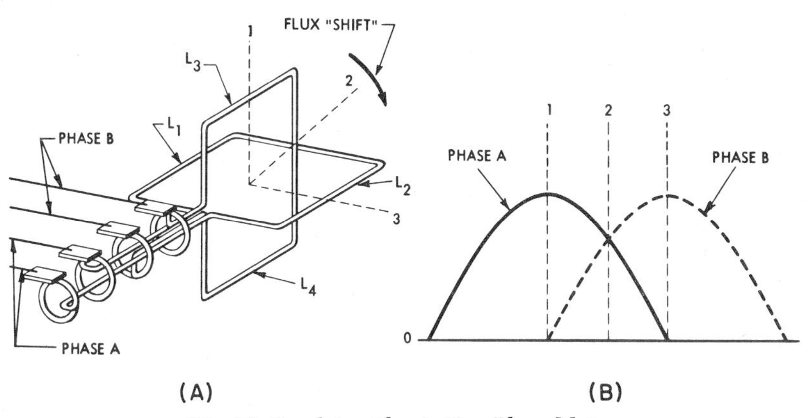

Fig. 18. Revolving Flux in Two-Phase Motor

by the two loops. Current flowing in the loops is represented by the curves in Fig. 18B, phase *A* representing the current in loop L_1–L_2, and curve I_2 representing the current in loop L_3–L_4. And, since these currents establish magnetic poles, the curves may represent variation of magnetic flux in these poles, as well as current in the loops.

At point *1* in both illustrations, the current in loop L_1–L_2 is at maximum value, creating an N pole in the upper face of the loop. At this instant, the current and the magnetism in loop L_3–L_4 are both zero. Referring to view A, the centers of the poles formed by the loop are along line *1*, an N pole being formed at the upper face and an S pole at the lower. At point 2, view B, the strength of current in each of the loops is the same so that both are equally effective in establishing the magnetic pole. In this case, the resulting pole is formed half way between them, as shown by line 2, view A. When the flow of current in the two loops reaches values indicated at point 3, that in loop L_1–L_2 will be zero while that in L_3–L_4 will be maximum. At this time, the location of the magnetic poles will be directly opposite the center of loop L_3–L_4.

The effect of current flow in the two loops has been to cause a shift of magnetic poles in a clockwise direction. As indicated in view A, an N magnetic pole moves from point *1* to point *2,* to point *3,* while an S magnetic pole, directly opposite the N pole, shifted in a clockwise direction. Although the armature is stationary, the magnetic poles shift as if fixed poles were turned mechanically in a clockwise direction and, if current flow is continued, the magnetic poles will circle the armature continuously, traveling around it at synchronous speed. In other words, two-phase alternating current flowing in a two-phase armature establishes a revolving magnetic flux.

Stator Winding

If the two loops are placed in slots on the inner circumference of the stator, as shown in Fig. 19, the rotation of magnetic flux will be

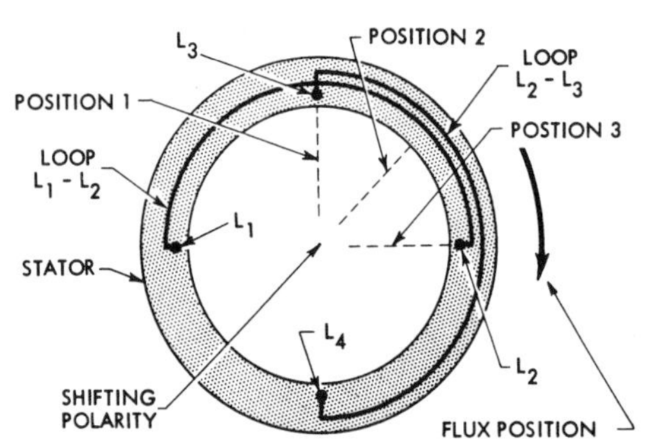

Fig. 19. Flux Rotation With Loops Placed on Motor Stator

exactly the same as if the loops were on the armature. An N pole will shift about the inside of the stator from positions *1,* to *2,* to *3,* while an S pole directly opposite it duplicates this rotation.

Revolving Flux in Three-Phase Stator

A revolving flux may be established with a three-phase stator winding in a manner similar to that of the two-phase winding. If three loops are placed on the stator, and three-phase current is supplied to them; it will move along the positions *1, 2, 3, 4, 5,* and *6* Fig. 20A, circling the stator at synchronous speed. Fig. 20B illustrates the relationship of currents and field poles in the three-phase stator.

Although, for the purpose of illustration, each winding is represented by a single loop, the windings of commercial units are composed of a great number of coils arranged in numerous slots around the inner circumference of the stator. The principle of operation, however, is exactly as presented here.

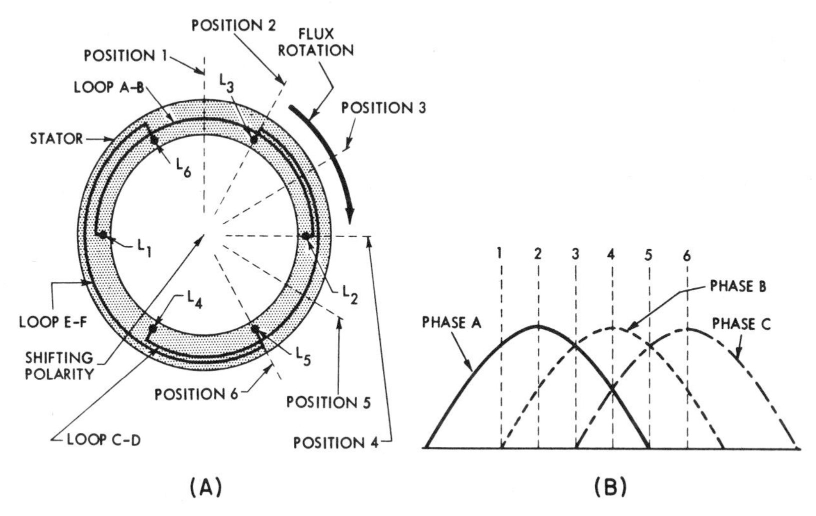

Fig. 20. Revolving Flux in Three-Phase Stator

Polyphase Synchronous Motor

In the polyphase synchronous motor, a set of field poles are mounted upon the rotating element. These poles are excited by means of collector rings and brushes which carry direct current to them as noted in Fig. 21. A three-phase winding on the stator provides a revolving flux which draws the field poles after the stator poles at synchronous speed. Rotation here is actually caused by the attraction of the revolving stator N pole for the rotor S pole, and the attraction of revolving stator S pole for the rotor N pole. In other words rotation is caused by attraction between unlike magnetic poles. As with the armature of the single-phase synchronous motor referred to earlier, the rotating member of the polyphase synchronous motor must be brought up to a point close to synchronous speed before current is applied to its electromagnets. The manner in which the polyphase rotor is brought up to speed will be explained shortly.

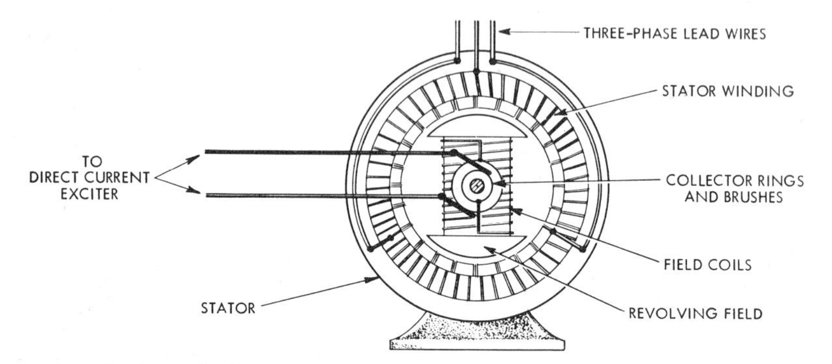

Fig. 21. Polyphase Synchronous Motor With Revolving Field Poles

Induced Poles in Cylindrical Rotor

The cylinder in Fig. 22 is made of copper or brass and is mounted upon a shaft so that it is free to turn. If the cylinder is placed inside a polyphase stator, poles will be induced in it. The revolving N flux is represented by the N magnetic pole in the figure. As it cuts across point *A* on the cylinder, it generates a voltage whose direction may be determined with the aid of the right-hand rule, always remembering that it is relative motion which counts.

As the N pole moves in a clockwise direction, the voltage created

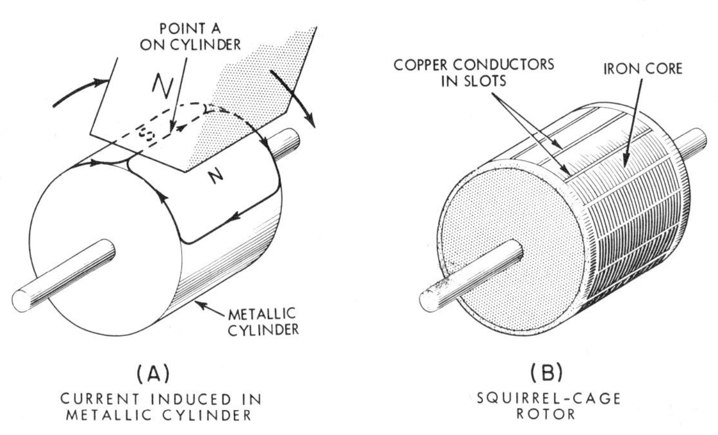

Fig. 22. Rotors

at *A* causes a flow of current as noted in the figure. The current flows from the front to the back of the cylinder. The current divides, half flowing along the face of the cylinder in one direction and half in the other. Two magnetic poles are thus created on the surface of the cylinder, an S pole to the left of *A* and an N pole to the right. As the revolving N flux moves in a clockwise direction, it repels the N pole of the cylinder away from it and attracts the S pole toward it. This attraction and repulsion causes the cylinder to rotate in the same direction as the revolving flux and, at the same time, the revolving S stator pole induces poles in that part of the cylinder close to it in the same way. The cylinder is commonly spoken of as a *rotor.*

Rotor of Induction Motor. A motor in which poles are induced in this manner is called an *induction motor* but the rotor is somewhat different from the elementary cylinder of Fig. 22A. It consists of an iron core with slots in its surface. The core is made up of thin sheets of iron, or laminations, and copper conductors are placed in the slots, Fig. 22B. This type of unit is called a *squirrel-cage* rotor.

Speed of Squirrel-Cage Induction Motor

The rotor of an induction motor does not revolve at synchronous speed. It rotates at some speed less than this amount, depending upon the load. The torque of the motor depends upon the attractive force between the stator poles and those induced in the rotor and, although the strength of the revolving stator poles is of constant value, the strength of the rotor poles depends upon the rate at which rotor conductors are cutting across lines of force. If the rotor were to turn at synchronous speed, its conductors would maintain their relative position with regard to the revolving stator poles, and they would not cut across magnetic lines. Consequently, there would be no voltage generated in them, and no current would flow in the rotor conductors.

In order to keep turning, then, the rotor must slip back gradually as it turns. That is, it must run at a speed somewhat lower than synchronous value. Thus, a 4-pole, 60-cycle induction motor may rotate at a speed of 1,790 r.p.m. at no load. With respect to the stator flux, the rotor is slipping backward ten revolutions per minute. When its conductors are cutting magnetic lines at this rate, the voltage generated in them is sufficient to force necessary current through them. The necessary current is the amount of current required to give the rotor poles enough strength that attraction between them and the stator poles may cause rotation against forces of friction.

When loaded, the drag on the rotor causes it to slip backward at a greater rate of speed until its conductors are generating a voltage high enough to produce the required current. The motor considered here, which runs at 1,790 r.p.m. at no load, may rotate at a speed of only 1,750 r.p.m. under full-load conditions. The difference between synchronous speed and full-load speed is termed the *slip* of the rotor. Here, the slip is equal to 1,800 r.p.m. minus 1,750 r.p.m., or 50 r.p.m.

Speed Control of Induction Motor. The speed of the ordinary squirrel-cage induction motor cannot be varied but, if the squirrel-cage is replaced by a winding of coils, speed variation becomes possible. Since the rotor winding is entirely independent of the stator, coils on the rotor may be arranged in any desired manner. They may be connected together to form a single-phase, two-phase, or three-

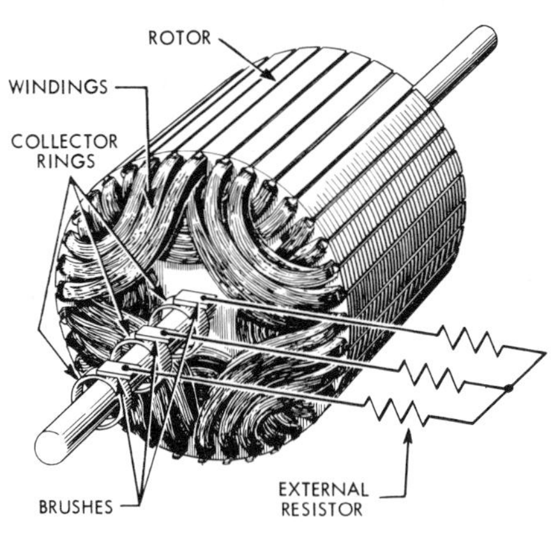

Fig. 23. Wound Rotor of Induction Motor

phase windings. Usually, they are connected three-phase, the terminals of the winding being brought out to three collector rings as shown in Fig. 23.

As the rotor slips backward, the voltage generated in the windings is carried from collector rings to suitable resistors by means of brushes and connecting leads as indicated in the figure. The amount of current which flows in the winding of the rotor depends upon two factors: the voltage generated by cutting lines of force and the resistance of the winding. If the resistance of the rotor winding is doubled, the voltage generated in it to produce a certain strength of field flux must be doubled; and for the voltage to be doubled the slip must be doubled. When the slip is 100 r.p.m., for a certain load, without any resistance in the rotor circuit, it must increase to 200 r.p.m. when the series resistance is made equal to the resistance of the rotor winding.

By arranging contact arms to vary the resistance in the external circuit, speed of the rotor may be adjusted at will. This type of unit is called a wound-rotor induction motor.

Starting Induction Motor. With large induction motors, it is necessary to limit starting current in a manner similar to that in which starting current of direct-current motors is limited. A resistance may be inserted in each supply wire in the case of a squirrel-cage motor, but the usual method is to reduce the supply voltage by means of a transformer. In the case of a wound-rotor motor, the starting current may be kept within reasonable bounds simply by inserting resistance in series with the rotor windings. The manner in which this fact is accomplished will be better understood after learning about the operation of the transformer.

It may now be explained that the rotor of the polyphase synchronous motor is brought up to a speed somewhere near synchronism by means of a squirrel-cage winding which is placed on the rotor. The winding is considerably lighter than it would be for an induction motor of this size. The electromagnets on the field poles are not excited until the rotor has attained the highest speed obtainable by means of the squirrel-cage winding. When this point is reached, current is supplied to the field poles, and the rotor pulls into step with the revolving flux.

Starting Single-Phase Induction Motor. As explained earlier, the single-phase motor is not *self-starting.* That is, it will not start when current is applied to its winding. It must be given a start by mechanical means. The polyphase induction motor is self-starting because of

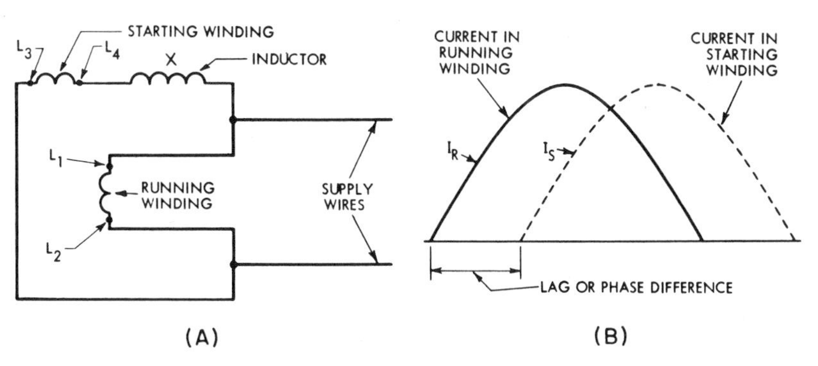

Fig. 24. Inductance Method of Creating Revolving Flux in Single-Phase Motor

its revolving flux. Now, the single-phase motor can be made self-starting by creating a form of revolving flux in its stator.

Fig. 24A represents a two-pole stator which has two loops, L_1–L_2 and L_3–L_4, the loops being at right angles with one another as are those of a two-phase winding. Loop L_1–L_2 is connected directly to the supply wires but loop L_3–L_4 is connected in series with inductance *X*. When current is supplied to these windings, the effect of the inductance is to cause the current in L_3–L_4 to lag behind that in L_1–L_2. This is illustrated in Fig. 24B. Here, curve I_R represents current in loop L_1–L_2, and curve I_S represents that in L_3–L_4.

The amount by which I_S lags I_R depends upon the value of inductance in circuit with L_3–L_4. When the inductance is of such a value that I_S lags I_R a considerable amount, a revolving field flux is produced similar to that of a two-phase motor. Under this condition, the single-phase unit is similar in operation to the polyphase unit; therefore, it is self-starting. After the rotor has attained considerable speed, the circuit of the starting winding represented by loop L_3–L_4 is opened, and the motor continues to operate on the running winding which is represented by L_1–L_2.

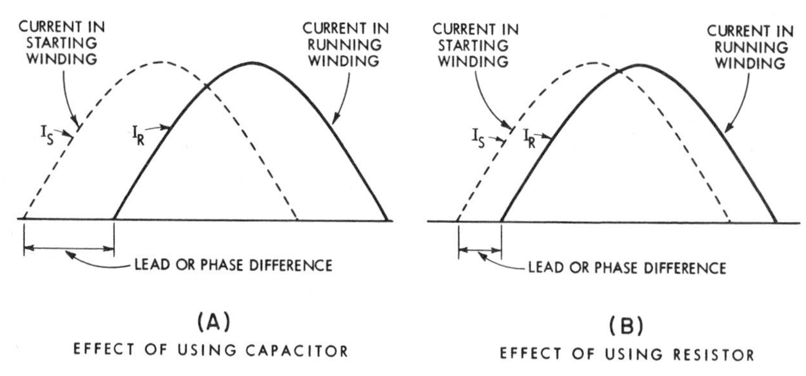

Fig. 25. Other Methods of Achieving Flux-Shift in Single-Phase Motors

If a capacitor is substituted for the inductance at *X*, the current in L_3–L_4 is caused to lead that in L_1–L_2 as indicated in Fig. 25A. The result is that a revolving field flux is created exactly as in the case when an inductance is used. The motor which has a capacitor in the starting circuit is termed a *capacitor motor*.

A similar result may be obtained by inserting a resistor in circuit with winding L_3–L_4. In this case, the current in the running winding lags behind that in the starting winding, Fig. 25B. The amount of lag obtainable by this method is not so great as that obtainable by either the inductance or the capacitance methods, but it is sufficient to produce the starting torque required for small loads. This resistance-start method is usually accomplished by including resistance in the winding itself. That is, a conductor of smaller cross section is used in winding L_3–L_4 than in winding L_1–L_2; therefore, its resistance is considerably higher as compared to its inductance.

Repulsion Motor

Another type of single-phase motor in common use is the repulsion motor. As shown in Fig. 26, it has an armature similar to that of a di-

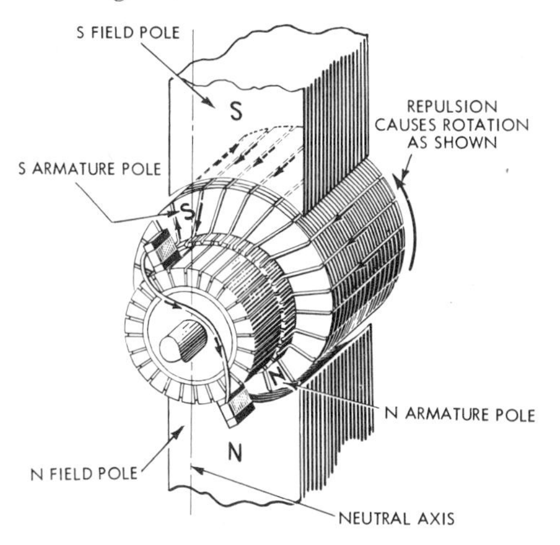

Fig. 26. Essential Elements of Repulsion Motor

rect-current motor, and a set of brushes which are connected together, or short-circuited, at the commutator. The alternating-current field coils induce current in the armature winding. This current establishes poles on the armature somewhat like in the ordinary direct-current motor, but on the vertical axis of the armature rather than the horizontal axis.

The polarities are such that at a given instant when the lower field pole is of N polarity, the lower armature pole is also of N polarity. When the field pole becomes S, the armature pole adjacent to it has become S. By shifting the brush axis slightly in one direction or the other, the armature will turn under the influence of repulsion between like poles.

One type of repulsion motor is arranged so that all the commutator segments are connected together after the motor is up to speed, and it then continues to operate as an ordinary squirrel-cage unit. Another type has a squirrel-cage winding in the bottom of the armature slots, in addition to the usual armature winding. The squirrel-cage winding has little effect until normal speed is approached, at which time it becomes sufficiently active to assist the commutated winding.

REVIEW QUESTIONS

1. Describe Barlow's wheel.
2. Discuss the left-hand motor rule.
3. What is meant by the term "counter-emf"?
4. Compare speed characteristics of shunt and compound motors.
5. Why does a series motor overspeed at no-load?
6. Define the term "horsepower."
7. How may the speed of a shunt motor be increased above normal?
8. What is the main reason that a shunt motor will not operate on alternating current?
9. Tell how a revolving flux is created in the stator of a two-phase motor.
10. Do you think the three-phase revolving flux superior to the two-phase revolving flux?
11. Tell how poles are induced in the rotor of an induction motor.
12. Could the wound rotor of a two-phase motor have a three-phase winding?
13. Why does an induction motor draw a large current at starting?
14. Compare use of inductance, capacitance, and resistance in the starting winding of a single-phase induction motor.
15. Upon what basic principle does the operation of a repulsion motor depend?

CHAPTER 11

TRANSFORMERS AND RECTIFIERS

TRANSFORMERS

Use of Transformers

As the name implies, a transformer transforms, or changes, something. One of the many uses of transformers is to change the high voltage supplied by the electric power company to a lower voltage, so it can be safely used in our homes. These transformers which are used by the electric company can be seen up and down the alleys in the city. They are in the form of large metal cans mounted on the poles just below the power lines, Fig. 1. In the country, they can be seen on the hi-line poles where the supply line to the farm is attached.

Line Material Co.

Fig. 1. Commercial Transformer Installation

Induction in Alternating-Current Loop. In Fig. 2A, a pair of copper loops are placed adjacent to one another, alternating-current supply wires being connected to one of them. From the study of inductance, it is evident that a voltage will be induced in the other loop when a varying current flows in the first one. The loop connected to the supply wires is termed the "primary" loop or coil in alternating-current discussions. That in which the voltage is induced is termed the "secondary."

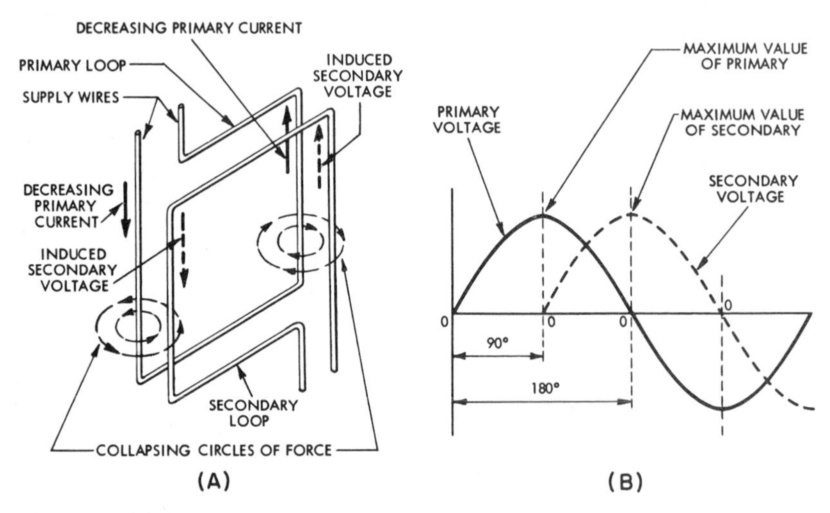

Fig. 2. Induction in Alternating Current Loop—Current Decreasing: A–Voltage Induced in Secondary Loop; B–Secondary Voltage Lags Primary Voltage by 90 Degrees

Since alternating current varies constantly between zero and maximum values of the sine curve, a continually changing voltage is induced in the secondary loop. Its outline duplicates that of the primary loop, as shown in Fig. 2B. Here, it is seen that the secondary voltage lags the primary voltage by one-half alternation, or 90 electrical degrees. The reason for the 90-degree lag can be readily explained.

One may recall, in connection with our study of inductance, that when current in a conductor starts to decrease, with resulting collapse of circles of force, voltage induced in the adjacent wire is in the same direction as the voltage in the first conductor. Referring to the figures, it will be noted that as primary current and voltage decrease from maximum to zero above-the-line, voltage induced in the secondary loop is also in the above-the-line direction.

When primary current reverses, and begins to increase from zero to maximum in the below-the-line direction, circles of force spread out, cutting across the secondary loop so as to maintain secondary voltage in its above-the-line direction. At first, this statement may sound contradictory. But reference to Fig. 3 shows that direction of the circles of force around the individual primary conductors has reversed, and their direction of cutting across the secondary conductors is changed. Application of the left-hand current rule confirms the result stated above.

Counter-EMF Generated in Alternating-Current Loop. When current flows in the secondary loop, by induction from the primary current, it creates circles of force which induce a voltage in the primary. This voltage, as with all induced voltages, lags the current which creates it by 90 electrical degrees. Fig. 4 shows it directly opposed to the supply voltage. While primary voltage increases from zero to maximum in the below-the-line direction, and then decreases again to zero to form a complete alternation, the voltage induced in the primary loop follows exactly the same pattern, but in the above-the-line direction. That is, it opposes the primary step by step. For this reason, it is termed a counter voltage, or counter-emf. This counter-emf is similar to that generated in the windings of a direct-current motor, and its function in the alternating-current transformer is basically the same.

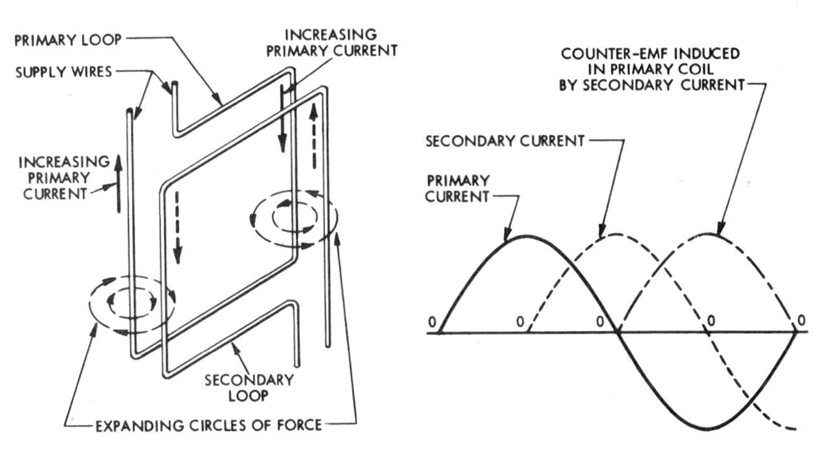

Fig. 3. Induction in Alternating Current Loop—Current Increasing

Fig. 4. Counter EMF in Alternating Current Loop

Elementary Transformer

Fig. 5A illustrates a simple transformer, consisting of primary and secondary loops mounted upon a laminated iron or steel core which forms a closed magnetic circuit. The core, like that in a direct-current electromagnet, increases the magnetic flux originated by the circles of force. The magnetic lines in the core of the transformer, with alternating current flowing in the primary coil, are the combined resultant of primary flux and the counter-flux of the secondary current. In effect, they constitute a single flux, and will be considered as such.

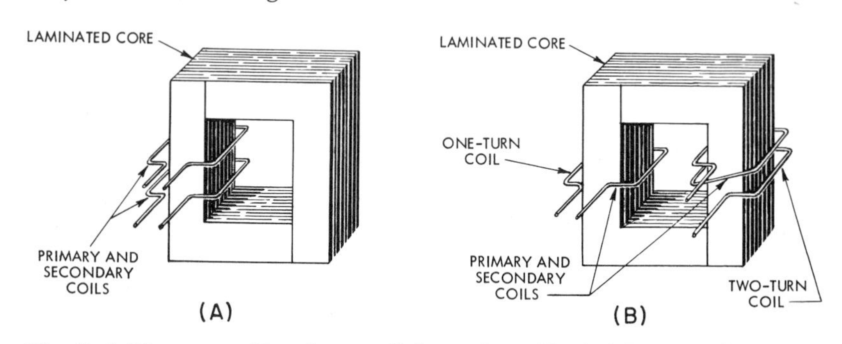

Fig. 5. A–Elementary Transformer, Coils on Same Vertical Leg; B–Elementary Transformer, Coils on Separate Legs

Since the iron magnetic path conducts lines of force with far greater ease than air, the primary coil may be placed on one leg of the transformer and the secondary on the other leg, without decreasing their mutual effects. Fig. 5B shows this arrangement, a primary coil of a single turn being placed at the left, and a two-turn secondary coil on the right. Both coils are exposed to the same magnetic flux, which sets up an induced voltage in the secondary winding and a counter-emf in the primary.

Step-Up Transformation. When the same number of magnetic lines cut across a coil of two turns, twice as much voltage is created as when this same flux cuts across a coil of one turn. The voltage induced in the secondary of the transformer in Fig. 5B, then, must be twice that generated in the primary as counter-emf.

Now, the counter-emf of a transformer, like the counter-emf in a direct-current armature, is only slightly less than the supply voltage. Suppose the supply is 6 volts and the counter-emf 5.9 volts. In this case, the secondary voltage is equal to twice 5.9, or 11.8 volts. Thus, the transformer accomplishes a transformation of voltage, taking 6 volts from the supply wires and changing the voltage to 11.8 for whatever use may be desired. This form of voltage change is termed a *step-up*, and the unit is known as a step-up transformer.

Step-Down Transformation. Consider, for the moment, that a 12-

volt supply line is connected to the coil of the right-hand leg of the core, so that it becomes the primary winding of the transformer. The magnetic flux cutting across the single-turn secondary winding will be the same as that cutting the two-turn primary winding. If the counter-emf of the primary winding is 11.8 volts, the voltage generated in the secondary will be only one-half this amount, or 5.9 volts. In this case, the voltage has been "stepped down," and the unit is known as a step-down transformer.

Current Available in Primary and Secondary Windings

The step-up transformer may appear to create something out of nothing, taking in 6 volts from the supply wires and providing 11.8 volts at the terminals of the secondary winding. Further investigation, however, will show otherwise.

The term *ampere-turns* was defined, in the study of electromagnetism, as the product of amperes and turns. There, it was pointed out that the strength of magnetic flux induced in an iron core was directly proportional to the number of ampere-turns in the magnetizing coil, or solenoid. The same rule applies to the basic transformer, which is nothing more than a pair of solenoids.

Since the counter-emf generated in the primary by current flowing in the secondary turns is approximately equal to the voltage induced in the secondary by current flowing in the primary turns, their ampere-turn values must be nearly equal. When the primary winding has a single turn and the secondary two turns, twice as much current may flow in the primary winding. Where the situation is reversed, and the primary has twice as many turns as the secondary, current in the primary winding is but one-half that in the secondary.

One should note that the product of volts and amperes is practically the same for the two windings. In the step-up transformer, a primary voltage of 6 and a current of 10 amperes ($6 \times 10 = 60$), Provide a secondary voltage of 12 and a current of 5 amperes ($12 \times 5 = 60$). The same facts, taken in reverse order, apply to the step-down transformer.

Turns-Ratio

With a 6-volt, single-turn, primary winding, a secondary voltage of approximately 12 volts was produced in a secondary winding of two turns. That is, twice as many turns in the secondary winding resulted in a secondary voltage twice as great as that in the primary. Or, considering the reverse order, a secondary with one-half the number of turns as the primary resulted in one-half the voltage of the primary. In the same way, the voltage of the secondary may be made four times that of the primary, or ten times, or twenty, or any chosen value, simply by making its number of turns that many times the number in the primary.

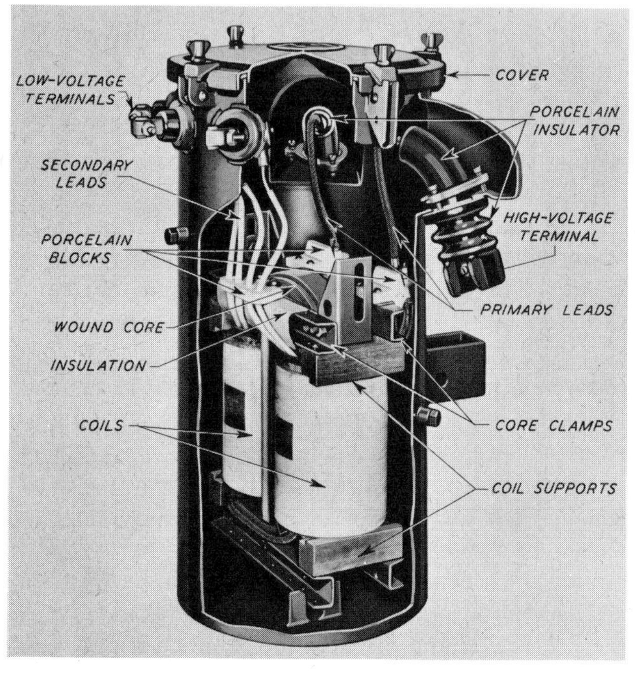

Line Material Co.

Fig. 6. Cut-away View of a Modern Transformer

This fact is expressed by saying that: The relationship between primary and secondary voltages in a transformer depends upon the turns-ratio of the two windings. The term *turns-ratio* means the result obtained by dividing the larger number of turns in one winding by the smaller number in the other. Where the secondary has two turns and the primary one turn, the turns-ratio is 2-to-1. Where the secondary has ten turns and the primary one, the turns ratio is 10-to-1. If the secondary has five turns and the primary thirty, the turns ratio is 6-to-1. In each case, it is necessary to take into consideration the matter of whether it is a step-up or a step-down transformer before applying the turns-ratio to determine the voltage of the other winding.

For purposes of illustration, transformers having but a few turns in primary and secondary windings have been considered. The ordinary commercial transformer, a cut-away view of which is shown in Fig. 6, employs primary and secondary windings that have hundreds or even thousands of turns, the actual number depending upon engineering design factors.

Transformers of the type shown in the illustration are filled with oil, or often with a non-inflammable liquid, which conducts heat from windings to the surface of the steel case, where it is dissipated into the atmosphere. Smaller ones, termed *dry* transformers, use a solid tar compound for transmitting heat from coils to case.

Transformer Ratings

Small transformers are usually rated in watts, the rating being obtained by multiplying primary current and voltage. Larger ones, such as that in Fig. 6, are rated in volt-amperes or kilovolt-amperes (thousands of volt-amperes), because actual power output of the unit depends upon power factor of its load.

This method of rating becomes necessary, since the windings are designed to carry only a certain maximum current without overheating. For example, a 500-volt, 50 kva (kilovolt-ampere) transformer could supply a load of 50 kilowatts when voltage and current were exactly in phase with one another, or at 100 per cent power factor, as it is expressed. Here, 500 × 100 × 1. (power factor) = 50,000 watts or 50 kilowatts. At 80 per cent power factor, however, it could supply only: 500 × 100 × .8 (power factor), or 40,000 watts, even though the current in the windings is 100 amperes in both cases.

Single-Phase Transformer Connections

The low-voltage winding of single-phase distribution transformers that supply power to our homes is ordinarily made in two sections. Schematic diagrams of a single-phase transformer with the secondary leads brought out for 230 v service is shown in Fig. 7A. Here, the two sections are connected in series, and the voltages induced in each section are added. In Fig. 7B the two secondary windings are connected in parallel. This connection is used to supply a heavy load requiring 115 v service.

It is common practice to ground the middle of the secondary winding, making it a neutral wire. Then the voltage between the neutral wire and each outside wire is 115 v. A practical wiring circuit that uses

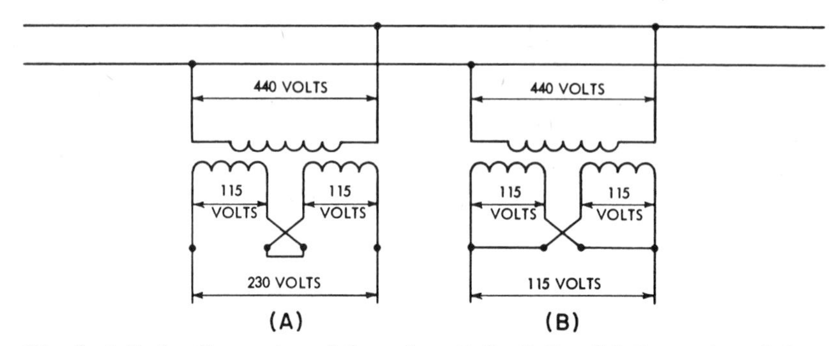

Fig. 7. A–Series Connection of Secondary Coils; B–Parallel Connection of Secondary Coils

this arrangement is illustrated in Fig. 8. The lamps and small appliances are connected between each outside wire and ground. The two outside wires, which supply 230 v, are used for electric ranges, hot-water heaters, and larger appliance motors. Note that the switches for the 115 v units are on the *hot* side of the unit; that is, the switch is between the outside wire and the unit being turned on. This removes the high voltage from the unit when it is not in operation. We also have fuses in the high-voltage lines, so that opening the circuit removes the high voltage. This, in turn, removes the danger of shock.

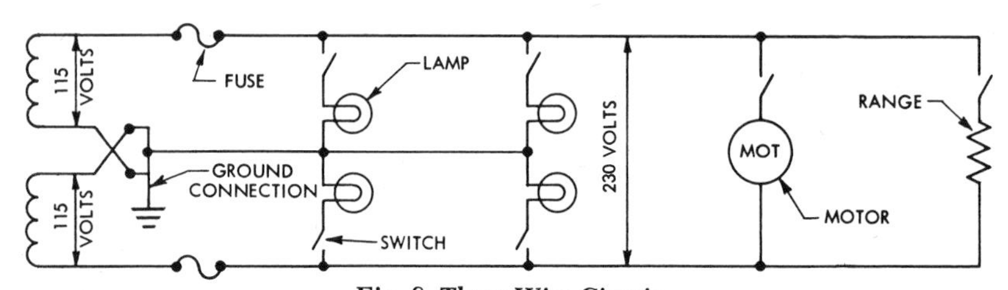

Fig. 8. Three-Wire Circuit

Grounding Single-Phase Transformers. The neutral of the three-wire, 115/230 v circuit is ordinarily grounded to afford protection to persons who may come in contact with the lighting circuit, as indicated in Fig. 8. If the neutral wire were not grounded, and if one of the outside wires comes in contact with the ground, the other side of the circuit would rise to a voltage above ground equal to the series voltage of the two winding sections.

Three-Phase Transformer Connections. Standardization of generating equipment, motors, and appliances, has brought about the acceptance of three-phase, 60 cycle current throughout the whole country. Except for network systems, which will be referred to later, a group of three single-phase transformers, known as a transformer bank, is usually employed in transforming three-phase current from one voltage to another. The three primary windings of the transformers, and the three secondary windings, are connected together in one of two ways: star or delta.

Voltage Relationships in the Star Connection. This connection, also known as the *Y* connection, is illustrated in Fig. 9A which shows three star-connected primary windings of transformers supplied by a "2200 volt," three-phase, power line whose voltage, between each pair of

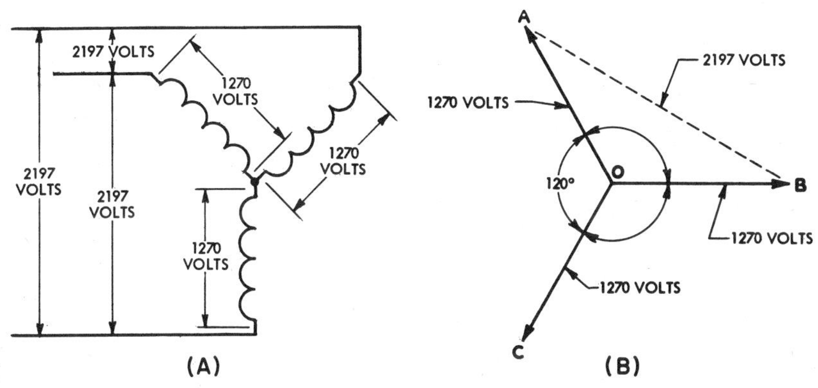

Fig. 9. A–Voltages in Star Transformer Bank; B–Diagrammatic View of Star Voltages

line wires is actually 2197. The voltage across each winding between the line wire to which it is connected and the common, or *star* point, is shown as 1270.

Fig. 9B shows how the voltage across the windings of a star-connected transformer bank may be determined, the illustration consisting of three equal arrows spaced 120 degrees apart (1/3 of a circle). From the study of three-phase generators, it will be recalled that three-phase voltages are so spaced. In the figure, the arrows *A-O*, *B-O*, and *C-O* represent the voltages across each of the three transformer windings in view Fig. 9A. The distance between the ends of any two arrows, such as *A* and *B*, is a measure of the voltage between any two supply wires.

Upon measuring the distance *A-B* very accurately, and comparing it with the lengths of any one of the three arrows, such as *A-O*, it is found to be 1.73 times as long. If the length, or value, of the arrow is known, the value of the outer distance is determined by multiplying the arrow value by 1.73. If the outer value is known, the arrow value may be determined by dividing the outer value by 1.73.

In the present instance, where the line voltage is known to be 2197, the arrow or transformer voltage is equal to 2197 divided by 1.73, or 1270 volts. Expressed in the form of a rule: Line voltage in a star-connected bank is equal to 1.73 times the star voltage.

Current Value in Star Connection. One should note that the current flowing into each of the windings is the same as that flowing in the line wire to which it is connected. Such is not the case with the other important form of connection, as will become apparent shortly. Meanwhile, it should be emphasized that: Line current in a star-connected bank is the same as transformer current.

Voltage Relationships in the Delta Connection. Fig. 10A illustrates a conventional delta connection, the three windings being connected to a three-phase supply line. It is seen that the voltage across each pair of line wires, 2197 volts, is that across the individual windings. Stated as a rule: Line voltage in a delta-connected bank is the same as transformer voltage.

Referring to Fig. 10B where each of the lines of the delta, or triangle, represent a transformer winding, it would appear by measuring the angles inside the triangle that voltages in the individual windings are only 60 electrical degrees (1/6 of a circle) apart instead of 120 degrees. Yet, the voltages of the three-phase supply line are certainly 120 degrees apart. What does this mean?

Fig. 10C will help solve the difficulty, because it shows how the three windings are actually connected. The three winding arrows are spaced 120 degrees apart, as in Fig. 9, but the star ends are not connected together. Instead, the star end of winding *A-O*, shown as A_1, is connected to the outer end of winding *B-O*. The star end of winding *B-O*, marked B_1, is connected to the outer end of winding *C-O*, and the star end of *C-O*, marked C_1, is connected to the outer end of *A-O*.

Referring again to Fig. 10B, the 120 degree relationship may be seen by checking the angles outside the triangle, the arrows being extended beyond the intersection point in each case. Perhaps, by way of obtaining a correct picture, the delta connection should always be drawn as in Fig. 10B. But the conventional method of representation is ordinarily used, without explanatory comment, in the interest of simplicity.

Current Values in the Delta Connection. The current from each supply wire, in Fig. 10A, flows into two transformer windings. Since voltages in the two windings are 120 degrees apart, their currents (assuming 100 per cent power factor) must be 120 degrees apart, the line current being the sum of the two. We found, in examining the star connection, that the sum of two equal voltages which are 120 degrees apart is equal to 1.73 times either one. Here, where the two currents are 120 degrees apart, the line current must be equal to 1.73 times either one. Expressed in the form of a rule: Line current in a delta-connected bank is equal to 1.73 times transformer current.

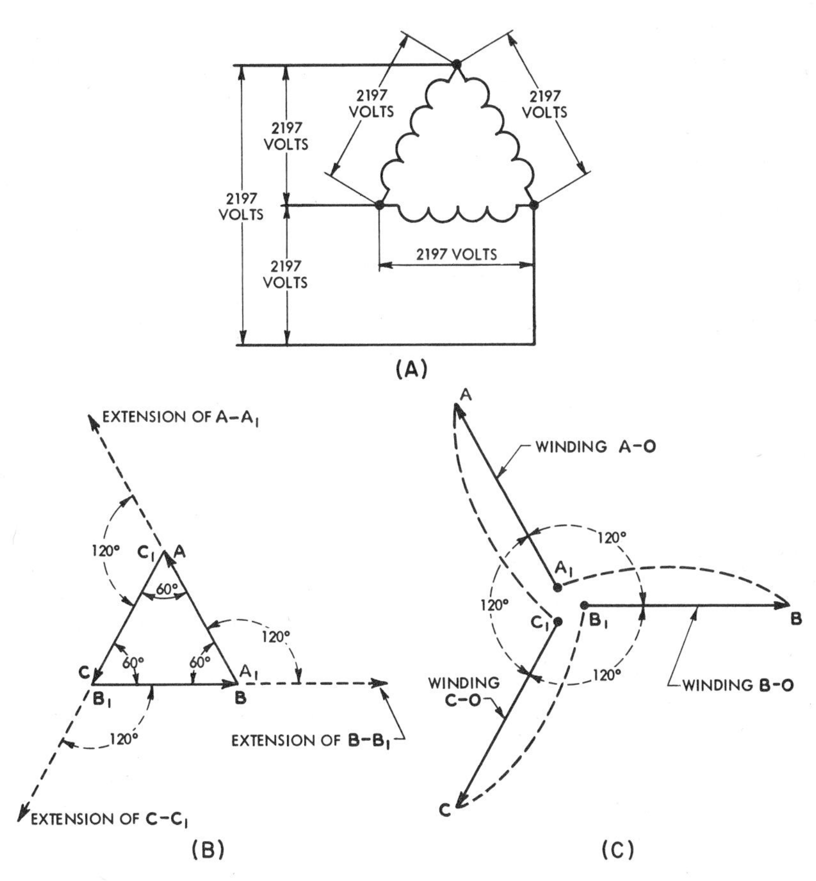

Fig. 10. A–Conventional Diagram of Delta Primary Windings; B–Angular Relationships in Delta Windings; C–Actual Connections Between Windings of Delta Transformer Bank

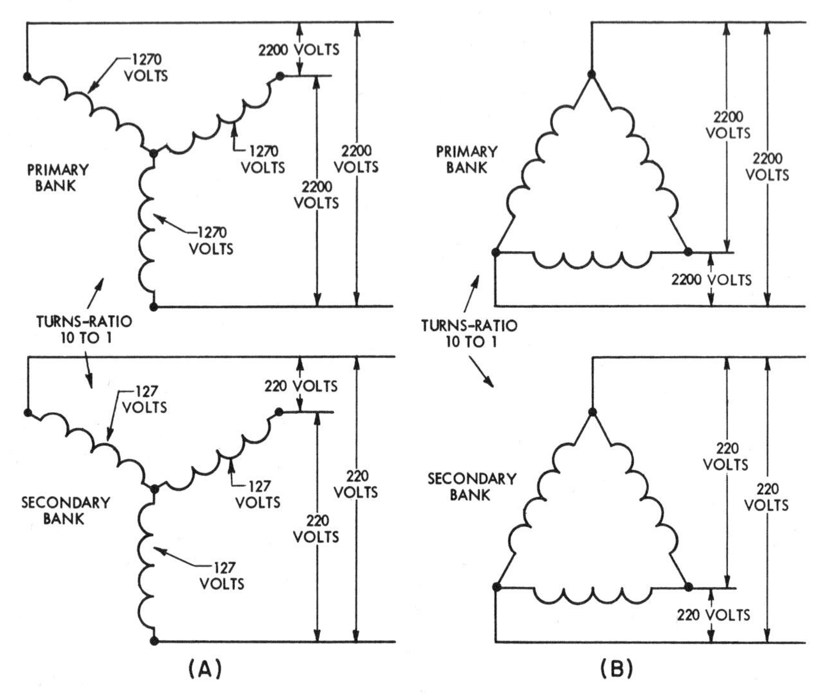

Fig. 11. A–Star-Star Transformer Bank; B–Delta-Delta Transformer Bank

Secondary Transformer Connections. As with primary windings, the secondary windings may be connected either star or delta to suit particular requirements. Fig. 11A shows in schematic form, the transformer bank of Fig. 9, both primary and secondary windings being connected star, this arrangement known as *star-star.* If the turns-ratio of the step-down transformers is 10 to 1, the voltage in each secondary winding will be 127 while that between secondary line wires is 220 (1.73×127).

Fig. 11B shows the transformer bank of Fig. 10, with both primary and secondary windings connected delta, and known as a *delta-delta* connection. With a turns-ratio of 10 to 1, the secondary voltage is 220 across each winding. Since each winding spans two secondary line wires, the secondary line voltage is, of course, 220.

If the transformer bank is connected *star-delta,* the primary remaining star, but the secondary being changed to delta, as in the more serviceable schematic form of Fig. 12A, secondary line voltage is 127 with a turns-ratio of 10-to-1. Should the transformers be constructed with a turns-ratio of 5.77-to-1, the primary winding remaining unchanged, the secondary voltage would be 220 as before (1270/5.77 = 220).

In Fig. 12B, which shows a *delta-star* connection, the secondary line voltage of a 10-to-1 set of windings becomes 381 (220 × 1.73 = 381). In this case, also, secondary voltage can be raised or lowered to any desired value by designing the windings to have a different turns-ratio.

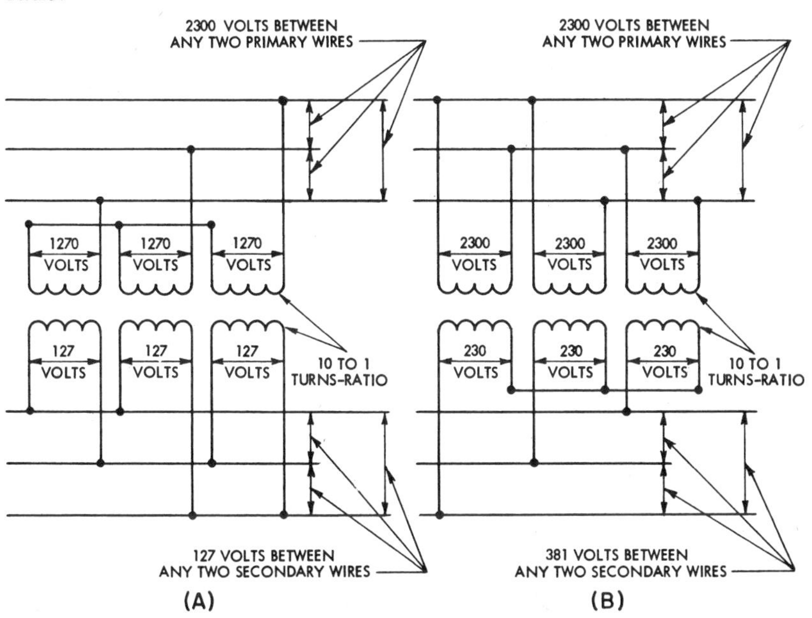

Fig. 12. A–Voltages in Star-Delta Transformer Connection; B–Voltages in Delta-Star Transformer Connection

Two Special Transformer Connections. Fig. 13 illustrates a delta-delta connection, the primary voltage 2300 and the secondary 230. Three secondary line wires: *A*, *B*, and *C* supply 230-volt motors and similar loads. A connection is made to the mid-point of one of the secondaries, as shown in the figure, and single-phase, three-wire lighting circuits are taken off the two line wires, *A* and *B* which are connected to the transformer secondary, and the tap wire which serves as a neutral conductor. The voltage between *A* and *B*, of course, is 230, while that between either one of them and the neutral wire is 115. It is common practice to run all four wires into a commercial or industrial plant for supplying both lighting and power requirements. Electricians call line *C* the *power leg*.

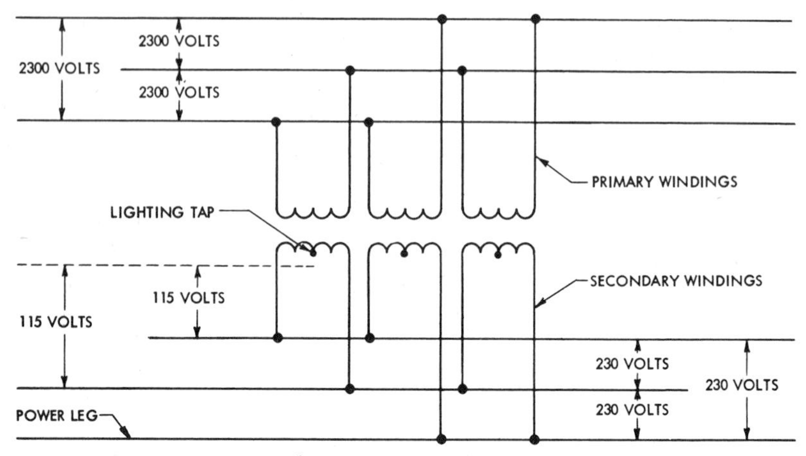

Fig. 13. Delta Secondaries with Lighting Tap

Fig. 14 shows the popular network arrangement used for both power and lighting. The basic connection is delta-star. Voltage between any line wire and star is 120, and that across any pair of the main wires, *A*, *B*, and *C*, is 208. A neutral wire is brought out from the star connection to serve as the common wire for lighting circuits. Lighting is connected between all three of the main wires and the neutral conductor, and power loads between any two, or all three, of the main conductors.

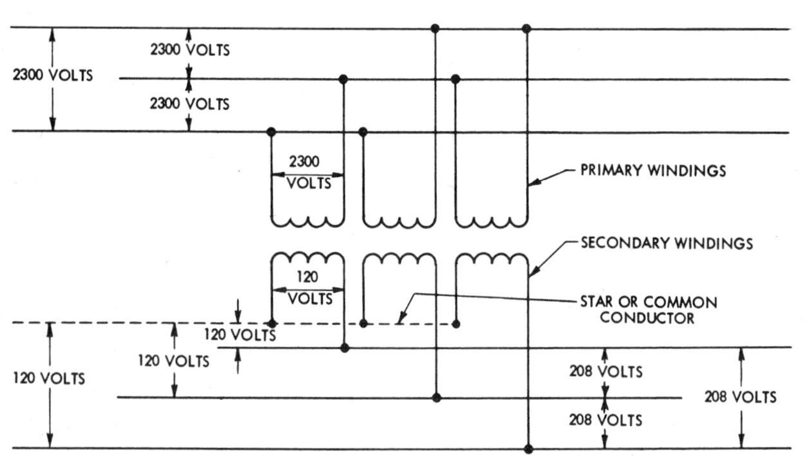

Fig. 14. Network Connection

The term *network* is applied to this arrangement because it was first employed in congested downtown areas of large cities where automatically-controlled units were desired in connection with feeder networks. In this particular application, all three sets of primary and secondary windings are wound upon a single core, the unit being arranged for rapid connection or disconnection as the feeder load changes or as local trouble occurs.

Power in Three-Phase Circuits. Total power input or output of an evenly loaded, or balanced three-phase transformer bank is equal to three times that of any one transformer. At 100 per cent power factor, this total equals: 3 × Voltage × Current. One fact to note, is that the voltage and current of the particular transformer winding must be employed in this calculation.

If the windings are connected star, we know that the transformer voltage equals line voltage divided by 1.73, but that transformer current is the same as line current. For the star connection, therefore, the calculation may be changed to read:

$$\text{Power} = 3 \times \frac{E}{1.73} \times I,$$

where E and I are line values.

If the windings are connected delta, we know that the transformer voltage is equal to line voltage, but that transformer current is equal to line current divided by 1.73. For the delta connection, the calculation reads:

$$\text{Power} = 3 \times E \times \frac{I}{1.73}$$

In either of these cases, the formula is the same as if written:

$$\text{Power} = 3 \times \frac{E \times I}{1.73}$$

Written in still another way, the formula reads:

$$\text{Power} = \frac{3}{1.73} \times E \times I$$

Now,

$$\frac{3}{1.73} = 1.73$$

In other words, 3 is the square of 1.73

To determine power taken from the line wires by the three-phase transformer bank, then, whether it is connected star or delta, we may write:

$$\text{Power} = 1.73 \times E \times I$$

And the same calculation will apply to power delivered to the secondary line wires by the secondary windings of the transformer bank. Indeed, this formula for determining power in a balanced three-phase circuit applies not only to transformers, but to any kind of three-phase load.

If the power factor of the circuit is other than 100 per cent, it is necessary to multiply the above value by that power factor. For example, if the power factor was 80 per cent, or .8, the formula would read:

$$\text{Power} = 1.73 \times E \times I \times .8$$

Autotransformer

The autotransformer, shown diagrammatically in Fig. 15, is employed for certain applications, especially where an assortment of voltages is required. The iron core is exactly like that of the ordinary transformer, but the usual primary and secondary windings are combined

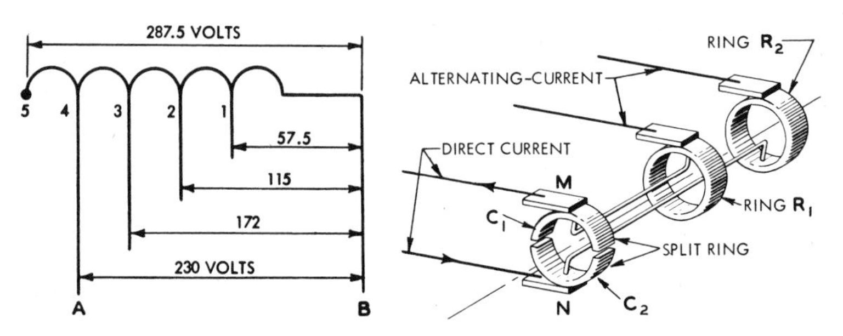

Fig. 15. Autotransformer **Fig. 16. Split-Ring Rectifier**

into one. As indicated in the figure, a number of voltages may be obtained by making tap connections to the winding at suitable points. Here, where the supply is 230 volts, intermediate voltages may be obtained between either of the supply wires, *A* and *B*, and a tap point.

The illustration shows that 57.5 volts may be obtained between wire *B* and tap point number 1; 115 volts between this wire and tap point 2; and 172.5 volts to point 3. Point 4, where supply wire *A* is connected, might well be the end of the winding if it were desired to obtain only voltages less than that of the supply. Where a higher voltage is desired, a tap may be taken from an extension of the winding beyond the supply tap, as at point 5. The value between this point and wire *B*, in the illustration, is seen to be 287.5 volts.

RECTIFIERS

Commutator Rectifier

Although all but a very small percentage of electricity is generated as alternating current, it is often necessary to have a supply of direct current. It might be obtained from a small direct-current generator, but it is much easier to change the alternating current into direct current, which is termed *rectification.* This can be done by one of several available methods.

One of the first methods devised for rectifying alternating current was the use of a *rectifying commutator.* Fig. 16 illustrates the device. The shaft of this unit is driven at a speed of 3,600 r.p.m. by means of a small synchronous motor. At one end of the shaft are two collector rings, R_1 and R_2. Current is carried from the supply lines to the rings by means of brushes. Ring R_1 connects with the half of the split ring C_1, and ring R_2 connects with the half C_2. Two brushes, *M* and *N*, bear against the split ring as it turns.

At the instant shown, current flows from the alternating-current supply wire to ring R_1, to split-ring C_1, to brush *M*, to the load, which requires a supply of direct current. At this moment, brush *M* is the negative brush. Current returns from the load to positive brush *N*, through split-ring C_2 and collector-ring R_2 to the other side of the alternating-current supply circuit.

When the current is passing through zero, however, the split ring changes brushes so that the C_2 half is in contact with brush *M* and C_1 with brush *N*. Current in the alternating-current supply wires changes direction now, flowing to ring R_2, to split-ring C_2, to brush *M*, to the load, to brush *N*, to R_1 to the other side of the supply wires. It will be noted that brush *M* is still the negative brush of the direct-current circuit. In other words, current through the load has not altered direction.

Current delivered to the direct-current load passes through zero twice during one cycle, but it always flows in the same direction. This is known as *pulsating* direct current. Current furnished by the usual direct-current generator is not pulsating; it maintains a steady value. For most applications, however, pulsating current is altogether suitable.

Electrolytic Rectifier

An early rectifier used to supply direct current of low value is the *electrolytic rectifier.* It resembles the electric cell in that it has two plates and an electrolyte. Two plates, one aluminum and the other lead, are placed in a solution of ammonium sulfate. When current flows, a coating is formed on the surface of the aluminum plate. This coating has the property of permitting current to flow in one direction more easily than in the other.

In other words, this device cuts off one half of every cycle of current flow. For this reason, it is said to be a *half-wave rectifier.* The electrolytic rectifier is not now in general use.

Dry-Disk Rectifier

The dry-disk rectifier, also known as a junction rectifier, makes use of the principle of the electrolytic rectifier: that certain combinations of metals permit current to flow in only one direction. Two of the more popular are the *selenium rectifier* and the *copper oxide rectifier.* The copper-oxide rectifier described here illustrates the manner of operation.

Fig. 17 shows a copper disk which is about 1¼ inches in diameter and about ⅛ inch thick. One face of the disk is polished copper. The

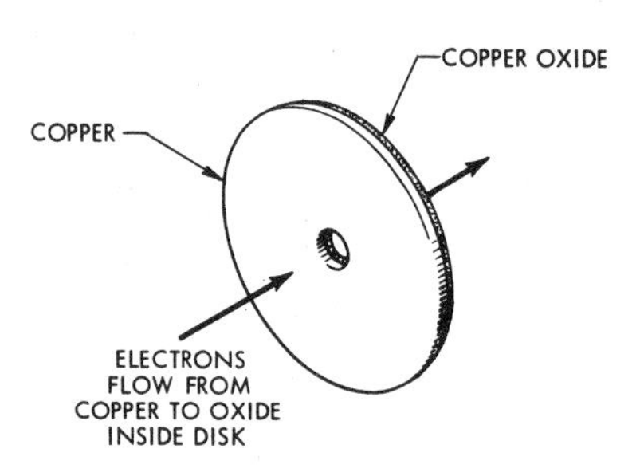

Fig. 17. Copper Rectifying Disc

other face of the disk has been burned so that the surface metal has combined with oxygen in the air to form a compound of copper which is called *copper oxide.* When an alternating voltage is applied to the opposite faces of the disk, current flows from the copper to the copper oxide face, but not in the reverse direction. That is, the disk rectifies alternating current in the same way that the electrolytic unit rectifies it.

The voltage across any disk should not exceed 5 or 6 v and is usually somewhat less than this value. When used on circuits of higher voltage, several disks are arranged in series, a lead washer being placed between each two disks in order to improve contact between them.

In its simplest form, this device is also a half-wave rectifier as shown in Fig. 18A and Fig 18B. Four such units may be arranged in a *bridge*

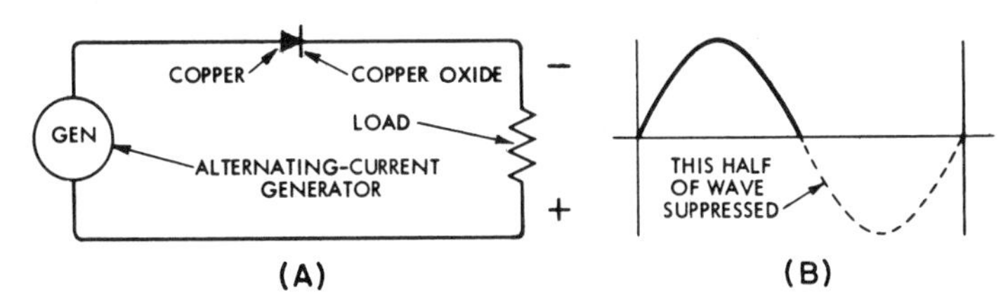

Fig. 18. Copper Disc as Half-Wave Rectifier

circuit to provide full-wave rectification. Fig. 19 represents this circuit. Current is supplied to the load by way of four copper oxide rectifying units: *A, B, C,* and *D*. In each case, the copper side of the disk is represented by an arrow and the copper oxide face is represented by a short, heavy line.

In Fig. 19A, the current flows from the supply wire that is negative at the moment to units *A* and *D*. It cannot pass through *D* because that is the copper oxide face, but it passes readily through unit *A* to the negative side of the load. After passing through the load, the current flows to the junction between units *D* and *C*. The current cannot flow through *D* because of the pressure of the negative supply line on the other side; therefore, the current flows through unit *C* to the positive supply wire.

When the supply voltage reverses polarity, the current flow through

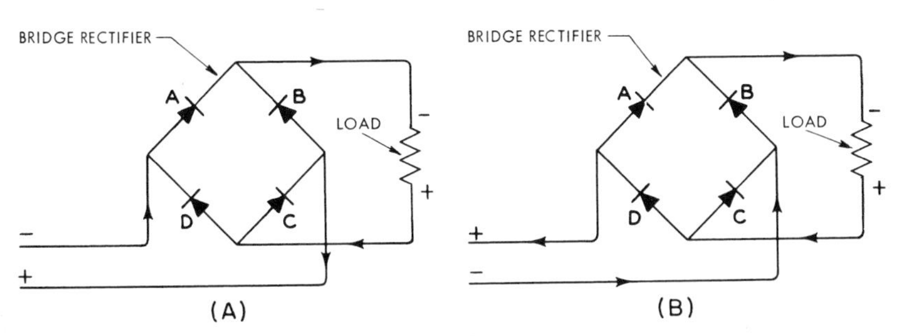

Fig. 19. Full-Wave Bridge Rectifier Circuit

the bridge rectifier is shown in Fig. 19B. This flow is from the positive terminal of the supply, through unit *B*, through the load (this direction remains unchanged), and through unit *D* to the negative supply terminal. We will note that the current flows through the load in the same direction during each alternation of the supply voltage, resulting in a full-wave direct-current supply to the load.

Electron Tube Rectifiers

We have considered the dry-disk type of rectifier and also the mechanical method. Another method of great importance in the electrical industry is rectification by means of electron tubes. These devices, however, take on several forms; and in large industrial applications lose any resemblance to a tube. We will consider them in three different groups: high-vacuum rectifiers, gaseous-tube rectifiers, and mercury-arc rectifiers.

High-Vacuum Rectifier. Our first step in this study will be to consider the operation of the most elementary vacuum tube. This tube is illustrated schematically in Fig. 20. There are but two elements in this

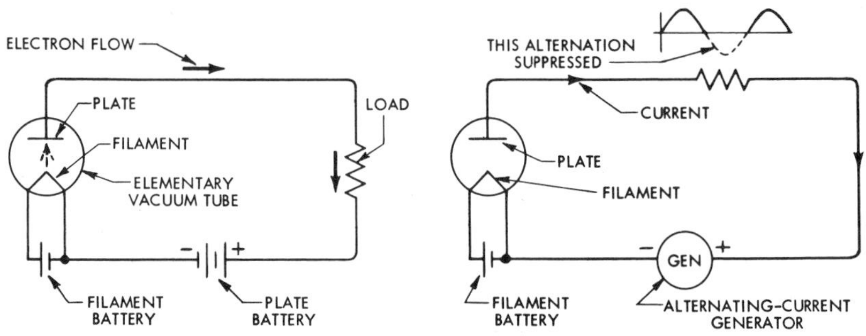

Fig. 20. Elementary Vacuum Tube Circuit

Fig. 21. Vacuum Tube as Half-Wave Rectifier

tube: the *plate* and the *filament*, rigidly mounted within the sealed glass envelope from which practically all of the air has been removed. The materials from which these elements are made vary according to the use to which they are to be put.

The metal plate has a connecting lead that passes through the glass envelope so that a connection can be made to it. The filament is a coil of fine resistance wire that has been coated with barium oxide or similar material. When a voltage is applied to the filament, it becomes very hot, and electrons are boiled from the coating on the wire.

With the tube connected in this circuit, the negatively charged electrons are attracted by the positively charged plate, and they move through the vacuum to the plate. This results in an *electron flow* from the filament to the plate *within the tube,* as shown by the dotted arrow. This current leaves the negative terminal of the battery and flows from the filament to the plate of the tube. The current then flows through the load, and from the filament lead it flows into the negative terminal of the plate supply.

If we were to reverse the polarity of the plate supply, connecting the negative terminal to the plate and the positive to the filament, only a moment's examination is needed to see why no current will flow. The current flow in the first instance was the result of the boiled-off electrons being drawn to the positively charged plate. If, in the second case, the filament is positive and the plate is negative, there are no electrons to be boiled off the plate and attracted by the positive filament. Since there are no electrons to move between the plate and the filament, there is no *electron flow.*

Fig. 21 shows the alternating-current circuit in which the high-vacuum rectifier is used and the resultant current through the load. When the terminal of the generator is positive, current will flow, but for the period that this terminal is negative, no current will flow. The resulting current flow is similar to that obtained when the electrolytic or dry-disk rectifier was used. When the rectifying unit is employed in this manner, it is known as a *half-wave rectifier.*

Full-Wave Rectifier. As we have noticed in studying the half-wave rectifiers, only half of the cycle is used in forcing current through the load. There is another form of rectifier, in addition to the bridge rectifier, that utilizes both cycles in forcing current through the load. This is known as the *full-wave rectifier.* Besides employing two rectifier tubes, this circuit must have the equivalent of two sources of voltage. Although a transformer with a lead connected at the center of the secondary winding is normally employed in this circuit, we will use two generators connected in series for the purpose of illustration.

The two generators, G_1 and G_2, and the two rectifiers, T_1 and T_2, are shown in Fig. 22. The polarities of the two generators, it will be noted, are such that when the right-hand terminal of G_1 is positive, the right-hand terminal of G_2 is also positive. And, when the polarity of G_1 reverses, the polarity of G_2 reverses at the same time. When the polarities are as indicated in Fig. 22, current flows from the negative terminal of G_2 upward through the load and through tube, T_2 to the positive terminal of G_2. During this time, no current is drawn from generator G_1, for the only way for current to return to the negative terminal would be from the plate of G_1. Since current will not flow through the tube in that direction and current will not flow from the positive

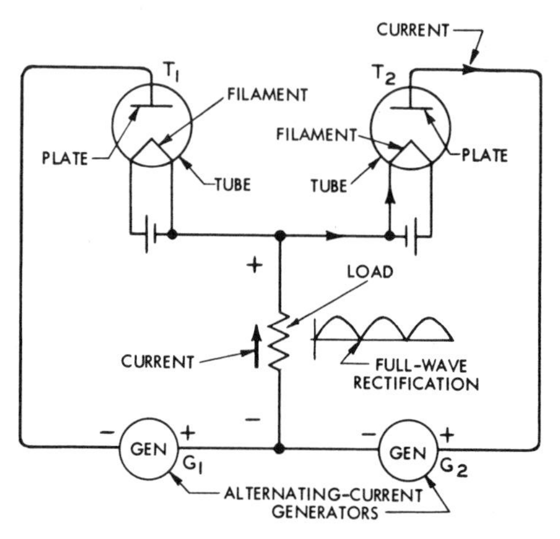

Fig. 22. Full-Wave Vacuum Tube Rectifier Circuit

terminal of a generator without returning to the negative terminal, no current will flow through G_1.

When the generators reverse polarity, and T_1 is connected to the positive terminal of G_1, current will flow upward through the load, and through it to the positive terminal of G_1. During this period, G_2 supplies no current to the load. The resulting current supplied to the load is a pulsating wave, as indicated to the right of the load.

Gas-Filled Rectifier. The main difference between the high-vacuum rectifier and the gas-filled rectifier is that the latter has gas within the glass envelope. This may be an inert gas—argon, neon, or xenon—or it may be a small amount of mercury, which becomes gaseous when the filament of the tube is heated. In each case the gas serves the same purpose: to increase conductance through the tube. The gas-filled rectifier is indicated schematically in Fig. 23. The most popular of these gas-filled tubes is the *mercury-vapor* rectifier. These tubes are arranged in a circuit in the same manner as the high-vacuum rectifiers.

Mercury-Arc Rectifier. In industrial applications, where higher amounts of current are desired than can be obtained from the high-vacuum or gas-filled rectifiers, we find application for the *mercury-arc* rectifier. This rectifier employs a small pool of mercury, a plate element and a starting element, the pool serves the same purpose as the filament of the other tubes; that is, it furnishes the supply of electrons.

The operation differs somewhat from that of the high-vacuum and the mercury-vapor rectifier. In this tube, conduction (current flow) will not begin when a positive voltage is applied to the plate. Conduction will only begin when a positive voltage is applied to the plate and an arc is established between the mercury pool and the plate.

There are different methods for establishing the arc. One is with a starting rod, Fig. 24, which can be tilted into the mercury pool and then removed. Although this method is not practical for a single-phase rectifier, it will serve for the purpose of explanation. A lower voltage is applied to this rod from a separate source, and when this rod is removed from the pool an arc is established between it and the mercury. The higher voltage, which is applied to the plate, takes over the arc and conduction occurs between plate and mercury during the part of the cycle that it is positive. For the time that it is of a negative polarity, no current will flow. It is necessary that the arc be maintained between the auxiliary plate and the mercury during the period that the rectifying plate is negative, or it must be started again when the rectifying plate becomes positive.

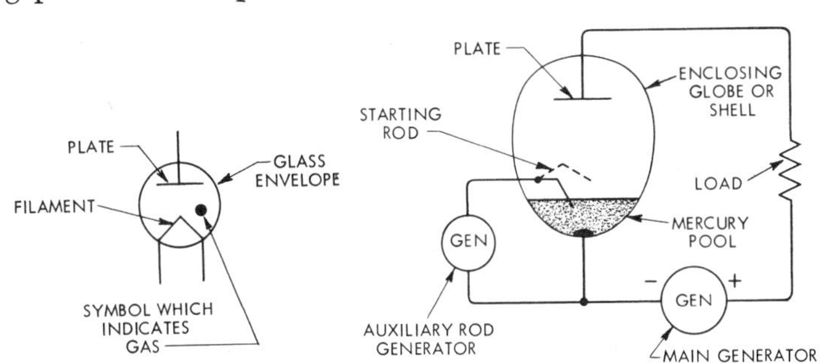

Fig. 23. Gas-Filled Tube **Fig. 24. Mercury Pool Tube**

The shortcomings of this elementary type of mercury-vapor rectifier are overcome in the modern commercial units. The rod is constructed of boron carbide which sparks continually, when a voltage is applied to it. An arc is established without the necessity of raising or lowering it. Fig. 25 is a cutaway view of a modern mercury-arc rectifier. Two of these units can be used to obtain full-wave rectification.

Polyphase Mercury-Vapor Rectifiers

In the polyphase rectifier, there are a number of plate elements, or anodes, in the upper portion of the steel enclosing tank. These anodes are connected to polyphase supply wires, and the arc is drawn be-

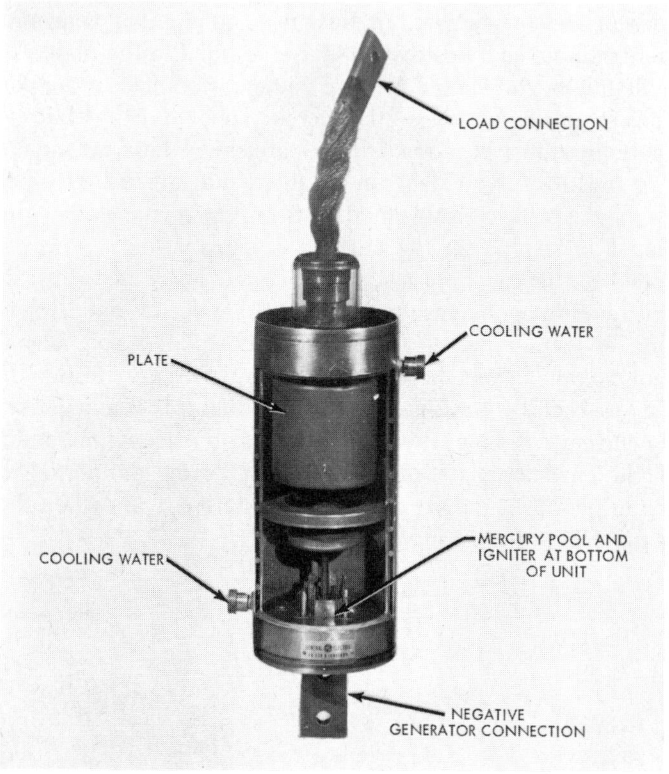

General Electric

Fig. 25. Ignitron Rectifier

tween one or more of them and the mercury pool in the bottom. As some of the anodes become negative and others positive, the arc shifts from one to the other, maintaining a steady flow of direct current to the load.

Another form of polyphase rectifier makes use of single-phase tanks, each containing an anode, a mercury pool, and a starting rod. They are connected to polyphase supply wires in such a way that current flow similar to that in the multi-anode tank is achieved by the whole group, which functions as a unit.

TRANSFORMERS AND RECTIFIERS

REVIEW QUESTIONS

1. Explain the process of induction in the alternating-current loop.
2. Discuss counter-emf in the alternating-current loop.
3. Why can't the transformer be used on direct current?
4. Define the expression "turns-ratio."
5. What is the relationship between primary and secondary ampere-turns?
6. Why are large transformers rated in kilovolt-amperes?
7. Outline voltage and current relationships in the three-phase star connection.
8. Outline these relationships as applied to the three-phase delta connection.
9. What form of connection is employed in the three-phase network system?
10. How is power determined in a three-phase system?
11. Describe the autotransformer.
12. How does a commutator rectifier work?
13. What basic fact explains operation of a dry-disk rectifier?
14. Make a simple sketch of a gaseous-tube rectifier.
15. Mention two types of polyphase rectifiers.

CHAPTER 12

ELECTRICAL MEASURING INSTRUMENTS

DIRECT-CURRENT METERS

Use of Meters

Electrical measuring instruments are used to find the values of electrical quantities. A voltmeter indicates the voltage of a circuit, an ammeter the current, and a wattmeter the power. Although there are a great number of different electrical measuring instruments, there are but three basic types.

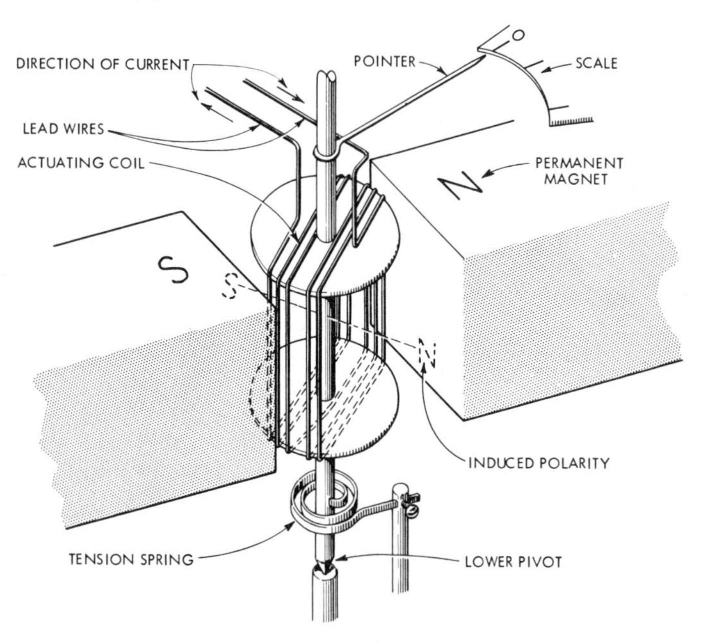

Fig. 1. Moving Coil Mechanism

Direct-Current Meters

Both the direct-current voltmeter and the direct-current ammeter operate on the principle of repulsion between like magnetic poles. Fig. 1 is used as an aid to understanding the operation of a direct-current meter. A coil of six turns is held in place by disks that are rigidly fastened to a shaft. The shaft and coil are centrally placed between the poles of a permanent magnet. The loop and shaft turn against the tension of the spring, which tries to hold them in the position shown.

When the meter is not in operation, and the coil is positioned as in Fig. 1, the pointer, which is attached to the shaft, indicates zero on the meter scale. Now we will assume that the meter is arranged in a circuit to read the desired electrical quantity—in this case it will be voltage or current. The method of connecting the meter will be explained in a moment. When the meter is connected, current will flow into the meter and through the coil. If the current flows as shown, the left-hand rule will indicate an N pole at one side of the coil and an S pole at the other. The repulsion between the N pole of the magnet and the N pole of the coil, and also the S pole of the magnet and the S pole of the coil, causes the coil and shaft to turn against the tension of the spring, moving the pointer across the scale.

The amount the coil rotates depends upon the strength of the repulsion between the two sets of like magnetic poles. Since the strength of the magnetic pole set up by the coil varies as the amount of current flowing through the coil, the amount of rotation is then in proportion

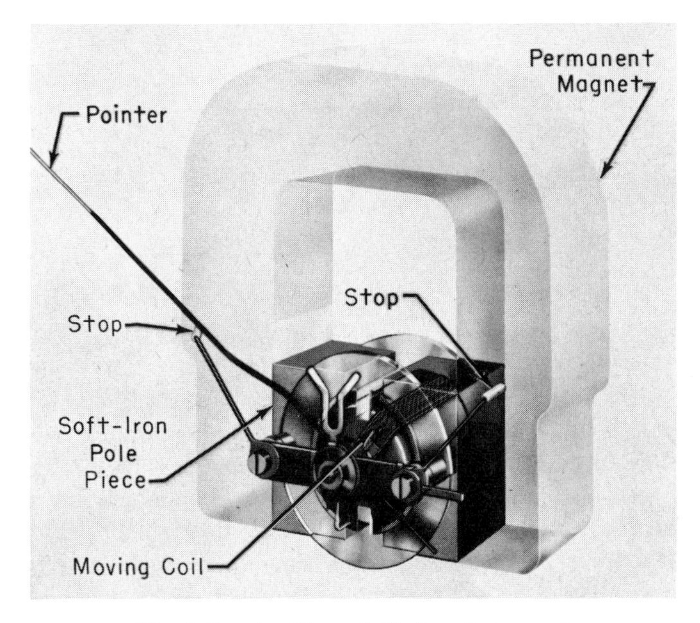

Fig. 2. Interior View of Modern Instrument

to the amount of current flowing through the coil. Therefore, we see that it is the amount of current flowing through the coil that is indicated by the pointer. The commercial version of the elementary moving coil for Fig. 1 has undergone many refinements. A modern moving-coil element is shown in Fig. 2.

Direct-Current Ammeter

Fig. 3A shows how an ammeter is connected in a circuit to measure current. Fig. 3B is the schematic of this circuit. The first point

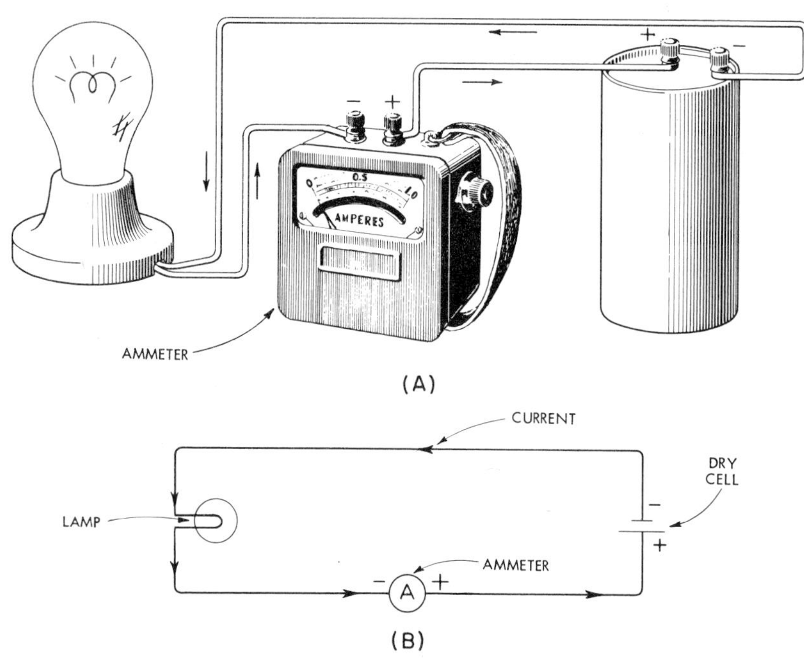

Fig. 3. Direct-Current Ammeter Connected in Circuit

to note is that the ammeter is connected in series with the battery, for the current flow that we wish to measure must pass through the meter. This brings forth a word of caution. If the ammeter is built to measure 5 amps, we must know for certain that less than 5 amps is flowing, for we must never permit more current to flow through the meter than the maximum reading on the scale. Should excessive current flow through the meter, the fine wire on the moving element may be heated to the melting point, and the meter will burn out. Even though the current may not be great enough to burn out the coil, the needle will move across the scale so rapidly that it will be badly bent when it strikes against the needle stop.

The second point to note in connecting a direct-current ammeter is the polarity. That is, the leads are attached so that the current flow is into the terminal that has a negative (−) marking. Connecting the meter in reverse can also damage the pointer.

Two-Range Ammeter. Fig. 4 represents the scale of a two-range ammeter. Below the scale markings are the numbers from 0 to 1, and above the markings we see the numbers from 0 to 5. Now we will connect the ammeter in the circuit of Fig. 5. This circuit consists of five

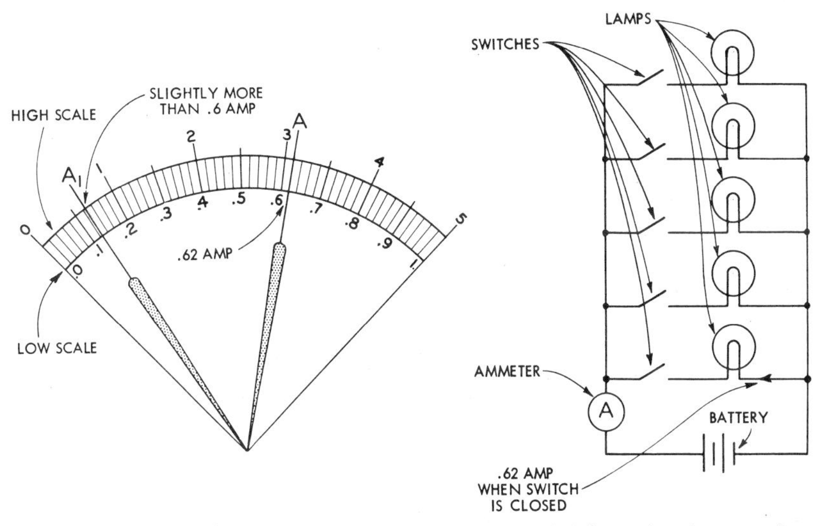

Fig. 4. Scale of Two-Range Ammeter

Fig. 5. Schematic Diagram of Test Circuit

identical lamps being operated by a battery. Switches are included in each branch so the lamps can be switched in and out at will. We will assume that each lamp draws about 0.5 amp when in operation; therefore, we can use the low range of the meter to measure the current flow through any one of the lamps without fear of damage to the meter. If we wish to measure the current flow when more than one lamp is in circuit, we must use the high range. However, we will first consider using the low range.

With the meter arranged to read on the low-range scale, and one switch closed, we can read the current flow on the ammeter dial.

This reading is indicated at point *A* in Fig. 4. We see that it is an indication between 0.6 and 0.8 of an amp. As a matter of fact, it is on the first mark above the 0.6 amp line. The long line between 0.6 and 0.8 amp indicates 0.7 amp as shown. If we count the number of spaces marked off between 0.6 and 0.7 amp, we will see that there are five, so each mark is 1/5 or 2/10 of the difference between 0.6 and 0.7 amp. These marks will then indicate 0.60, 0.62, 0.64, 0.66, 0.68, and 0.70 amp. From this we know that our reading is 0.62 amp.

Should the meter have been arranged to read on the high range, its position would be as shown at A_1. Since there are 10 divisions between *0* and *1,* each division indicates 0.1 amp. The pointer is somewhere between 0.6 and 0.7, but we cannot tell exactly where, as we could on the low range. This shows us that the pointer position is most easily and accurately read when using the lowest possible range.

Let us suppose that we are going to switch in all five lamps. We immediately know that we must use the high range, for, if the same current flows through each lamp, the total current will be 3.1 ($0.62 \times 5 = 3.1$) amps. Looking at the high-range scale, Fig. 4, we see that the pointer must rest on the first mark beyond the No. 3 line. This is shown as position *A,* for 3.1 amps on the high-range scale is the same as 0.62 on the low-range scale. Since this deflection of the meter will be caused by 0.62 amp flowing through the meter, we must find some means whereby 3.1 amps can be measured while only permitting 0.62 amp to flow through the meter coil. We will do this by diverting, or *shunting,* part of the current around the meter. The remainder of the current, that which is not shunted around the meter, will be used to deflect the pointer.

Ammeter Shunt. For the moment, let us examine two resistors in

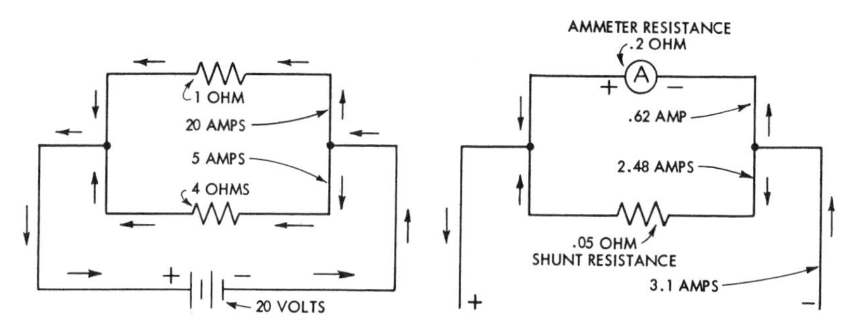

Fig. 6. Current Division Between Two Resistors in Parallel

Fig. 7. Current Division Between Ammeter and Shunt

parallel, Fig. 6. The schematic shows the values of these resistors to be 1 ohm and 4 ohms, and the supply voltage is 20 v. We can find the current flow by determining the equivalent resistance and then employing Ohm's law. However, it will better serve our purpose to find the current through each resistor separately. Current through the 1-ohm resistor is

$$I = \frac{E}{R}$$

$$I = \frac{20}{1}$$

$$I = 20 \text{ amps}$$

and the current through the 4-ohm resistor is

$$I = \frac{E}{R}$$

$$I = \frac{20}{4}$$

$$I = 5 \text{ amps}$$

The total current is the sum of these two currents, or 25 amps ($20 + 5 = 25$). Here, part of the 25 amps flows through one resistor and part through the other. One-fifth flows through the 4-ohm resistor, and $\frac{4}{5}$ flows through the 1-ohm resistor. Now, if we can apply this same idea to the ammeter, we will solve our problem of diverting part of total current around the ammeter. This case has been chosen because when the meter reading is 3.1 amps we want only one-fifth of the amount, or 0.62 ($3.1 \div 5 = 0.62$) to flow through the coil.

With the ammeter in a similar circuit, Fig. 7, we can immediately see that placing a resistor, having a resistance of $\frac{1}{4}$ the value of the ammeter coil, in parallel with the meter will direct $\frac{4}{5}$ of the current around the meter. With the meter coil having a resistance of 0.2 ohms, the diverting resistor, which is called a meter *shunt*, must have a resistance of 0.05 ohm ($0.2 \div 4 = 0.05$). Then $\frac{1}{5}$ of the current ($3.1 \div 5 = 0.62$) will flow through the meter and $\frac{4}{5}$ of the current ($0.62 \times 4 = 2.48$) will flow through the shunt. By using a shunt to divert a definite portion of the current, we can use the meter to measure higher values of current than that for which the meter was originally built.

In practice, it is rarely necessary to calculate the value of an ammeter shunt. Ammeters are furnished with accurately-calibrated resistors which are marked with their ampere-ratings instead of their resistance. Thus, where the ammeter has a full-scale rating of 5 amperes, shunts may be furnished for 15 amperes, 30 amperes, or whatever range is desired.

Direct-Current Voltmeter

The same meter movement can be used for measuring current and for measuring voltage, but the voltmeter has a current limiting resistor of a definite value in the circuit at all times. Fig. 8 shows how

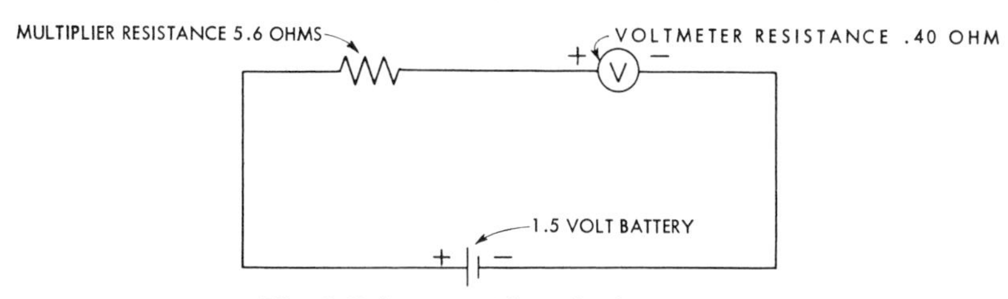

Fig. 8. Voltmeter with Multiplier Resistor

this meter is used to measure voltage. This is the schematic of a 0–250 milliammeter, having a resistance of 0.4 ohm. Let us suppose that we desire full-scale deflection when measuring 1.5 v. The resistance needed in series with the meter can be determined with Ohm's law, for we know the voltage and the current necessary to produce this deflection to be 1.5 and 0.25, respectively.

$$R = \frac{E}{I}$$

$$R = \frac{1.5}{0.25}$$

$$R = 6 \text{ ohms}$$

This is the total value of resistance to limit the current to 0.25 amp, and we know the resistance of the meter is 0.4 ohms. Therefore, the current limiting resistor plus the meter must have a resistance of 6 ohms. This means that the current-limiting resistor, R_m, which is called a *multiplier*, has a resistance of 5.6 ohms $(6.0 - 0.4 = 5.6)$.

Connecting the Voltmeter. Since the voltmeter is constructed to measure voltage drop, it must be connected across that which is causing the voltage drop, Fig. 9. The same caution must be exercised with the voltmeter as was with the ammeter—proper polarity must be noted, and the voltage being read must not be greater than the meter range.

Returning to Fig. 9, we will connect the positive voltmeter lead at point *A* and the negative lead at point *B*, which is the midpoint of the resistor. Since point *B* is the midpoint of the resistor, the voltage drop between points *A* and *B* will be one-half of the battery voltage, or 0.75 v. Knowing the resistance in the meter circuit, and voltage across the meter circuit, we can calculate the current flow through the meter.

$$I = \frac{E}{R}$$

$$I = \frac{0.75}{6}$$

$$I = 0.125 \text{ amp}$$

Since 0.250 amp will cause full-scale deflection of the meter with a reading of 1.5 v, 0.125 amp will deflect the meter to the midpoint, which will give a reading of 0.75 v. Should we wish to measure the voltage between points *B* and *C*, we will have to move lead L_2 to point *C* and L_1 to point *B*. If we merely shift lead L_1 to point *C*, the meter will read in reverse, because we are not observing the proper meter polarity.

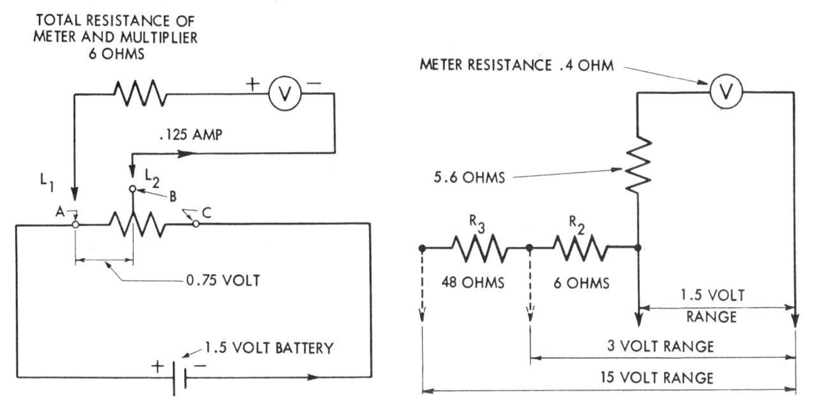

Fig. 9. Method of Using Voltmeter to Determine Voltage Drop

Fig. 10. Extending Voltmeter Range by Adding Multipliers

Extending Voltmeter Range. The voltmeter in Fig. 10 is the same as that in Fig. 9, but two resistors have been added. These multiplying resistors are to extend the range from 1.5 v to 3.0 v and 15 v. We know that the meter will give full-scale deflection of 1.5 v when 6 ohms are in the circuit. The next step is to obtain full-scale deflection of 3.0 v. The approach to this problem is the same as for determining the value of the 5.6 ohms resistor. We know that the applied voltage will be 3.0 v and the current flow will be 0.250 amp, so we can use Ohm's law to find the total resistance.

$$R = \frac{E}{I}$$

$$R = \frac{3}{0.25}$$

$$R = 12 \text{ ohms}$$

Since we already have 6 ohms in the circuit, we need to add only 6 ohms in series with the meter circuit. Fig. 10 shows this as R_2. Now,

Weston Electrical Instrument Corp.

Fig. 11. Two-Range Voltmeter

if we move the lead, L_1, to point *B*, we will have a total of 12 ohms in the circuit, and 3 v will cause full-scale deflection. To increase the range to 15 v, we will repeat the process.

$$R = \frac{E}{I}$$

$$R = \frac{15}{0.25}$$

$$R = 60$$

The additional resistor, R_3, will have a value of 48 ohms $(60 - 12 = 48)$, for we already have 12 ohms in the circuit. A commercial version of this type of meter is shown in Fig. 11. The various terminals for the different ranges can be seen on the top of the meter.

The Ohmmeter

The *ohmmeter* is used to read resistance values, and the same meter movement which was used for the ammeter and the voltmeter can be adapted to this service. In practice, however, it is desirable to employ a meter requiring less current to produce full-scale deflection, but we will use this meter to describe the principle of the ohmmeter. Fig. 12 shows the basic ohmmeter circuit, containing a battery,

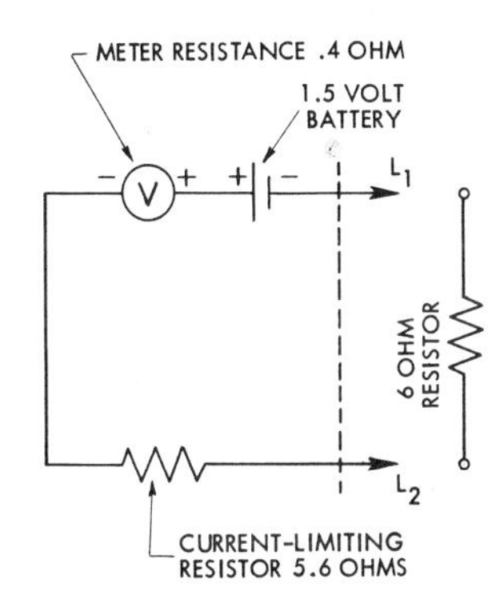

Fig. 12. Ohmmeter Circuit

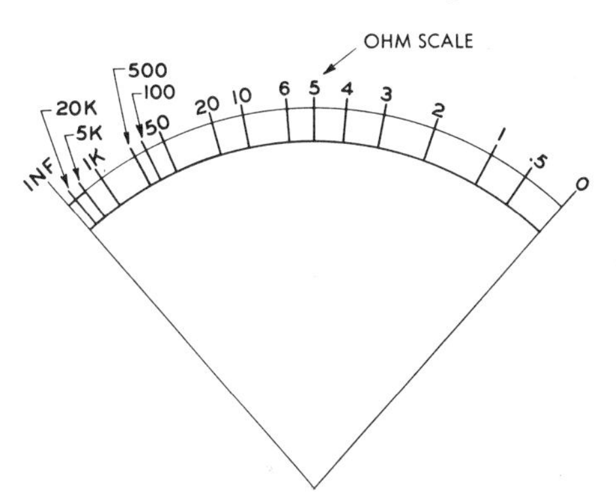

Fig. 13. Back-up Scale of Ohmmeter

meter, and current limiting resistor. With a 1.5-volt battery, we will select a 5.6-ohm current-limiting resistor. This value is chosen so that when L_1 is touched to L_2 the meter will read full scale—indicating that there is no resistance between points L_1 and L_2. This will show zero ohms at the right of the ammeter scale, and maximum at the left; therefore this is known as a *backup scale*.

If we assume that the leads are connected across the resistor R, which has a value of 6 ohms, the pointer would indicate midscale. We have a circuit resistance of 12 ohms and a voltage of 1.5 v, so

$$I = \frac{E}{R}$$

$$I = \frac{1.5}{12}$$

$$I = 0.125$$

and 0.125 amp will cause midscale deflection. This point on the meter is marked as 6 ohms instead of 0.125 amp. The additional points on the ammeter scale, Fig. 13, can be determined in a similar manner.

We should note that the pointer deflection becomes less as the resistance increases, for the greater the resistance, the less the value of current flow for a given voltage.

The Volt-Ohm-Milliammeter

In practice, it is common to combine a voltmeter, ohmmeter, and milliammeter into one unit. The method of employing a meter for these various operations is shown in the elementary circuit of Fig. 14.

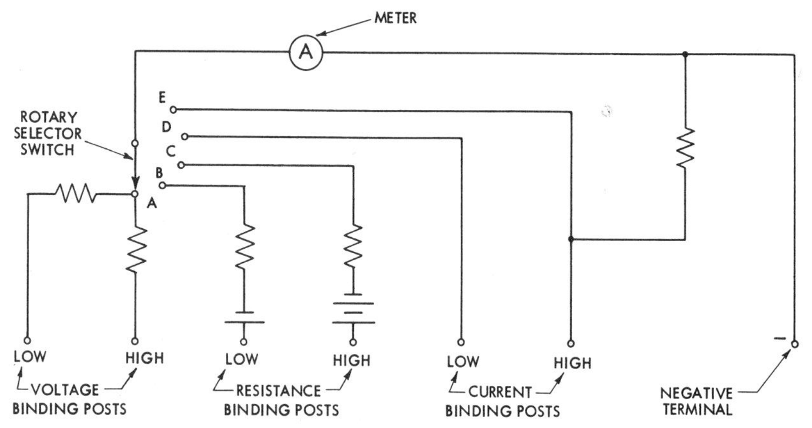

Fig. 14. Internal Circuit of Volt-Ohm-Milliammeter

The negative lead wire of the meter is permanently connected to negative binding post of the instrument. The positive side of the meter can be moved to various positions by means of a switch, and the positive lead, which is used to connect into the circuit, can be connected to the binding post giving the desired reading.

When the meter switch is in position *A*, the multipliers are in circuit for measuring high or low voltages, depending upon which binding post is selected. With the switch in position *A*, and the lead connected to the low-voltage binding post, the reading will be taken from the low-voltage scale.

Switching the meter to *B*, and the lead to the low-resistance binding post, we have the battery and limiting resistor for a low-range ammeter. In position *C* and connected to the high-resistance post, we have inserted a battery of higher voltage for the high-resistance range.

At D and the low-current binding post, we have the basic movement of the meter. A meter shunt is inserted when we switch to E and the high-current binding post.

No values for the resistors have been given, for they will vary with different meters. Furthermore, we have made these calculations during our discussions of the different meters. The commercial versions of this meter have a more complicated switching arrangement, resulting in several ranges for each unit being measured, and eliminating the need for moving the lead from post to post for different measurements. The commercial units also have methods for compensating for variations of the battery in the ohmmeter and the provisions for measuring alternating as well as direct current.

Rectifier Instruments

Most instruments employed with direct current are of the permanent-magnet type. They would not be suitable, without change, for use on alternating current. Through the use of very small instrument rectifiers, however, direct-current voltmeters may be adapted for alternating current. The commercial instruments of this type employ a bridge rectifier in series with the multiplying coil.

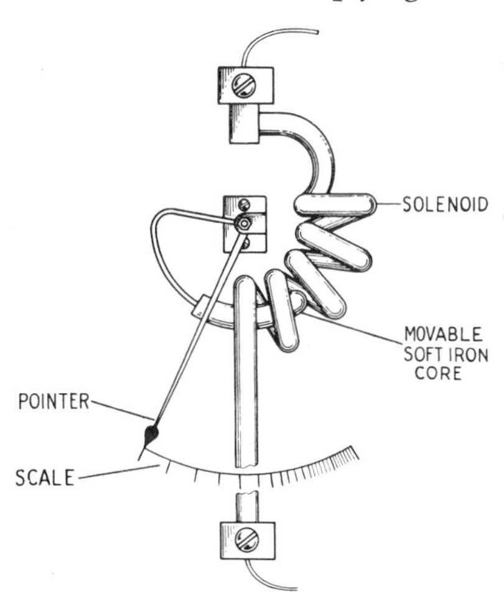

Weston Electrical Instrument Corp.

Fig. 15. Solenoid Instrument Mechanism

Solenoid Instruments. The instrument of Fig. 15 can be employed to measure voltage or current in alternating- or direct-current circuits.

When used as an ammeter, the coil has but few turns of heavy wire; but, when used as a voltmeter, the coil has many turns of fine wire. Current through the solenoid pulls the soft-iron core into the solenoid.

Inclined-Coil Instrument. Fig. 16 shows the mechanism of an *inclined-coil instrument.* Here, the iron vane is attached to the shaft at

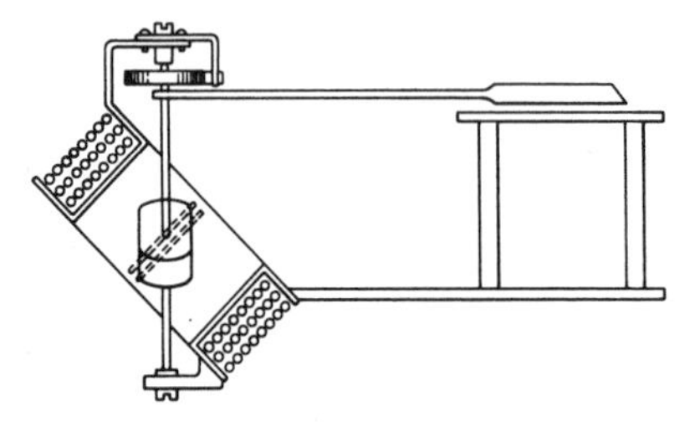

Fig. 16. Inclined-Coil Mechanism

somewhat of an angle to the horizontal, and the coil is also placed so that it is at an angle to the shaft. When current flows in the coil, mag-

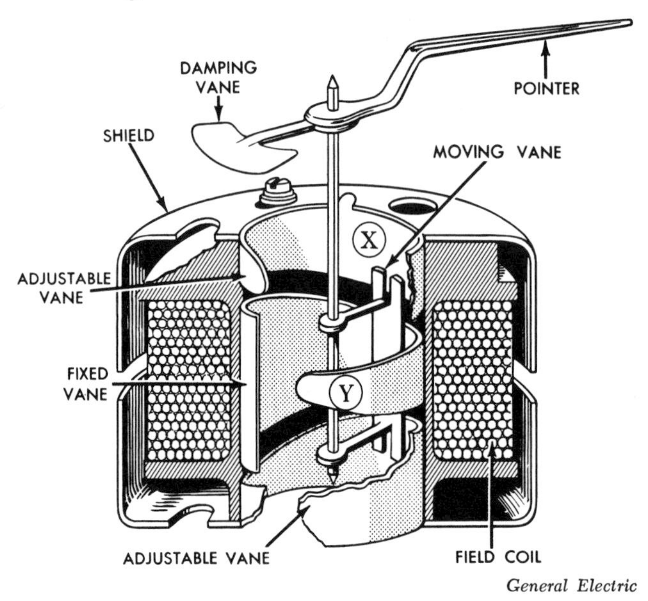

General Electric

Fig. 17. Repulsion-Vane Instrument Mechanism

netic lines of force pass through the iron vane, causing magnetic poles to form in it. Forces of attraction and repulsion between magnetic poles in the vane and those of the coil result in a torque which is proportional to the strength of current in the coil. The vane tends to swing around so that it approaches a position as indicated by the dotted outline in the figure. Its torque is opposed by a spring, and the reading is indicated by the distance which the pointer moves over the scale.

Repulsion-Vane Instrument. Another type of moving vane instrument is illustrated in Fig. 17. There are two iron vanes, *X* and *Y*. When current flows in the coil, both vanes are magnetized so that they have N poles at one end and S poles at the other. Vane *X* is fastened to the side of the coil. Vane *Y*, attached to the shaft, is free to move against the restraining pressure of the spring. Repulsion between like poles of *X* and *Y* causes *Y* to move, the torque depending upon the strength of the magnetic poles. The strength of the magnetic poles depends upon the strength of current in the coil, and the degree of movement is indicated on a calibrated scale.

Wattmeter

The wattmeter incorporates features of the ammeter and voltmeter. The construction is somewhat similar to the direct-current voltmeter, except that the permanent magnet is replaced by an electromagnet, Fig. 18.

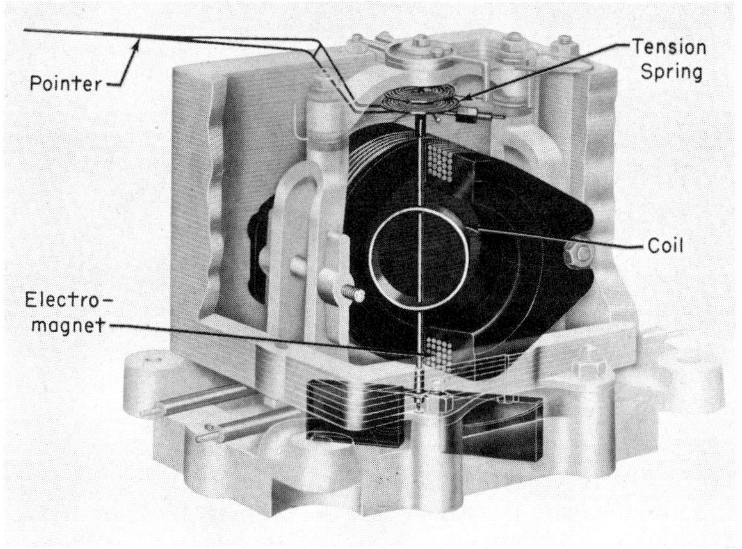

Weston Electrical Instrument Corp.

Fig. 18. Wattmeter

The field coils are connected in series with one of the circuit wires, as an ammeter; and the moving coil is connected across the circuit wires, as a voltmeter. Torque developed by the moving element depends upon the voltage of the circuit and the current flowing in the circuit and, since watts equal volts times amperes, the scale is calibrated to read in watts, or kilowatts.

Watthour Meter

When the electric power company supplies electricity to our homes, we are required to pay for this service. The meter employed to measure the amount of electric power we must pay for is called a *watthour* meter. Fig. 19 illustrates this meter, and it can be seen in the basement or on the side of practically every home.

Duncan Electric Mfg. Co.

Fig. 19. Kilowatt-Hour Meter

Now we will see what is meant by the unit watt-hour and why it is used. If we turn on a 100-watt lamp and operate it for one hour, more power would be required than to just turn it on and then turn it off again in a moment. Therefore, we must be able to measure the amount of power being used and the length of time it is used. The watthour meter is built on the principle of a small motor, and the speed of the motor varies as the amount of power being used in the measured circuit. If we operate a 100-watt lamp for ten hours, the rotor of a tiny motor will revolve at a certain speed and, at this speed, a pointer is moved through a gear train and indicates one kilowatt hour. If two lamps were put in operation, however, the motor would turn twice as fast and would indicate two watt hours in the same period of time.

Since the watt-hour is a small unit of power, the modern commercial instruments are built to record thousands of watt-hours, or kilowatt-hours.

REVIEW QUESTIONS

1. Name three basic types of electrical instruments.
2. What elementary principle governs operation of the direct-current ammeter and voltmeter.
3. Describe an ammeter shunt.
4. Is it often necessary, in practice, to calculate the value of an ammeter shunt?
5. What is a milliameter?
6. How is the range of a voltmeter extended?
7. What type of scale is used on the ohmmeter?
8. Describe a volt-ohm-milliammeter.
9. How are direct-current instruments adapted for use on alternating current?
10. Can alternating-current instruments, generally, be used on direct current?
11. Sketch a solenoid instrument.
12. What is the principle of the inclined-coil ammeter?
13. In the repulsion-vane meter, strength of the magnetic poles is dependent upon what factor?
14. Name two meters whose basic elements are incorporated into the wattmeter.
15. What instrument is employed to measure amount of electric power used in a home?

CHAPTER 13
ELECTRIC WAVES

Basic Considerations

Preceding chapters have brought out the fact that a flow of alternating current is but a series of electrical waves. This form of current is transmitted commercially at frequencies of 25, 50, and 60 cycles, the latter predominating because it has been found most suitable for generation and distribution. This chapter, however, deals with much higher frequencies, audible sound covering a range from nearly zero to a maximum of 15,000 cycles per second, while radio frequencies run to many million cycles.

In the telephone, sound waves created by vocal chords generate electrical waves having a range covering approximately 200 to 3000 cycles. At the far end of the telephone line, these electrical waves are reconverted to sound waves. In a radio broadcasting station, sound-created waves are mixed with, or imposed upon, other electric waves generated at frequencies a thousand or ten thousand times as great. Photoelectric devices function by virtue of light waves, whose frequencies are many times greater than that of radio.

Electric waves, in the telephone, are confined to the circuit wires in which current is flowing. Radiated waves are not confined to wires, but pass through the atmosphere from a transmitting station to a receiver at some remote location.

These waves of extremely high frequency behave differently in many respects from those which are easily confined to electrical conductors. Yet, their existence depends upon the electron just as the presence of an electric current in a wire depends upon the electron. Radiated electric waves are not composed of electrons, but are a product of electronic activity. They are detected and utilized at receiving stations through their ability to free electrons from atoms in electrical conductors. These waves induce voltages in conductors in much the same way that lines of force surrounding the primary winding of a transformer induce voltages in the secondary winding.

The Telegraph

In telegraphy, information is transmitted from one point to another by means of sound. The operator at the sending station manipulates a telegraph key, which is actually a small switch, thereby controlling flow of current in a wire that connects sending and receiving stations. A solenoid, part of the sounding device at the receiving end, attracts and releases its armature as the key at the other end allows current to flow, or cuts it off, the armature making a clicking sound as it strikes against the metal core of the solenoid.

But the clicking sound of the key at the sending station does not travel over the wire to the sounder. All that passes is a current of electricity which is interrupted at specific intervals by the key, to designate dots and dashes upon which telegraphic communication is based. In other words, telegraphy is achieved by mechanically-created electrical impulses, and not by sound-created electrical waves.

The Elementary Telephone

The telephone, also, transmits information by virtue of sound. Vibrations heard at the distant end of the circuit, however, are exact duplicates of those delivered at the transmitting end. The current flowing in the line wires is not a series of long or short impulses, but is a complicated series of electric waves closely approximating the pattern of sound waves that created it.

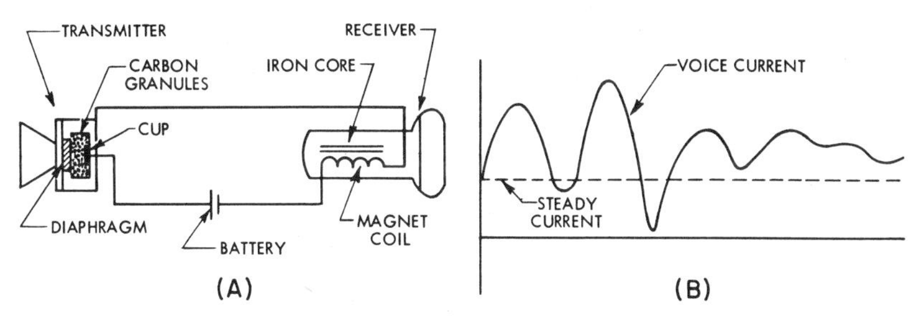

Fig. 1. A–Simple Telephone Circuit; B–Flow of Current in Circuit

Fig. 1A illustrates a simple telephone circuit. When a person speaks into the transmitter, sound vibrations strike against the diaphragm, a thin iron disc whose outer rim is fastened rigidly in the hard-rubber case, but whose center is quite flexible. The diaphragm compresses granules of carbon which are held in a shallow cup, the pressure varying slightly with each modulation of the speaker's voice. The metal base of the cup connects to one terminal of the battery. The other battery terminal connects to one end of the magnet coil in the receiver, and the second lead of the coil is attached to a wire that is attached to the diaphragm.

The complete circuit is from negative battery to magnet coil, to diaphragm, to carbon granules, to cup, to positive terminal of the battery. As the transmitter diaphragm moves in response to voice vibrations, carbon granules are rapidly compressed and released. The resistance of circuit wires and solenoid is small as compared to that of the carbon granules, whose total resistance is varied widely as they are compressed and released in the cup. The rate of current flow in the whole circuit, then, is made to vary largely in accordance with oscillations of the diaphragm.

The receiver includes an iron diaphragm similar to that of the transmitter. A varying current in the electromagnet results in attraction and release of the disc in a manner similar to the action of the transmitter diaphragm. Vibrations of the receiver diaphragm, therefore, create sound waves that reproduce the voice of a person speaking into the transmitter.

Fig. 1B represents flow of current in the circuit. When no sound is being delivered to the transmitter, the current maintains a steady value as shown by the dotted line. As sound enters the transmitter, circuit current varies rapidly, the shape and strength of the *waves* changing from instant to instant. The current flowing in the wires is a direct current which never falls below the zero line, although touching it occasionally.

Two-Way Telephone System. Since it is necessary to talk and to listen at both ends of the telephone line in order that conversation

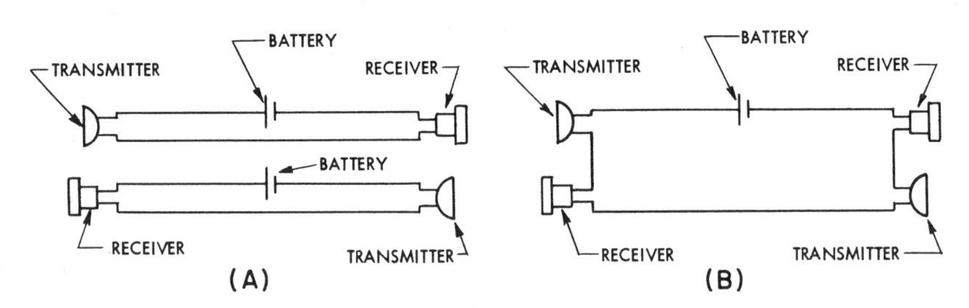

Fig. 2. A–Separate Circuits of Two-Way Conversation; B–Composite Circuit for Two-Way Conversation

may be carried on, it might appear that two separate units are required as in Fig. 2A, each completely distinct from the other. Such is not the case, the desired result being obtained through combining sets of units as in Fig. 2B, the battery sending current to all four series-connected devices.

Modern Intercommunication System. Fig. 3A illustrates a small but complete telephone arrangement, often referred to as an intercom system. It is employed for local communication between offices of a large

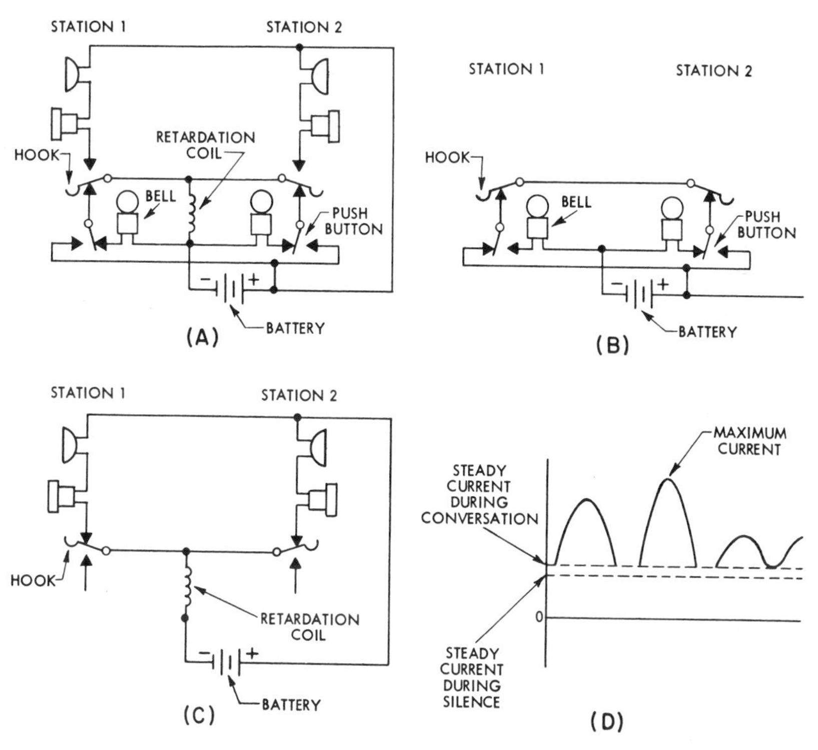

Fig. 3. A–Modern Intercommunicating System; B–Ringing Circuit; C–Talking Circuit; D–Effect of Retardation Coil

business concern, or between lobby, tenants, and janitor of an apartment house. Although but two stations are shown here, the system may be expanded to include any desired number of locations.

Each station has a transmitter, a receiver, a hook upon which the receiver hangs when not in use, a double-contact push button, and a signal bell. The hook really constitutes the blade of a double-throw switch. When raised, it establishes contact with the free terminal of the receiver. In the lower position, it makes contact with the movable lever of a double-contact push button. In its normal state, the push button contacts one side of the telephone bell. When pressed, it touches a wire that leads to the positive terminal of the battery.

Fig. 3B shows the ringing circuit. The party at Station *1*, desiring to talk with Station *2*, touches the push button, thereby making contact to the left. Current flows from the negative battery terminal to one end of each of the signal bells. Since Station *1*'s button is depressed, the circuit of the local bell is open at that point. At Station *2*, however, current flows through the closed contact of the push button to the hook switch, then to the hook switch of Station *1*, to the left contact of the push button, and to the positive terminal of the battery, completing the circuit so that Station *2*'s bell rings.

With the lifting of Station *2*'s receiver, the circuit of the local bell is broken at the hook switch. It should be noted that the retardation coil is in parallel with the signal bells. But the coil impedance is comparatively high, so that its presence does not affect flow of ringing current to the bells.

The talking circuit is outlined in Fig. 3C. When both receivers are off their hooks, ringing circuits to both bells are interrupted, and the talking circuit established. Current flows from the negative battery terminal, through the retardation coil, then through the parallel combinations of receiver and transmitter to the positive terminal of the battery. Since this current is of a low, steady value, the retardation coil offers little opposition to it.

When the person at Station *1* talks into his transmitter; varying pressure on the carbon granules tends to set up a complicated pattern of voice-current waves, as already noted. Here, the retardation coil becomes important. Although it allows the steady battery current to pass through readily enough, it tries to reject the highly-inflected voice-created waves. Basically, they are direct-current waves, but their continually varying nature is similar to that of high-frequency alternating current to which the coil offers great impedance.

Therefore, the coil permits a somewhat increased steady current to flow, as noted in Fig. 3D, but the "high-frequency" portion of the wave must dissipate itself by flowing through the circuit composed of the transmitters and receivers in series. Were it not for the retarding effect of the coil, the complex voice-current waves would prefer the low resistance offered by the battery to that of the comparatively higher resistance offered by the transmitter and receiver at Station *2*. Little current would pass through Station *2*'s receiver, and the voice from Station *1* could not be heard there.

A More Advanced Telephone Unit. Fig. 4 shows a talking circuit on which conversation is possible between distant locations. Small step-up transformers are employed, the primary winding in each case, being connected in series with the transmitter and a local battery. The secondary windings connect to the line wires, along with the two receivers. Voice currents in the primary windings are stepped up by the secondaries to a value desirable for long distance transmission. The transformers are termed *repeat coils* in trade language. Their action is such that an alternating form of voice current flows in the secondary circuit.

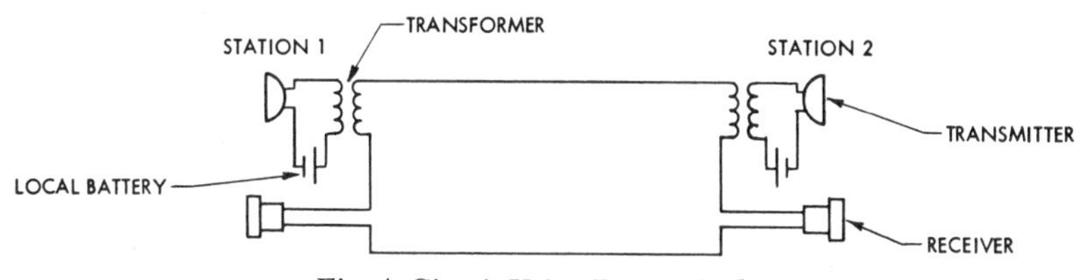

Fig. 4. Circuit Using Repeat Coils

In practice, one may talk with thousands of other stations, connections being made through a large switchboard, either manual or automatic. A central battery supplies exciting current to the transmitters, so that local batteries are not required.

RADIATED WAVES

Simplified Theory of Radio Waves

Fig. 5A shows a capacitor whose plates are connected to the terminals of a high-frequency generator, or oscillator. The upper wire is the antenna of a radio transmitting station, the lower wire a *counterpoise* or else that portion of the earth directly underneath the antenna, usually known as *ground.* At the instant shown, the antenna is of negative polarity, having an excess of electrons. In seeking to attract positively-charged atoms, the electrons establish strain lines or loops in the air space between antenna and Earth, similar to lines of force which surround an electrical conductor when carrying current.

As the generator polarity changes, strain loops try to collapse back toward the antenna. But when the frequency is extremely high, some of the loops do not have sufficient time. Before they can do so, others have formed between them and the conductor. A force of repulsion exists between loops, somewhat like repulsion between similar magnetic poles. Hence, some are propelled into space, as indicated by Fig. 5B.

These loops are a form of energy. That is, they have the power to do work. As the current in the antenna oscillates at the rate of several million times per second, a continuous series of loops is repelled into

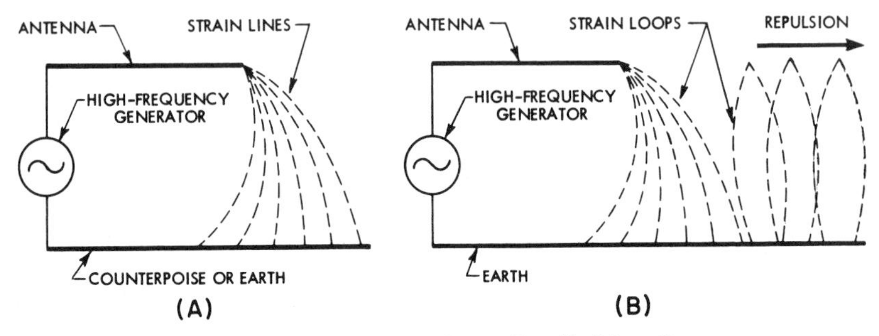

Fig. 5. A–Strain Loops; B–Loops Repelled Into Space

space, moving away from the antenna as waves, and at a speed which approximates that of light. The complete theory of radio-wave production is highly complicated, involving certain factors not mentioned here.

Receiving Radio-Telegraph Waves. The radio receiving set in Fig. 6 has a loop, or closed type of antenna connected to it. Two groups of

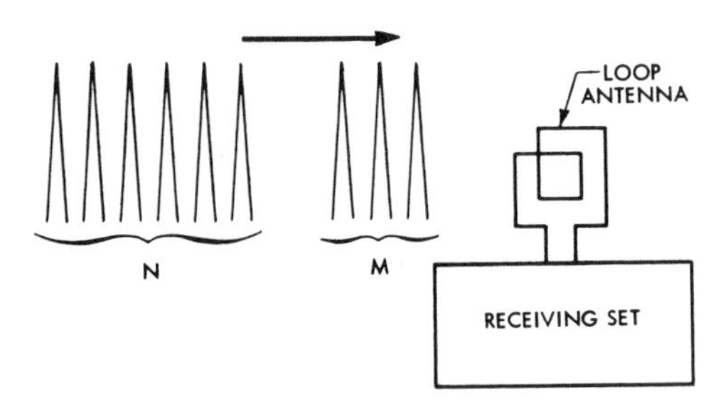

Fig. 6. Dot and Dash Signal Approaching Antenna

radio waves are approaching the antenna, one group, *M*, consisting of three waves, and another group, marked *N*, consisting of six waves. They were created by a telegraph key at the transmitting station. When the key was depressed for a short space of time to indicate a dot, group *M* resulted, when depressed twice as long, group *N* resulted. The whole series of waves, then, represent a dot and a dash.

As the first group cuts across the wires of the antenna, it frees electrons from atoms, just as magnetic flux cutting across the conductors of a generator frees electrons in the armature conductors. A flow of current takes place in the circuit which includes the antenna and the receiving device attached to it. The second group, following a short blank space, sets up current flow whose duration is twice that of the first instance. The receiving device amplifies the weak signal current, and delivers it to the listener as a dot-and-dash sound.

Messages can be telegraphed with the aid of radiated waves, therefore, in the same way they are transmitted over wires in the ordinary telegraph system. But there is one important difference. Wire transmitted telegraphy, as noted earlier, consists of mechanically-contrived impulses, whereas radio-transmitted telegraphy is actually in the form of electric waves.

Tuning the Radio Receiver. The receiving device will be affected more strongly by radio waves if it is tuned to them. To *tune* a circuit,

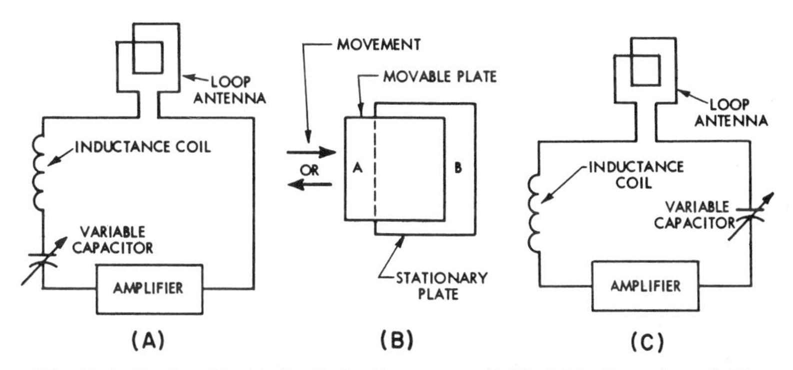

Fig. 7. A–Tuning Circuit for Series Resonance; B–Variable Capacitor; C–Tuning Circuit for Parallel Resonance

means to make it resonant to the frequency at which the waves are transmitted from the sending antenna. A circuit is termed resonant when its inductance and its capacitance are of equal value.

Fig. 7A indicates how the condition of resonance may be attained. The essential elements are a coil and a capacitor whose value can be changed by turning a knob so that a movable plate offers more or less of its surface to the fixed plate of the unit. This device is illustrated in Fig. 7B, where plate *B* can be moved horizontally to vary that portion of its area which is directly opposite plate *A*.

The capacitor is adjusted until its ohmic reactance is equal to the ohmic inductance of both inductance and antenna. Since relative reactance of inductances and capacitances varies with each change of frequency, the capacitance must be altered to suit the particular frequency it is desired to pick up.

Current flow in the circuit includes antenna, inductance, capacitor, and an amplifier. The purpose of the amplifier is to increase the strength of signal current received by the antenna, and to change the electrical waves into sound waves. The receiving antenna, instead of being in the form of a loop, might have been a capacitor similar to the sending antenna, consisting of an overhead wire and the Earth.

When coil and capacitor are connected in series, as in Fig. 7A, they are said to produce series resonance if inductive and capacitive reactances are equal. When connected in parallel, as in Fig. 7C they

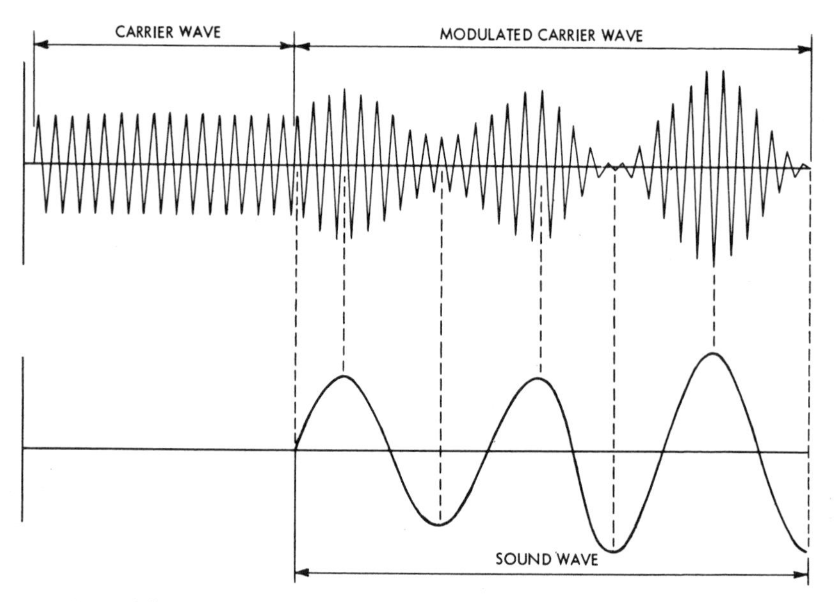

Fig. 8. Modulation of Carrier Wave with Sound Wave Produces Radio Waves of Varying Amplitude

produce a condition of parallel resonance if inductive and capacitive reactances are equal. The series-resonant circuit provides the lowest possible, or nearly zero, reactance. The parallel-resonant circuit provides the highest possible reactance. As will be noted later, the parallel-resonant circuit is most generally used in broadcast receivers.

Modulating Radio Waves

In order that sound may be transmitted by means of radio waves, whose frequencies are so much higher than those of the highest-pitched sound which can be heard, it is necessary to cause the radio waves to vary in some way. And the manner in which the radio, or carrier, waves are varied must depend entirely upon sound in order that sound may be recovered from them at the distant radio receiver.

Fig. 8 shows how a series of radio carrier waves generated at the transmitting station by an *oscillator* is altered by mixing it with a series of waves created by voice or musical instrument. The two sets of waves are combined at the radio-broadcasting station, by a device called a mixer or *modulator*, the process being termed *modulation*. Since the amplitude of the radio waves is altered, this method is termed *amplitude modulation*. Another scheme, termed *frequency modulation*, alters the frequency of the radio wave. Waves sent out by the transmitting antenna of a broadcasting station, then, are modulated waves.

Vacuum Tube

Before considering the manner in which modulated waves are handled by the radio receiver, it is necessary to examine the vacuum tube.

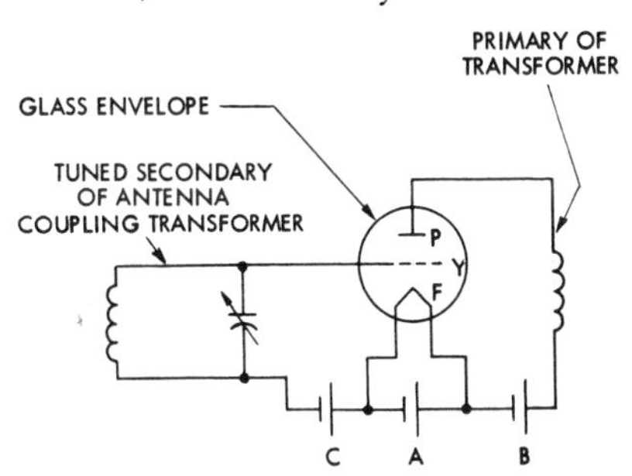

Fig. 9. Triode Vacuum Tube

As indicated in Fig. 9, a vacuum tube consists of a glass envelope, plate *P* which is charged positively, filament *F*, and a third element, *Y*, which is called a *grid*. The grid is charged, or polarized, negatively. Because the tube has three essential elements, plate, grid, and filament, it is known as a triode. There are many other types, having more or fewer elements, as the case may be, but the triode is the basic form. The enclosing globe can be either of glass or of metal.

The heated filament gives off electrons which are attracted by the positively-charged plate, these electrons forming a current of electricity that flows through the primary winding of the transformer and the polarizing battery on its way back to the filament. If the grid is given a negative polarity, or bias, some of the electrons from the filament will be forced back through repulsion between like charges. The grid battery, termed a *C-battery,* is able to impose and to hold a negative charge upon the surface of the grid because the filament and the grid, with the air space between them, constitute a small capacitor.

The extent to which the grid is effective in repelling electrons back to the filament, and thus limiting the rate of current flow in the plate circuit, is governed by the strength of the charge upon the grid. This value is determined by the voltage of the C-battery. Now, if some method were devised for altering the charge upon the grid by incoming radio waves, the flow of current in the plate circuit would become variable, the grid acting like a valve.

The Vacuum Tube as an Amplifier. In a certain vacuum tube the plate voltage is 100, the plate current 50 milliamperes (.05 ampere) when the charge imposed on the grid by its C-battery is 2 volts. If the grid charge is increased to 3 volts, the plate current decreases to 30 ma. (milliamperes). If the grid charge is decreased to 1 volt, the current in the plate circuit increases to 70 ma.

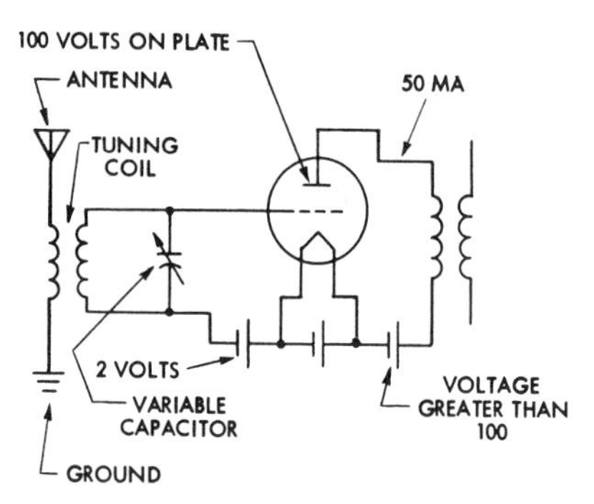

Fig. 10. Amplifier Tube

This principle is applied, Fig. 10, to amplify the strength of a signal received by the antenna. The steady plate current of 50 ma. flows through the primary winding of a transformer whose impedance is 500 ohms. A negative signal of 1 volt received by the antenna, adds to the 2 volts of the C-battery, inducing a grid charge of 3 volts, and decreases plate current from 50 ma. to 30 ma. A positive signal of 1 volt received on the antenna and transferred to the grid, decreases the charge there to 1 volt, the plate current rising to 70 ma.

The swing of 20 ma. on either side of the average plate current flow of 50 ma. creates a voltage across the windings of the transformer. According to Ohm's law, its value is equal to: 0.02 ampere × 500 ohms, or 10 volts. This voltage swing duplicates in form the 1-volt positive and negative variation of the antenna signal voltage, but it is ten

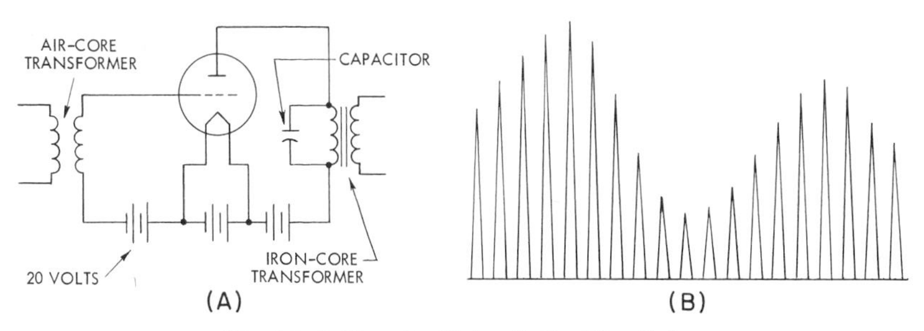

Fig. 11. A–Detector Tube; B–Rectifier Tube

times as great. If this amount is not yet strong enough for listening purposes, the voltage may be imposed upon the grid of a second amplifying tube. For the present, it is sufficient to note that the vacuum tube has amplified a voltage received at the antenna.

The secondary winding of the antenna tuning transformer and a variable capacitor are connected for parallel resonance, the desired signal imposing the highest obtainable voltage on the grid of the tube. Flow of current resulting from signals of lesser or greater frequencies does not build up sizeable voltages because combinations of inductance and capacitance have a much lower impedance at frequencies even slightly different from the resonant one.

Detection. Fig. 11A represents the next stage in a simple amplifier. The secondary winding of the transformer is connected to the grid of another tube. The transformer is of the air-core variety, no iron or other magnetic material being employed in its construction.

The value of C-bias used in this instance, 20 volts, is such that no current flows in the plate circuit. When an incoming positive voltage wave reaches the grid, the negative bias of 20 volts is decreased, and current begins to flow in the plate circuit. An incoming negative voltage wave merely increases the negative potential of the grid. Since the plate current is already at zero value, it cannot be further decreased. As a result, only positive halves of radio-frequency waves, Fig. 11B, are effective with respect to current flow in the plate circuit.

The primary winding of an iron-core, or audio, transformer is connected in the plate circuit of the tube. A small capacitor is attached to the terminals of this winding. If both positive and negative portions of radio waves were active toward increasing and decreasing plate-current flow, this capacitor would charge and discharge rapidly so that no current would pass through the primary of the transformer.

But, since the radio-frequency waves have been rectified, small charges from each half-wave build up on the plates of the capacitor, its voltage charge following the outline of low-frequency voice waves as noted in Fig. 11B. The capacitor, therefore, discharges through the primary of the audio transformer, a current which approximates the voice-frequency outline. This process of separating the sound portion of the transmitted wave from the radio-frequency portion is termed *detection.* The result is exactly the opposite from modulation, and might well be called *de-modulation.* Other methods of detection are sometimes employed in radio receiver, all of them accomplishing their purpose through rectification of incoming radio-frequency waves.

A Basic Radio Receiving Set

An elementary receiving set is outlined in Fig. 12. Starting at the left end of the figure, the tuned-secondary winding of the antenna coupling unit is connected to the grid of a radio-frequency (abbreviated RF) amplifier tube. The plate of this tube is in circuit with the primary winding of an RF transformer. The secondary winding of

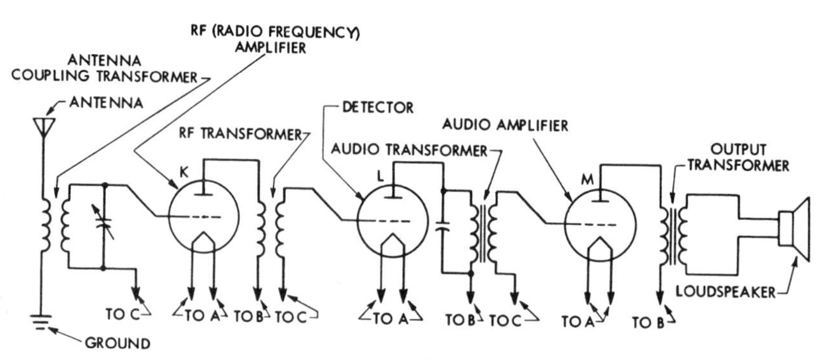

Fig. 12. Basic Radio Receiving Set

this transformer is attached to the grid of the detector tube whose plate leads to the primary winding of an audio-frequency (abbreviated AF) transformer. A small capacitor spans the terminals of this winding. The secondary coil of the AF transformer feeds the grid of an AF amplifier, the plate of this tube connecting to the primary winding of the output transformer. The secondary of the output transformer supplies the voice coil of the loudspeaker.

Tracing through the whole unit, a signal from the antenna is chosen by the tuned circuit and passed on to the RF tube where it is amplified and passed to the RF transformer. Here, the signal is amplified further before turning it over to the detector tube for processing, and delivery to the AF transformer. The AF transformer amplifies the audio wave and passes it to the grid of the AF amplifier tube. From the plate of this tube, the primary winding of the output transformer takes the resulting audio signal and modifies its voltage to suit requirements of the loudspeaker.

Television Transmitter

A television transmitter is a device for modulating radio-frequency waves so that pictures may be created on television screens at points remote from the sending station. The radio carrier wave cannot be altered to suit a visual pattern in the same manner as a voice pattern. The reason, is that visual patterns are of much higher frequency than carrier waves, whereas voice patterns are of much lower frequency than carrier waves. In television, therefore, the carrier wave is modulated, primarily, according to intensity of light at continually moving spots on a light-sensitive screen at the sending station. Just how pictures may result from this method will become apparent shortly.

The Camera Tube. The heart of a television transmitter is the camera, or image, tube. It has three essential parts, aside from the enclosing globe: a photoelectric screen, a focusing lens, and an electron gun. The electron gun is a combination of electrically-charged elements and an electron-emitting filament, the charges on the elements or plates causing electrons which pass between them to "shoot" toward particular spots on the screen.

The Photoelectric Screen. The screen, shown in Fig. 13B resembles the simple capacitor of Fig. 13A, but the front plate of the screen consists of a thin coating of photoelectric compound sprayed upon a piece of insulating material which rests against a metallic back plate. This photoelectric coating and the metal, together with the insulation between them form an immense number of small capacitors, each tiny speck of photoelectric material making a separate capacitor, in conjunction with that portion of metal directly opposite it.

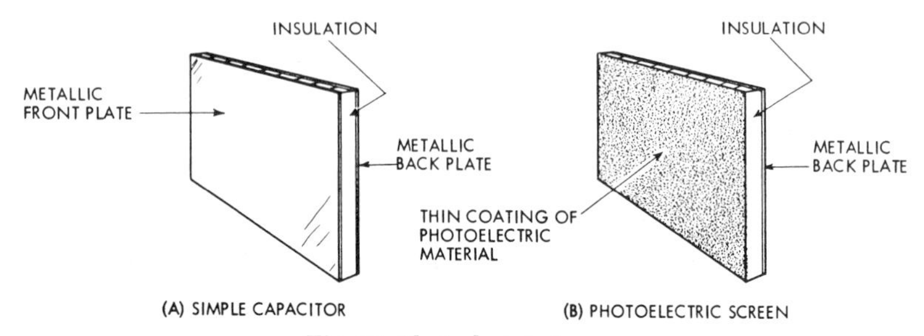

Fig. 13. Photoelectric Screen

Fig. 14 illustrates how the screen is affected by light. The photoelectric material has the property of giving up electrons when a ray of light touches upon it, the number of "lost" electrons depending upon the intensity of the light beam. In the figure, a weak pencil of light releases two electrons when it touches spot *A*. A stronger pencil releases three electrons at *B*, and the strongest pencil of the three releases five electrons at *C*.

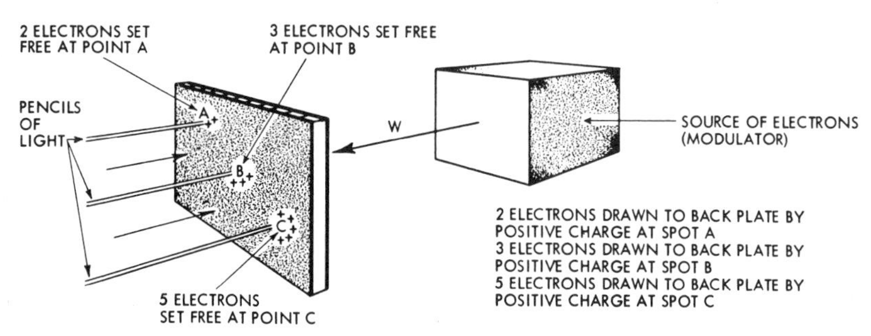

Fig. 14. Electrons Liberated from Photoelectric Screen by Light

In each case, the small area of screen is left positively charged by the loss of electrons, *A* having a charge of two units, *B* three units, and *C* five units. If a source of electrons, *M*, is attached to the back plate by wire *W*, two electrons will be drawn to the back plate by the charge at *A*, three by the charge at *B*, and five by the charge at *C*.

Fig. 15 illustrates what occurs when a beam of electrons is now made to sweep across the front plate from left to right, starting at the top and working to the bottom. The spot at *A* absorbs two electrons, that at *B* absorbs three electrons, and that at *C* absorbs five electrons. Neutralization of the positive charge at *A* releases two electrons which

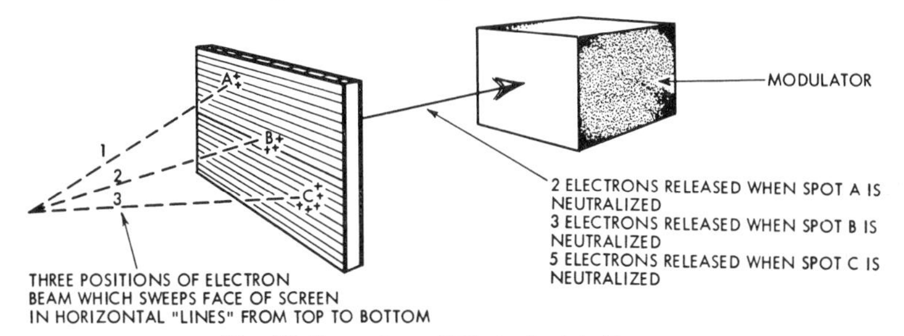

Fig. 15. Sweeping of Photoelectric Screen

seep backward over wire *W* to the source of electrons. In the same way, neutralization of *B*'s charge releases three electrons, and *C*'s, five electrons.

How Television Works

Keeping in mind facts learned about the photoelectric screen, basic principles governing television operation may be readily understood. In *Step One,* Fig. 16A, reflected light rays from objects in a scene are picked up by a lens in the image tube. Lens *L* focuses the rays onto photoelectric screen S at the far end of the tube, causing each small spot to lose electrons according to intensity of light in that area. The cloud of electrons given off by the screen is attracted to, and absorbed by, a positively-charged anode which has been omitted from the illustration for reasons of simplicity.

Step Two, Fig. 16B, starts when a shutter cuts off light rays to lens *L,* screen S being left dark, but with an electrostatic, or image, charge upon its surface. This positive image charge draws a mass of electrons from source *M* to the back plate of the screen, the total number of such electrons depending upon the sum of all positive charges on the face of the screen.

Before passing to Steps Three and Four, it should be explained that screen *R,* in the receiving tube, takes in the whole end of the unit. This portion of the tube is coated, on the inner surface, with material that glows when electrons strike upon it, the glow persisting a fraction of a second after the electron hits.

Step Three, Fig. 16C, begins with the shutter still closed, lens *L*

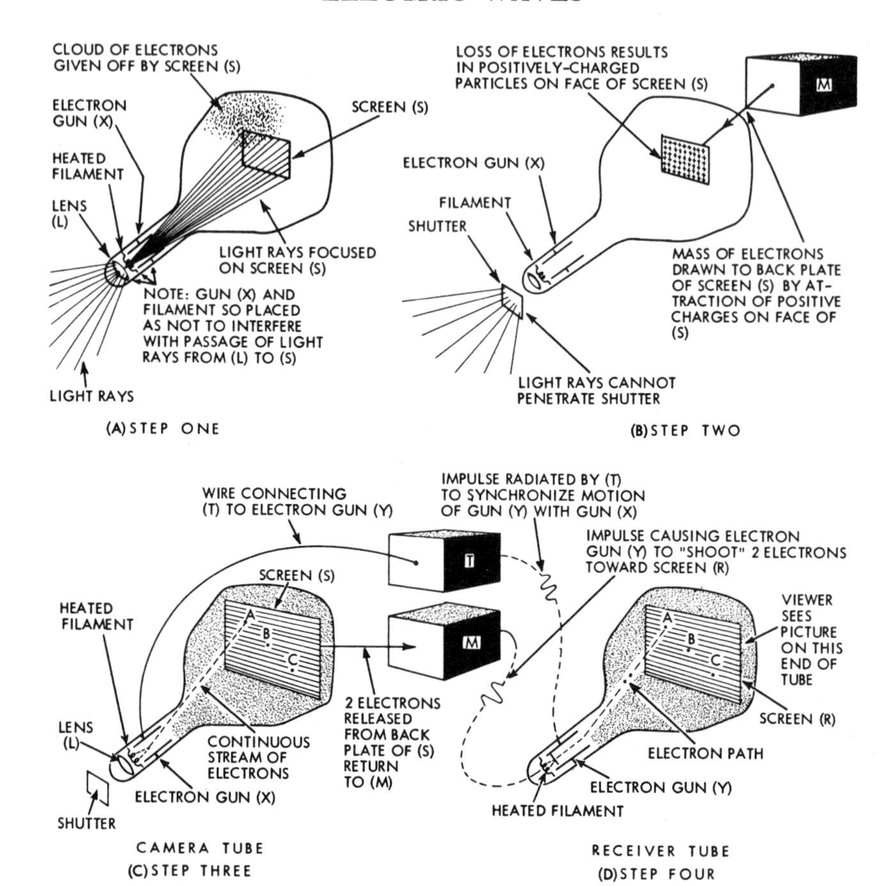

Fig. 16. A–Step One; B–Step Two; C–Step Three; D–Step Four

and screen S dark, but with electron gun *X* actively directing a stream of electrons toward screen S. Sweep generator *T* controls movement of the electron beam from gun *X*. *T* also radiates an impulse which is picked up by the television receiving set, and which keeps electron gun *Y* of the receiving tube in step with electron gun *X*, *Y* duplicating every movement of *X*.

Thus, when the electron beam from *X* is neutralizing spot A on screen S, electron gun *Y* is aimed at a similarly located spot on receiving screen *R*. There is one notable difference between operation of guns *X* and *Y*, however. The beam from gun *X* is a steadily flowing stream of electrons. That from gun *Y* is a series of bursts or clusters of electrons. The reason will become apparent shortly.

Step Four deals with Fig. 16C and Fig. 16D. It was shown in Fig. 15, that when spot *A* with a positive charge of two units is neutralized, two electrons return along the wire from the back plate of the screen to modulating device *M*. When the electron beam of Fig. 16C is directed to spot *A* on screen *S*, and two electrons are released, modulator *M* radiates an impulse which, in the receiving set, causes electron gun *Y* to "shoot" two electrons to spot *A* on screen *R*.

When the electron beam from *X* neutralizes spot *B* on screen *S*, three electrons are sent to modulator *M*, and an impulse is generated there which causes gun *Y* to send a cluster of three electrons to similar spot *B* on screen *R*. In the same way, five electrons are delivered to gun *Y* when *X* neutralizes spot *C* on screen *S*.

Now, since intensity of light spots created on screen *R* depends upon the number of electrons which strike that particular area, spot *B* on screen *R* will be brighter than *A*, and spot *C* will be brightest of all. In other words, spots created by light rays striking screen *S* in Step One are duplicated by electrons which strike screen *R* in Step Four. And, since pictures are nothing but arrangements of light spots which vary in intensity, whole scenes observed at a transmitting station may be *recreated* at every receiving set within range of the transmitted signal.

Tracing the sequence of operations, a lighted picture becomes an electrostatic image in the camera tube, and an electronic image becomes a lighted picture in the receiving tube. The shuttering arrangement allows thirty separate pictures to be thrown on the screen during the space of one second, electron gun *X* sweeping the whole screen and thus causing the necessary impulses to be sent out during the small fraction of a second that screen *S* is dark. It is worth noting that the wave radiated by the transmitting station is made up of the carrier wave, the gun synchronizing waves, the modulating waves, and the voice waves. The receiving equipment separates the various portions from the carrier wave, and utilizes them as explained above.

Radar

During the Second World War, a system for detecting the presence and location of remote objects came into use. This method of detecting unseen distant bodies with the aid of high-frequency radiated waves is termed *radar*. It is based upon the principle that solids reflect waves of extremely high frequency in much the same way that a mirror reflects rays of light.

Fig. 16 shows such waves sent out by a transmitting antenna. They are radiated in short bursts, with blank spaces between. The waves strike the distant object which, in this case, is a ship. The metallic surface of the ship reflects the waves, sending them in the opposite direction to be picked up by the receiving antenna. The distance of the ship from the sending station may be determined by finding the length of time for a wave to be reflected back to the sender.

Since this period of time may be as small as a millionth of a second, it is necessary to provide a quick and accurate method for performing the calculation. The problem is solved with the aid of a tube similar to the television receiving unit. It contains an electron gun, and has a fluorescent screen in the flared end.

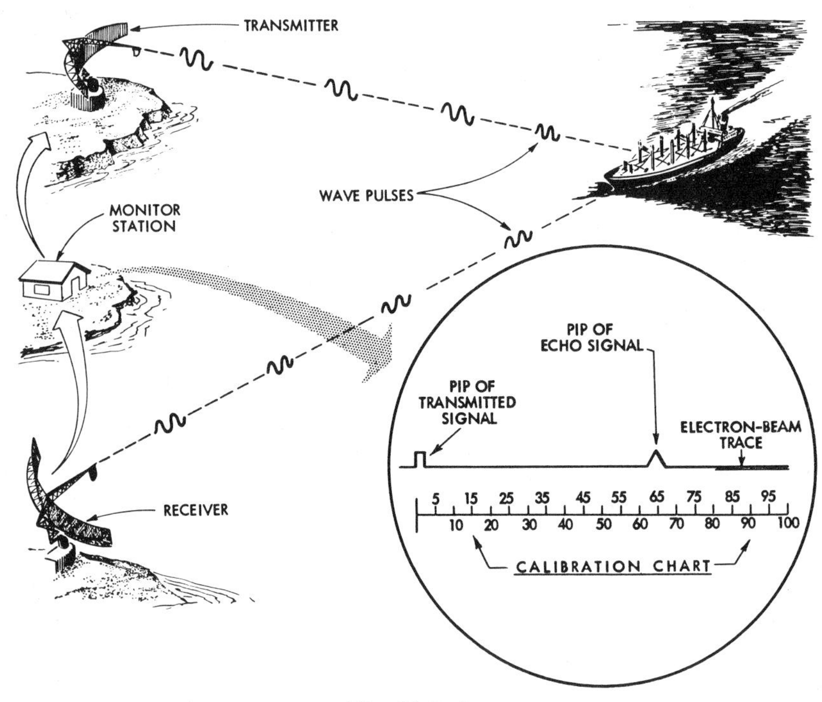

Fig. 17. Radar

A line is drawn across the middle of the screen, Fig. 17, that is graduated to indicate units of distance, starting from zero at the left and continuing in regular steps toward the right until the maximum range of the device is marked. An electron gun is caused to *scan* this line in the blank periods between bursts projected by the sending antenna.

At the instant a train of waves leaves the antenna, the gun begins to sweep across the line in the middle of the screen, and registers a small hump known as a *pip,* in the scanning line. As the reflected waves reach the receiving antenna, the electron gun is again excited by them and a second pip appears in the line. The fluorescent material continues to glow for a fraction of a second, the pip remaining at the same point on the graduated line. And, since the graduations indicate distance, the location of the distant object may be readily fixed. Variations of this principle are used for navigational and safety equipment.

REVIEW QUESTIONS

1. What is the fundamental difference between telegraph and telephone in the transmission of intelligence from one remote point to another?
2. Why is a retardation coil necessary in the intercom system?
3. Why are repeat coils used on telephone lines?
4. Tell how a radio set picks up radiated waves.
5. Compare reactances of series-resonant and parallel-resonant circuits.
6. What purpose is fulfilled by the modulator at a radio broadcasting station?
7. Discuss the action of the grid when a signal wave is delivered to it.
8. Outline the process of amplification with a vacuum-tube triode.
9. What essential purpose does a detector tube perform?
10. Does the modulating apparatus impose a visual pattern on the T-V carrier wave?
11. What is an electron gun?
12. Describe the photoelectric screen of a camera tube.
13. Discuss the scanning process.
14. What particular elements of T-V receiver and T-V transmitter must be synchronized?
15. Why doesn't a radar receiving antenna pick up signals directly from the sending antenna?

CHAPTER 14

AUTOMATION ELECTRICAL DEVICES

Automation

Automation is concerned with the automatic performance of industrial tasks. To this end, mechanical and electrical means are employed instead of human labor. Aside from vacuum tube amplifiers, electrical devices most commonly associated with these processes may be classified in four general groups.

Those permitting simple operations to be performed at some distance from the control center of the machine, the group, or the process under consideration.

Those making use of a beam of light for starting or stopping a machine or process.

Those employing dynamic amplification to control heavy machinery through the expenditure of a small amount of energy.

Those in which electronic methods are used to control motor speed.

Selsyn Systems

The term Selsyn is applied to a device which permits control of distant operations. Its principles will be explained with the aid of illustra-

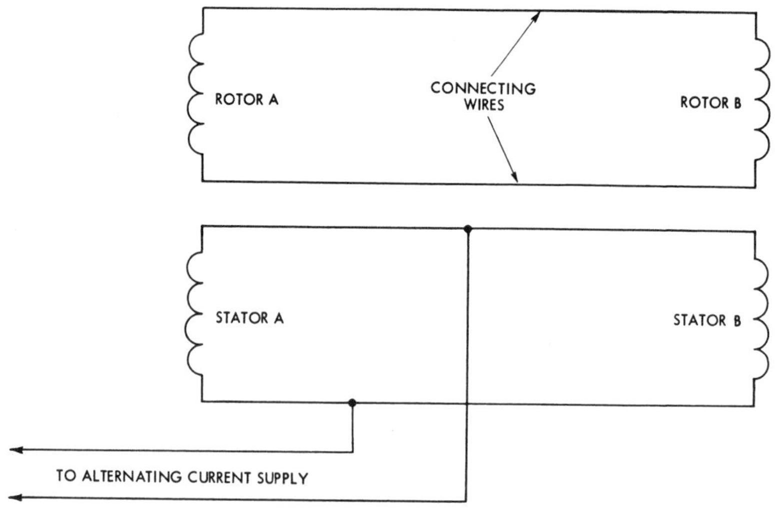

Fig. 1. Basic Selsyn Arrangement

tions. Fig. 1 shows the two units, *A* and *B*, the latter at some distance from the former. Each consists of a stationary member, the stator, and a movable rotor, the general appearance being that of a small alternating-current motor. The two stators are connected to the same alternating current supply circuit. The rotors of the two units are connected together.

If the rotor of device *A*, called the transmitter, is turned through a small angle, as in Fig. 2, the rotor of the receiver, *B*, will tend to turn through the same angle. The reason for the turning action on the part of the rotor may be more readily understood when it is realized that although the selsyn has the general appearance of a motor, its basic principle is more like that of a transformer. The two windings connected to the alternating current supply may be thought of as primary transformer windings, the rotating members as secondary windings.

When the two rotors occupy similar positions, as in Fig. 1, voltages induced in them are equal and opposite so that no current flows in the connecting wires. If the position of rotor *A* is altered, however, as in Fig. 2, voltages induced in the secondaries are no longer equal, and current flows between them. This current may cause rotor *B* to move, rotation continuing until the voltages in the two rotors are again equal, and current ceases to flow.

The elementary form illustrated here possesses certain defects.

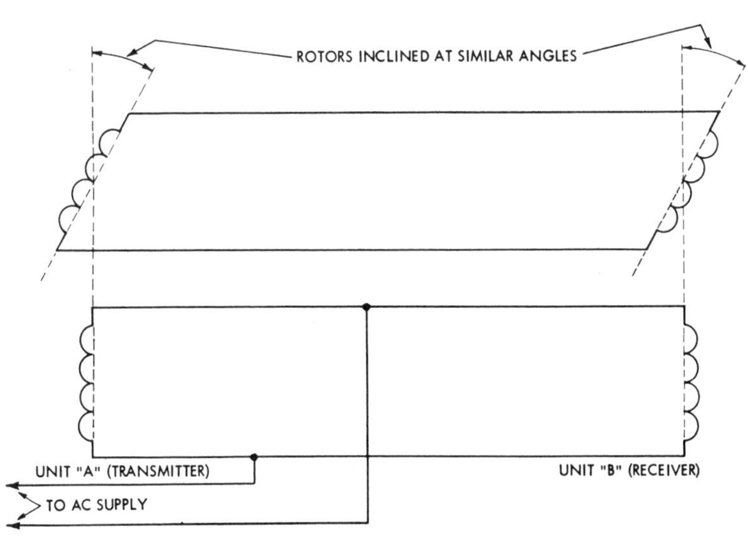

Fig. 2. Principle of Selsyn Operation

First, the rotor of the receiver tends to lock on "dead center"; and second, when it does move it may as readily turn in one direction as the other. That is, the receiver may turn to the left in Fig. 2 instead of to the right. The addition of a second winding at right angles to the first helps to overcome both these difficulties. However, the best arrangement is that of Fig. 3, where rotors have three windings spaced around the circumference at equal distances, like three-phase motor windings.

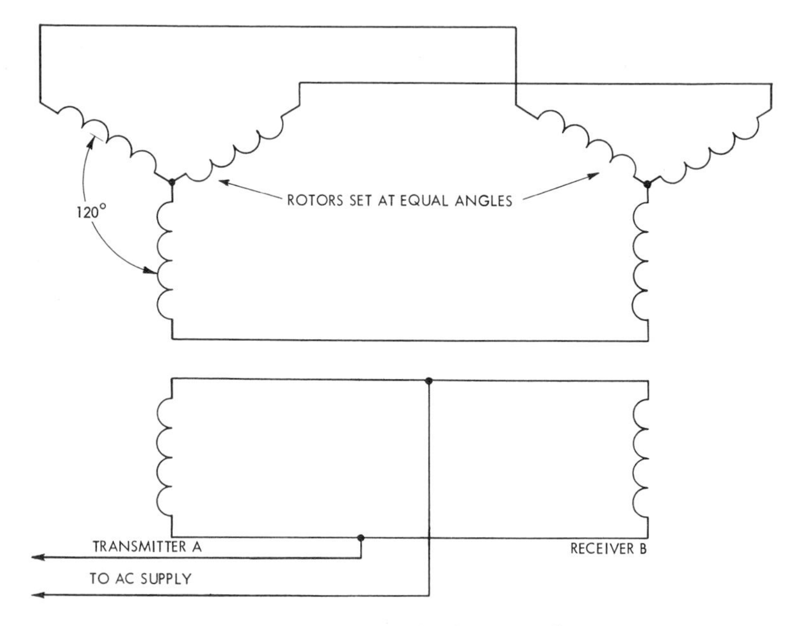

Fig. 3. Selsyn Units with Three Windings

When the transmitter rotor is turned, the receiver rotor duplicates its movement closely, having no tendency to lock, and turns through an identical angle. This form of rotor winding, therefore, is the one which is customarily used. In the commercial selsyn unit, the three part winding is usually the stator, and the single winding, connected to the supply wires, is the rotor. The devices work equally well in either case, because relative motion is the determining factor.

Selsyns are used to indicate the exact position of some distant piece of apparatus, for automatic control of liquid level in tanks, for transmission of signals or information to remote points, for the operation of valves or switches; wherein manipulation of objects from some other point is desired. In systems designed for the purpose, continuous motion imparted to a transmitter by a drive motor may be passed on to one or more receivers, all of them remaining exactly in step with the transmitter.

Phototube Circuits

Fig. 4 shows the basic construction of the phototube; a two-element vacuum tube. The anode is a vertical wire in the middle of the tube, the cathode a half-cylinder of sheet metal, usually copper,

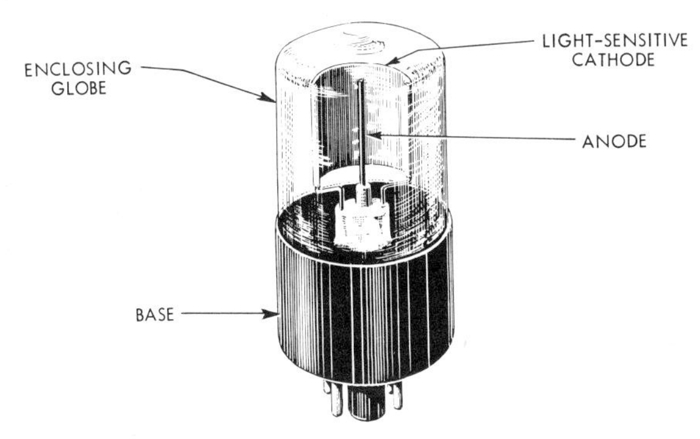

Fig. 4. Phototube

placed to one side of the anode. The copper is first silver-plated, then sprayed on the inner surface with a light sensitive compound. The anode is made positive so that it will attract electrons which are given off by the cathode when rays of light strike the inner surface. Although the resulting flow of current is quite small, it can be made use of, in connection with an amplifier tube, to accomplish practical results.

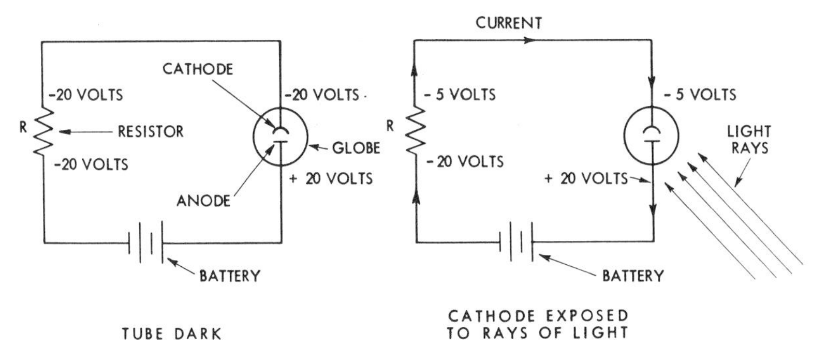

Fig. 5. Operation of Phototube

Fig. 5 illustrates the basic phototube circuit, which contains a battery whose positive terminal is connected to the anode, and a resistor *R* connected in series with the battery and the cathode. At the instant shown in view *A*, no current flows in the circuit, since there is no light striking the phototube. The anode is polarized 20-volts positive, cathode of the tube is 20-volts negative.

When light strikes the cathode, as in view *B*, electrons given off are attracted to the anode, setting up a flow of current in the circuit. The ohmic value of *R* is such that a drop of 15 volts takes place in it, the negative potential of the cathode decreasing to 5 volts. When no light fell upon the cathode, Fig. 5A, the negative potential at this point was 20 volts.

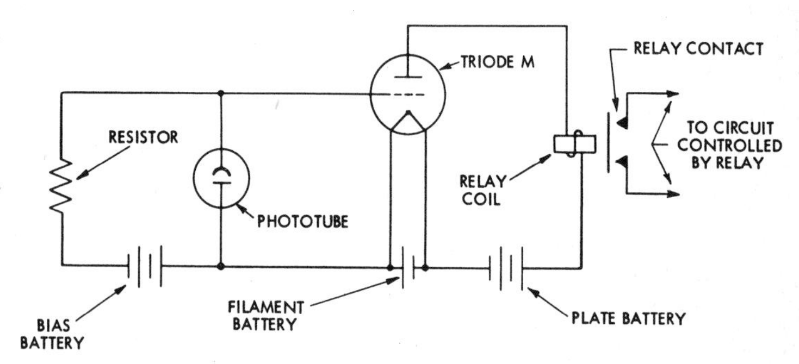

Fig. 6. Phototube Used to Control a Relay

Fig. 6 shows the manner in which the local phototube circuit may be combined with amplifying tube *M*, to operate a relay. In the figure, the upper end of the phototube circuit is connected to the grid of *M*, and a relay coil is inserted in the plate circuit. When no light strikes the phototube, the cathode end of this tube and the grid of *M* are at a negative potential of 20 volts. This high negative polarization of *M*'s grid permits only a small current to flow in the plate circuit; a current so small that it would be insufficient to operate the relay.

If light rays fall upon the phototube cathode, however, the negative polarization of *M*'s grid is reduced from 20 volts to 5 volts. In this condition, current flow in the plate circuit increases greatly so that the relay contacts close and the external circuit becomes active. Should the light source fail the negative polarization of *M*'s grid would become 20 volts, current in the plate circuit would fall, and the relay contacts would open.

Phototubes have wide application in commercial or industrial operations, ranging from that of causing doors to open automatically as a person approaches, to that of positioning castings on a machine tool. They are used to actuate burglar and fire-alarm signals, to count objects on a moving belt, to locate flaws in the output of sheet metal mills, and to insure safety in the use of machine tools.

Dynamic Amplification

Electronic devices amplify power through the use of electron tubes. The tubes themselves do not create power, but merely control the power made available by batteries, transformers and generators. In the same way, dynamic amplifying circuits control power delivered to them by driving engines and motors.

A basic example of dynamic amplification is shown in Fig. 7, where motor *M* driver excites *E*, and diesel engine *D* drives main generator *G*, and *G* furnishes power to operate motors of a huge crane. The value of current flowing in *G*'s armature circuit depends upon the amount of current flowing through its field coils. This quantity is governed by the output of *E*'s armature, and *E*'s output depends upon the current flowing through its own field coils. Current is supplied to them by an external direct current source, the current flow being controlled by variable resistor *R*, which is connected in series with the coils.

An operator who manipulates *R* to regulate current which has a maximum value of 1 ampere, is able to control the output of *G*, which amounts to 1500 amperes, the amplification being 1500 to 1. The power is increased in two steps; 25 units of amplification being supplied by the motor through the excitor that it drives, and 60 units be-

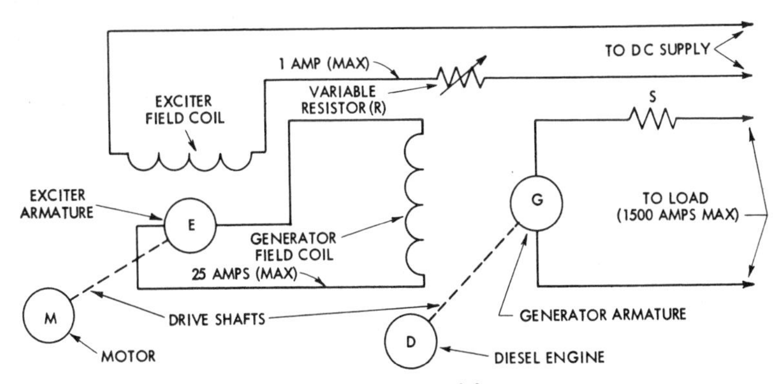

Fig. 7. Dynamic Amplification

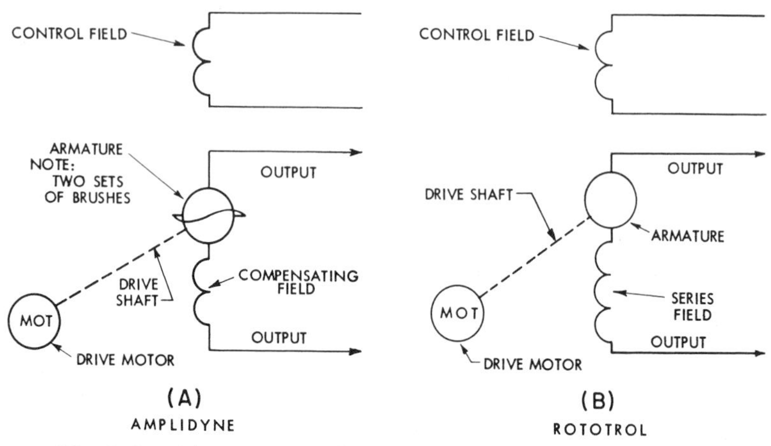

Fig. 8. Special Devices Employed in Dynamic Amplifying Circuits

ing supplied by diesel engine through the generator which it drives. The total amplification from the two separate steps is equal to 25×60, or 1500 times.

If a shunt S, in one of the generator leads, is employed in conjunction with suitable apparatus to limit the main generator's output automatically, the arrangement will fall under the general classification of automation.

Special apparatus has been developed in the field of dynamic amplification. Fig. 8 shows two such devices. View *A* illustrates the *amplidyne*, which finds numerous applications. It could be inserted in Fig. 7 to take the place of exciter *E*, the resultant amplification being much higher than is possible with the ordinary exciter unit. The amplidyne has two sets of brushes, one of which is short-circuited. A similar unit is the *rototrol*, View *B*, which has a specially designed magnetic system and which obtains initial excitation from its series field winding.

Electronic Motor Control

Fig. 9 represents a simplified circuit of an electronic motor control system. The armature of the shunt motor is connected to an alternating current supply line, in series with a rectifier tube. Its field coils are supplied by a second rectifier tube.

The average strength of current flowing in both armature and field circuits may be readily controlled by network systems which vary the grid voltages supplied to the rectifiers. If, under a certain condition of load, a decrease in armature speed is required, the grid bias of the armature rectifier may be adjusted to decrease the average strength

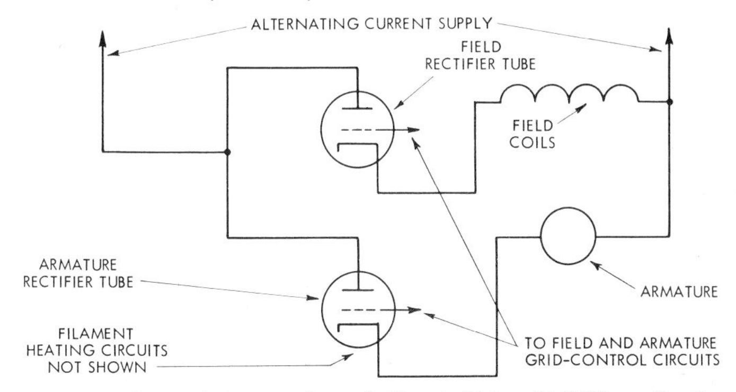

Fig. 9. Electronic Motor Control Circuit Using Half-Wave Rectifiers

of current flow in the armature circuit. In this way, speed of rotation may be altered between zero and maximum values. During this period, it is assumed that field current was maintained at maximum value.

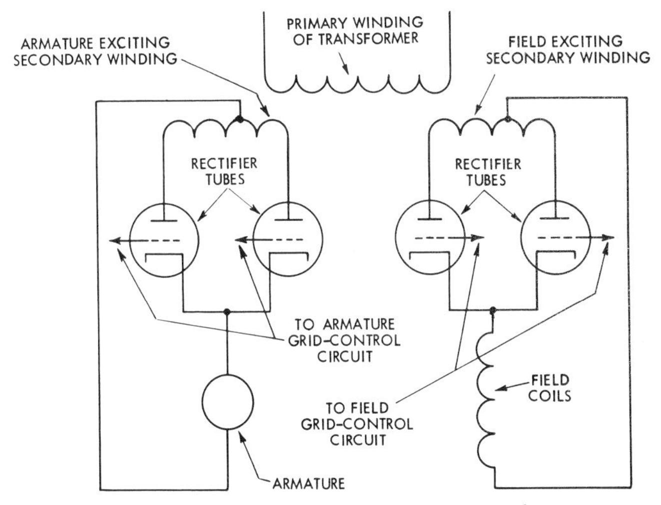

Fig. 10. Electronic Motor Control Circuit Using Full-Wave Rectifiers

Suppose, instead, that with armature current at full value, a still higher speed is desired. The field current can be weakened by variation of the grid voltage so that a speed increase results. Only half-wave rectification is possible with the arrangement of Fig. 9. Fig. 10 illustrates the more efficient full-wave circuit which is employed in the commercial unit.

REVIEW QUESTIONS

1. Describe briefly, a Selsyn circuit.
2. As to principle of operation, what other electrical device does the Selsyn most nearly resemble?
3. Do you think the three windings of the commercial unit have three-phase voltages induced in them?
4. How many elements does the phototube have?
5. Which element of the phototube is affected by light?
6. Outline operation of the phototube-relay circuit.
7. What is meant by the term dynamic amplification?
8. If the exciter in Fig. 7 is replaced by an amplidyne unit, will a larger or smaller drive motor be required to furnish the 25-ampere current to the generator's field coils?
9. How is the speed of the electronic motor control system manipulated?
10. What would happen if both field and armature in an electronic motor control system currents were reduced at the same time?

DICTIONARY of Electrical Terms

Including Symbols, Formulas, and Tables.

ELECTRICAL FORMULAS

OHM'S LAW

Ohm's Law is a method of explaining the relation existing between voltage, current, and resistance in an electrical circuit. It is practically the basis of all electrical calculations. The term "electromotive force" is often used to designate pressure in volts. This formula can be expressed in various forms.

To find the current in amperes:

$$\text{Current} = \frac{\text{Voltage}}{\text{Resistance}} \quad \text{or} \quad \text{Amperes} = \frac{\text{Volts}}{\text{Ohms}} \quad \text{or} \quad I = \frac{E}{R}$$

The flow of current in amperes through any circuit is equal to the voltage or electromotive force divided by the resistance of that circuit.

To find the pressure or voltage:

$$\text{Voltage} = \text{Current} \times \text{Resistance} \quad \text{or} \quad \text{Volts} = \text{Amperes} \times \text{Ohms} \quad \text{or} \quad E = I \times R$$

The voltage required to force a current through a circuit is equal to the resistance of the circuit multiplied by the current.

To find the resistance:

$$\text{Resistance} = \frac{\text{Voltage}}{\text{Current}} \quad \text{or} \quad \text{Ohms} = \frac{\text{Volts}}{\text{Amperes}} \quad \text{or} \quad R = \frac{E}{I}$$

The resistance of a circuit is equal to the voltage divided by the current flowing through that circuit.

POWER FORMULAS

One horsepower = 746 watts One kilowatt = 1000 watts

DIRECT-CURRENT CIRCUITS

$$\text{Power in Watts} = \text{Volts} \times \text{Amperes}$$

To find current in amperes:

$$\text{Current} = \frac{\text{Watts}}{\text{Voltage}} \quad \text{or} \quad \text{Amperes} = \frac{\text{Watts}}{\text{Volts}} \quad \text{or} \quad I = \frac{W}{E}$$

$$\text{Current (of a motor)} = \frac{\text{Horsepower} \times 746}{\text{Volts} \times \text{Efficiency}} \quad \text{or} \quad I = \frac{\text{hp.} \times 746}{E \times \text{Eff.}}$$

To find the pressure or voltage:

$$\text{Voltage} = \frac{\text{Watts}}{\text{Current}} \quad \text{or} \quad \text{Volts} = \frac{\text{Watts}}{\text{Amperes}} \quad \text{or} \quad E = \frac{W}{I}$$

Power in Watts = Volts × Amperes × Power Factor

To find current in amperes:

$$\text{Current} = \frac{\text{Watts}}{\text{Voltage} \times \text{Power Factor}} \quad \text{or}$$

$$\text{Amperes} = \frac{\text{Watts}}{\text{Volts} \times \text{Power Factor}} \quad \text{or} \quad \mathbf{I} = \frac{\mathbf{W}}{\mathbf{E} \times \mathbf{P.F.}}$$

$$\begin{matrix}\text{Current} \\ \text{(of a motor)}\end{matrix} = \frac{\text{Horsepower} \times 746}{\text{Volts} \times \text{Power Factor} \times \text{Efficiency}} \quad \text{or}$$

$$\mathbf{I} = \frac{\text{hp.} \times 746}{\text{E} \times \text{P.F.} \times \text{Eff.}}$$

TWO-PHASE ALTERNATING-CURRENT CIRCUITS

Power in Watts = Volts × Amperes × Power Factor × 2

To find current in amperes in each wire:

$$\text{Current} = \frac{\text{Watts}}{\text{Voltage} \times \text{Power Factor} \times 2} \quad \text{or}$$

$$\text{Amperes} = \frac{\text{Watts}}{\text{Volts} \times \text{Power Factor} \times 2} \quad \text{or} \quad \mathbf{I} = \frac{\mathbf{W}}{\mathbf{E} \times \mathbf{P.F.} \times \mathbf{2}}$$

$$\begin{matrix}\text{Current} \\ \text{(of a motor)}\end{matrix} = \frac{\text{Horsepower} \times 746}{\text{Volts} \times \text{Power Factor} \times \text{Efficiency} \times 2}$$

THREE-PHASE ALTERNATING-CURRENT CIRCUITS

Power in Watts = Volts × Amperes × Power Factor × 1.73

To find current in amperes in each wire:

$$\text{Current} = \frac{\text{Watts}}{\text{Voltage} \times \text{Power Factor} \times 1.73} \quad \text{or}$$

$$\text{Amperes} = \frac{\text{Watts}}{\text{Volts} \times \text{Power Factor} \times 1.73} \quad \text{or} \quad \mathbf{I} = \frac{\mathbf{W}}{\mathbf{E} \times \mathbf{P.F.} \times \mathbf{1.73}}$$

$$\begin{matrix}\text{Current} \\ \text{(of a motor)}\end{matrix} = \frac{\text{Horsepower} \times 746}{\text{Volts} \times \text{Power Factor} \times \text{Efficiency} \times 1.73}$$

The power factor of electric motors varies from 80% to 90% in the larger size motors. The efficiency likewise varies from 80% on a small motor to 90% on a large motor.

SINGLE-PHASE, TWO-PHASE, AND DIRECT-CURRENT CIRCUITS

To find size of conductor required:

$$\text{Circular Mils} = \frac{21.6 \times \text{Current in Amperes} \times \text{Distance in Feet}}{\text{Volts Drop}}$$

To find the voltage drop in a circuit:

$$\text{Volts Drop} = \frac{21.6 \times \text{Current in Amperes} \times \text{Distance in Feet}}{\text{Circular Mils}}$$

To find current flowing:

$$\text{Current} = \frac{\text{Circular Mils} \times \text{Voltage Drop}}{21.6 \times \text{Distance in Feet}}$$

To find allowable length of circuit for given voltage drop or loss:

$$\text{Length of Circuit} = \frac{\text{Circular Mils} \times \text{Voltage Drop}}{21.6 \times \text{Current in Amperes}}$$

THREE-PHASE ALTERNATING-CURRENT CIRCUITS

To find size of conductor required for a three-phase circuit:

$$\text{Circular Mils} = \frac{10.8 \times \text{Current in Amperes} \times \text{Distance in Feet} \times 1.73}{\text{Volts Drop}}$$

To find voltage drop in a three-phase circuit:

$$\text{Volts Drop} = \frac{10.8 \times \text{Current in Amperes} \times \text{Distance in Feet} \times 1.73}{\text{Circular Mils}}$$

To find current in a three-phase circuit:

$$\begin{matrix}\text{Current} \\ \text{(Amperes)}\end{matrix} = \frac{\text{Circular Mils} \times \text{Voltage Drop}}{10.8 \times \text{Distance in Feet} \times 1.73}$$

To find length of a three-phase circuit for a given voltage drop:

$$\text{Distance in Feet} = \frac{\text{Circular Mils} \times \text{Voltage Drop}}{10.8 \times \text{Current in Amperes} \times 1.73}$$

COPPER WIRE TABLE

Gauge No.*	Diameter in Mils	Cross Section Area		Ohms per 1000 Feet 25°C (=77°F)	Pounds per 1000 Feet
		Circular Mils	Square Inches		
0000	460.	212000.	0.166	0.0500	641.
000	410	168000.	.132	.0630	508.
00	365.	133000.	.105	.0795	403.
0	325.	106000.	.0829	.100	319.
1	289.	83700.	.0657	.126	253.
2	258.	66400.	.0521	.159	201.
3	229.	52600.	.0413	.201	159.
4	204.	41700.	.0328	.253	126.
5	182.	33100.	.0260	.319	100.
6	162.	26300.	.0206	.403	79.5
7	144.	20800.	.0164	.508	63.0
8	128.	16500.	.0130	.641	50.0
9	114.	13100.	.0103	.808	39.6
10	102.	10400.	.00815	1.02	31.4
11	91.	8230	.00647	1.28	24.9
12	81.	6530.	.00513	1.62	19.8
13	72.	5180.	.00407	2.04	15.7
14	64.	4110.	.00323	2.58	12.4
15	57.	3260.	.00256	3.25	9.86
16	51.	2580.	.00203	4.09	7.82
17	45.	2050.	.00161	5.16	6.20
18	40.	1620.	.00128	6.51	4.92
19	36.	1290.	.00101	8.21	3.90
20	32.	1020	.000802	10.04	3.09
21	28.5	810.	.000636	13.1	2.45
22	25.3	642.	.000505	16.5	1.94
23	22.6	509.	.000400	20.8	1.54
24	20.1	404.	.000317	26.2	1.22
25	17.9	320.	.000252	33.0	0.970
26	15.9	254.	.000200	41.6	.769
27	14.2	202.	.000158	52.5	.610
28	12.6	160.	.000126	66.2	.484
29	11.3	127.	.0000995	83.4	.384
30	10.0	101.	.0000789	105.	.304
31	8.9	79.7	.0000626	133.	.241
32	8.0	63.2	.0000496	167.	.191
33	7.1	50.1	.0000394	211.	.152
34	6.3	39.8	.0000312	266.	.120
35	5.6	31.5	.0000248	335.	.0954
36	5.0	25.0	.0000196	423.	.0757
37	4.5	19.8	.0000156	533.	.0600
38	4.0	15.7	.0000123	673.	.0476
39	3.5	12.5	.0000098	848.	.0377
40	3.1	9.9	.0000078	1070.	.0299

*The gauge number refers to American Wire Gauge, often called Brown & Sharpe Gauge, that is used for copper wire. A mil is $\frac{1}{1000}$ of an inch.

Comparison of Centigrade and Fahrenheit Thermometers

Water boils at......... 100 degrees Centigrade (C. or Cent.) / 212 degrees Fahrenheit (F. or Fahr.)

Water freezes at....... 0 degrees Centigrade (C. or Cent.) / 32 degrees Fahrenheit (F. or Fahr.)

Cent.	Fahr.	Cent.	Fahr.	Cent.	Fahr.
0	32.0				
1	33.8	36	96.8	71	159.8
2	35.6	37	98.6	72	161.6
3	37.4	38	100.4	73	163.4
4	39.2	39	102.2	74	165.2
5	41.0	40	104.0	75	167.0
6	42.8	41	105.8	76	168.8
7	44.6	42	107.6	77	170.6
8	46.4	43	109.4	78	172.4
9	48.2	44	111.2	79	174.2
10	50.0	45	113.0	80	176.0
11	51.8	46	114.8	81	177.8
12	53.6	47	116.6	82	179.6
13	55.4	48	118.4	83	181.4
14	57.2	49	120.2	84	183.2
15	59.0	50	122.0	85	185.0
16	60.8	51	123.8	86	186.8
17	62.6	52	125.6	87	188.6
18	64.4	53	127.4	88	190.4
19	66.2	54	129.2	89	192.2
20	68.0	55	131.0	90	194.0
21	69.8	56	132.8	91	195.8
22	71.6	57	134.6	92	197.6
23	73.4	58	136.4	93	199.4
24	75.2	59	138.2	94	201.2
25	77.0	60	140.0	95	203.0
26	78.8	61	141.8	96	204.8
27	80.6	62	143.6	97	206.6
28	82.4	63	145.4	98	208.4
29	84.2	64	147.2	99	210.2
30	86.0	65	149.0	100	212.0
31	87.8	66	150.8		
32	89.6	67	152.6		
33	91.4	68	154.4		
34	93.2	69	156.2		
35	95.0	70	158.0		

Decimal Equivalents

Fraction	Decimal
1/64	.015625
1/32	.03125
3/64	.046875
1/16	.0625
5/64	.078125
3/32	.09375
7/64	.109375
1/8	.125
9/64	.140625
5/32	.15625
11/64	.171875
3/16	.1875
13/64	.203125
7/32	.21875
15/64	.234375
1/4	.25
17/64	.265625
9/32	.28125
19/64	.296875
5/16	.3125
21/64	.328125
11/32	.34375
23/64	.359375
3/8	.375
25/64	.390625
13/32	.40625
27/64	.421875
7/16	.4375
29/64	.453125
15/32	.46875
31/64	.484375
1/2	.5
33/64	.515625
17/32	.53125
35/64	.546875
9/16	.5625
37/64	.578125
19/32	.59375
39/64	.609375
5/8	.625
41/64	.640625
21/32	.65625
43/64	.671875
11/16	.6875
45/64	.703125
23/32	.71875
47/64	.734375
3/4	.75
49/64	.765625
25/32	.78125
51/64	.796875
13/16	.8125
53/64	.828125
27/32	.84375
55/64	.859375
7/8	.875
57/64	.890625
29/32	.90625
59/64	.921875
15/16	.9375
61/64	.953125
31/32	.96875
63/64	.984375
1	1.

GRAPHICAL SYMBOLS

SYMBOL	OBJECT	SYMBOL	OBJECT
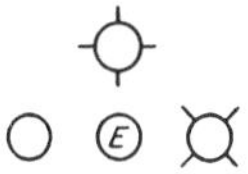 E CEILING OUTLET		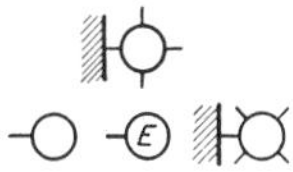 E WALL OUTLET	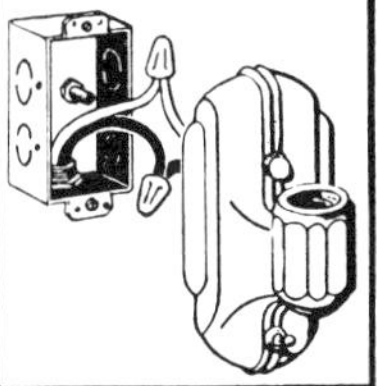
 B B BLANKED OUTLET		D DROP CORD	
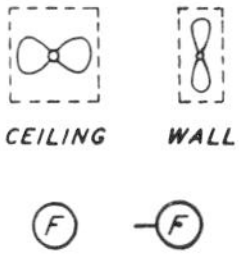 CEILING WALL F F FAN OUTLET	 VENTILATING FAN	 J J JUNCTION BOX	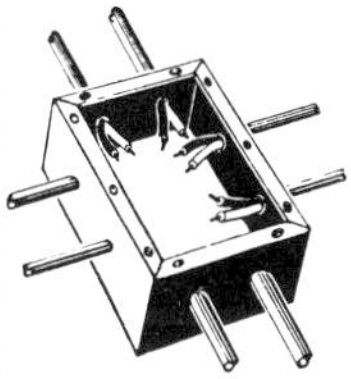
 L PS L LAMP HOLDER		 S S PS PULL SWITCH	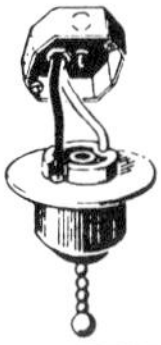
X EXIT OUTLET C CLOCK OUTLET V OUTLET FOR VAPOR DISCHARGE LAMP		 2 DUPLEX CONVENIENCE OUTLET	
 W.P. WEATHERPROOF CONVENIENCE OUTLET		R RANGE OUTLET	

Symbols Used on Architectural Plans

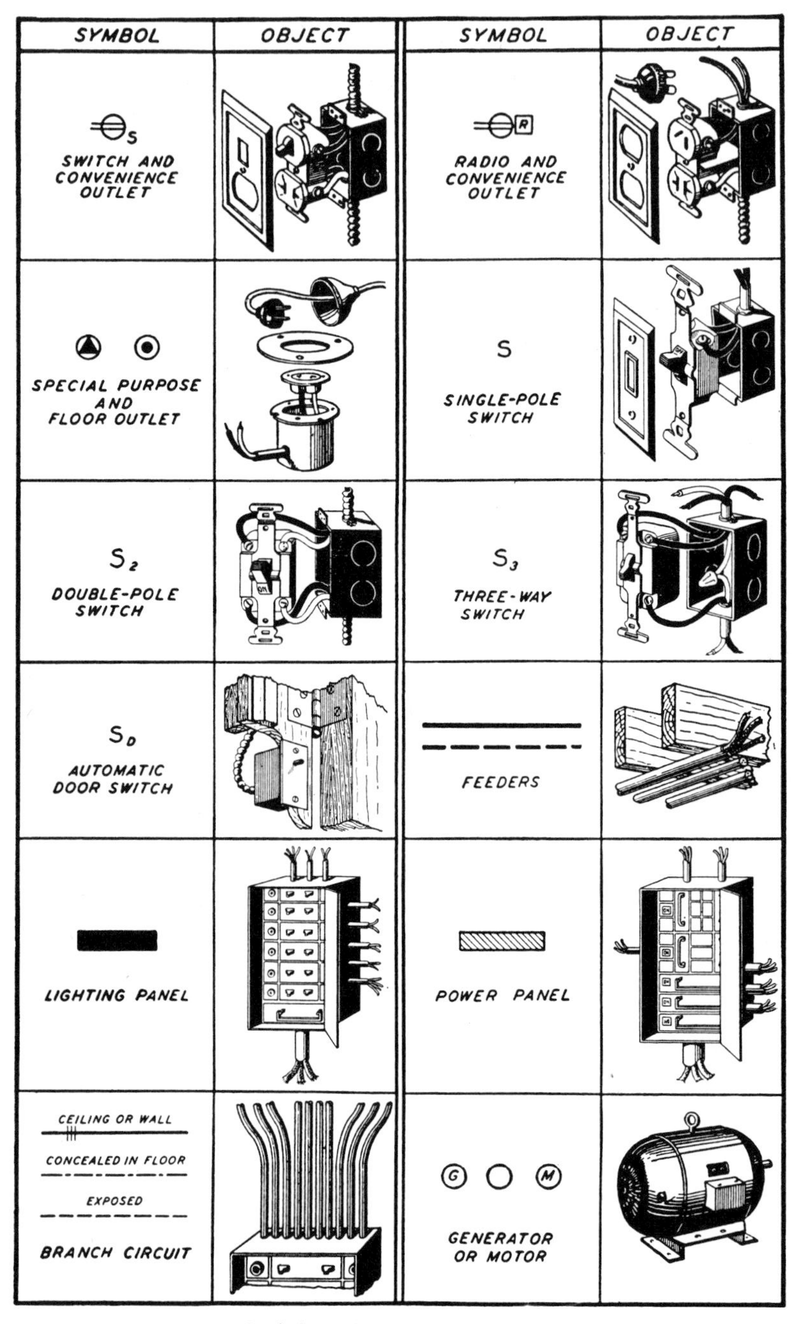

Symbols Used on Architectural Plans

NONMAGNETIC CORE		MAGNETIC CORE	
SYMBOL	OBJECT	SYMBOL	OBJECT
OR FIXED		OR FIXED	
OR ADJUSTABLE		OR ADJUSTABLE	
OR ADJUSTABLE BY TAPS		OR ADJUSTABLE BY TAPS	
MAGNETIC CORE		(A) BLOWOUT COIL OR (B) SERIES OR SHUNT OPERATING COIL	A B
SYMBOL	OBJECT		
OR VARIABLE			

Inductor, Reactor, Coil, and Field Symbols

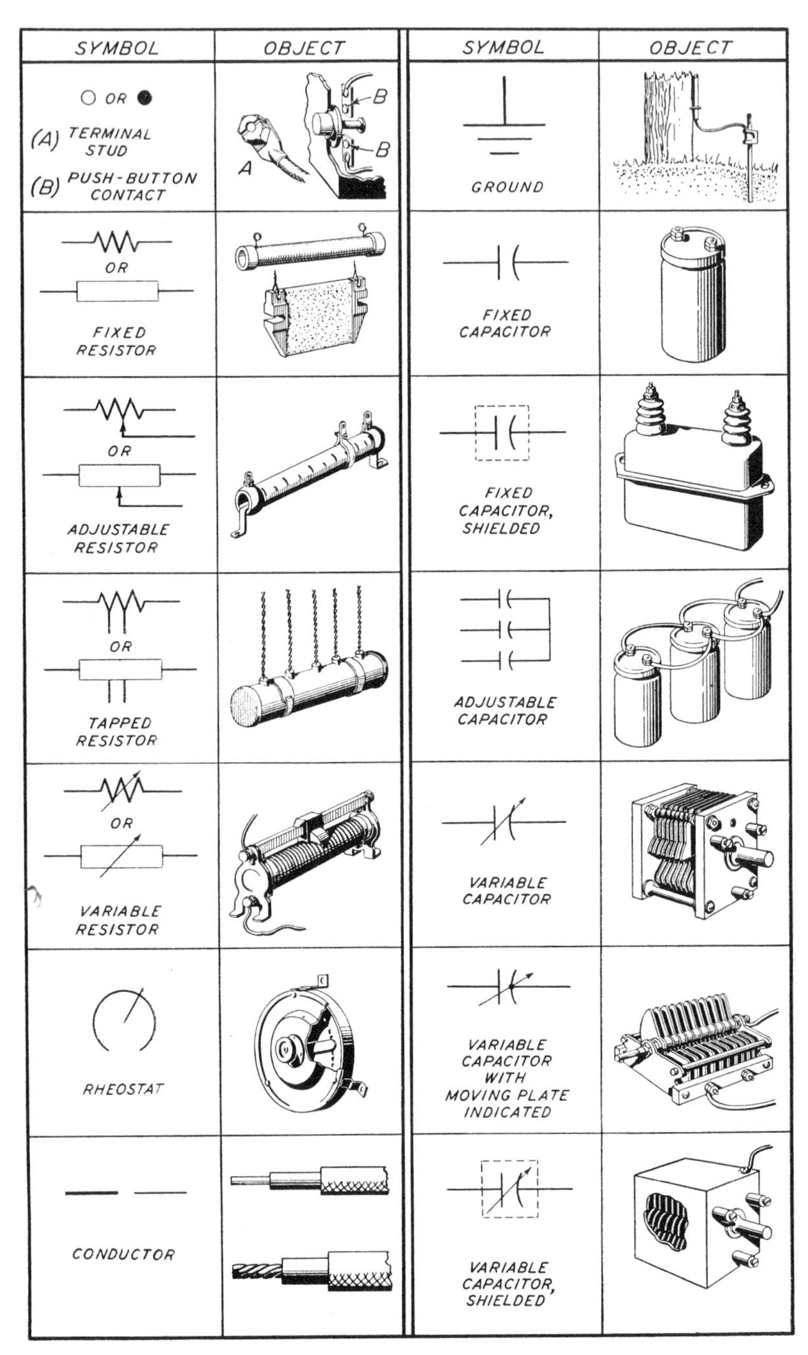

Resistor and Capacitor Symbols

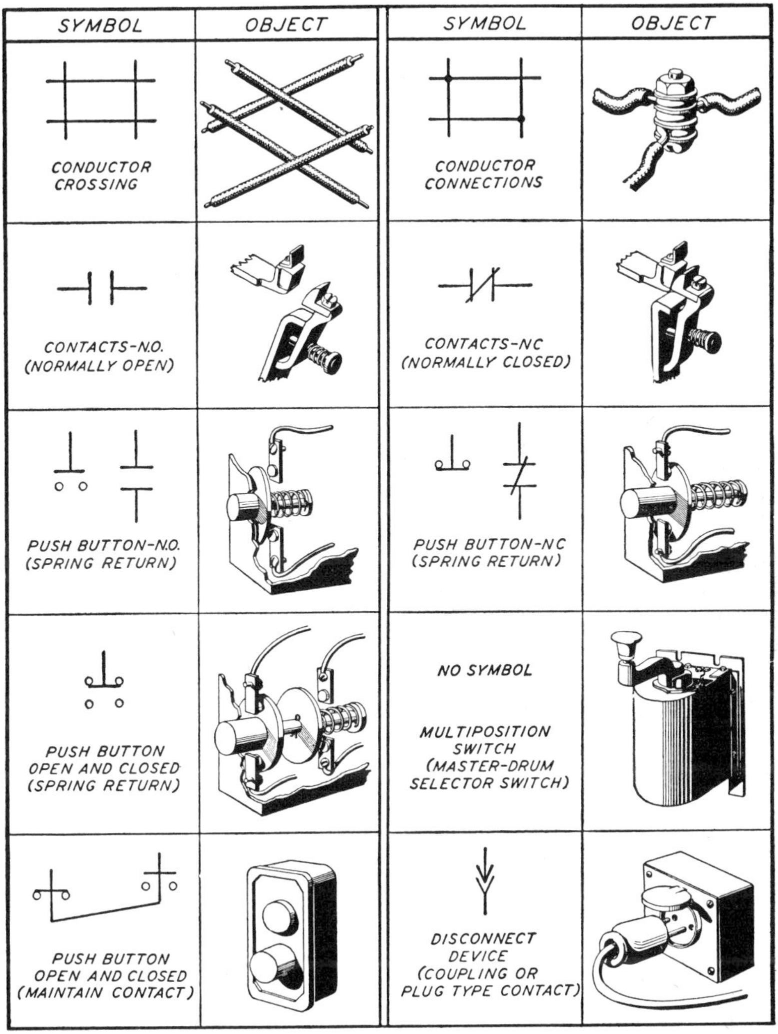

SYMBOL	OBJECT	SYMBOL	OBJECT
CONDUCTOR CROSSING		CONDUCTOR CONNECTIONS	
CONTACTS-N.O. (NORMALLY OPEN)		CONTACTS-NC (NORMALLY CLOSED)	
PUSH BUTTON-N.O. (SPRING RETURN)		PUSH BUTTON-NC (SPRING RETURN)	
PUSH BUTTON OPEN AND CLOSED (SPRING RETURN)		NO SYMBOL MULTIPOSITION SWITCH (MASTER-DRUM SELECTOR SWITCH)	
PUSH BUTTON OPEN AND CLOSED (MAINTAIN CONTACT)		DISCONNECT DEVICE (COUPLING OR PLUG TYPE CONTACT)	

Contact and Push-Button Symbols

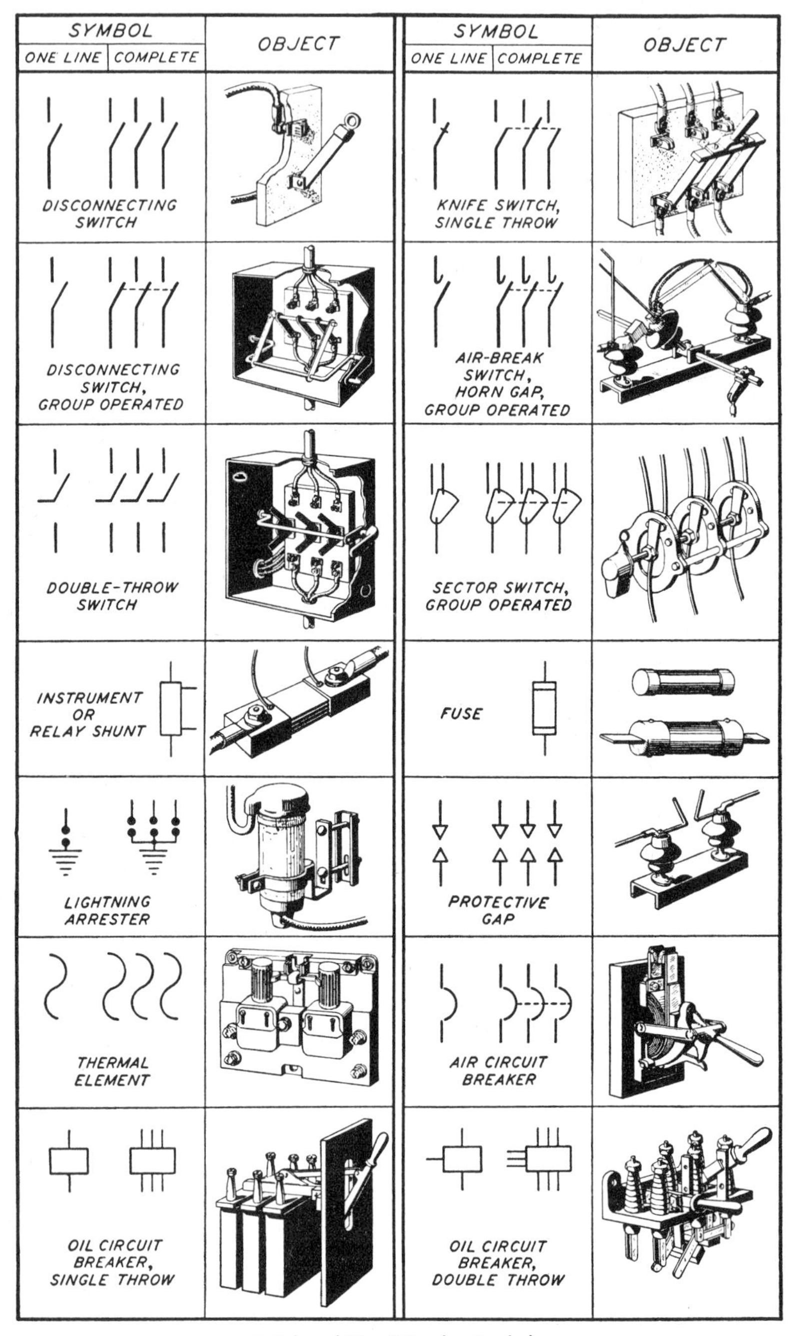

Switch and Circuit-Breaker Symbols

GRAPHICAL SYMBOLS

SYMBOL (ONE LINE / COMPLETE)	OBJECT	SYMBOL (ONE LINE / COMPLETE)	OBJECT
OR OR SINGLE-PHASE TWO-WINDING TRANSFORMER		OR OR POLYPHASE TWO-WINDING TRANSFORMERS	
OR OR THREE-WINDING TRANSFORMER		OR OR AUTO TRANSFORMER	
OR OR TRANSFORMER WITH TAPS		OR OR CONSTANT CURRENT TRANSFORMER	
OR OR OR OR OR 1 2 3 CURRENT TRANSFORMER		BUSHING CURRENT TRANSFORMER	
OR OR OR WITH IN PLACE OF INDUCTION VOLTAGE REGULATOR		CAPACITANCE BUSHING	
HALF WAVE DRY OR ELECTROLYTIC RECTIFIER		AC DC DC AC FULL WAVE RECTIFIER	

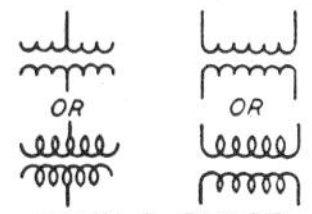

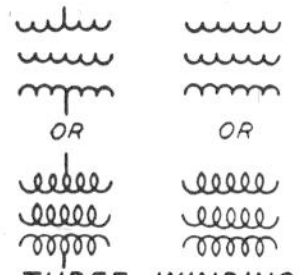

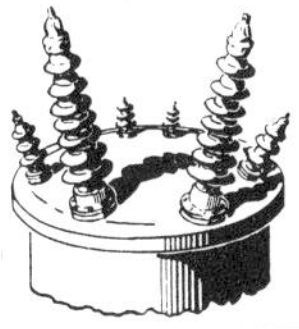

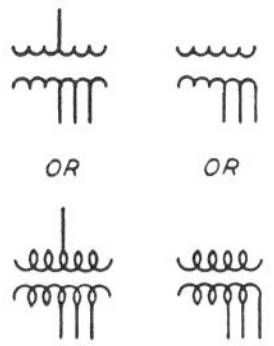

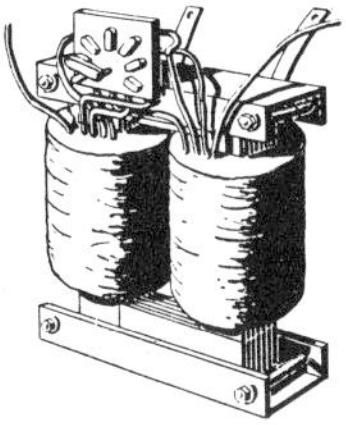

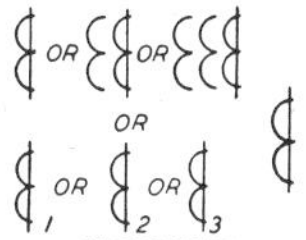

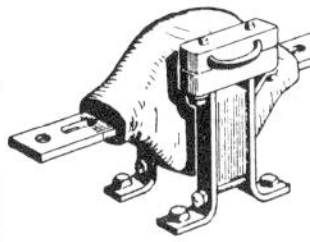

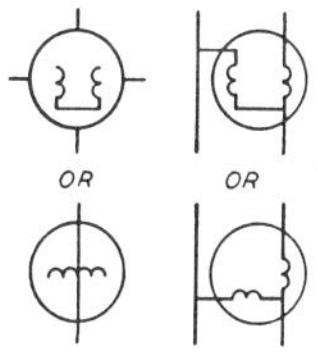

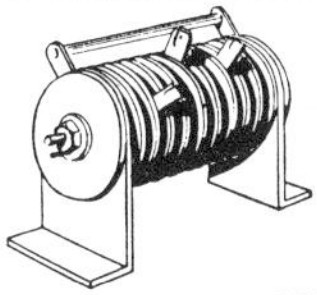

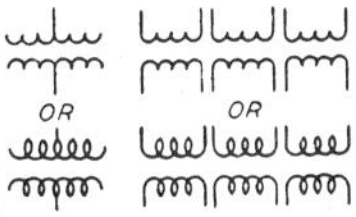

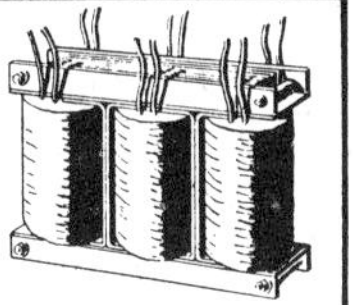

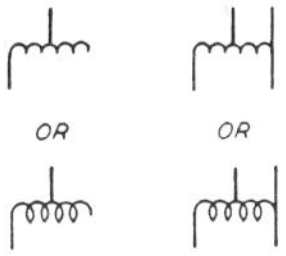

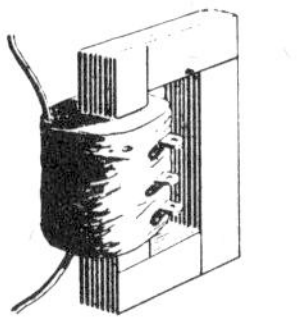

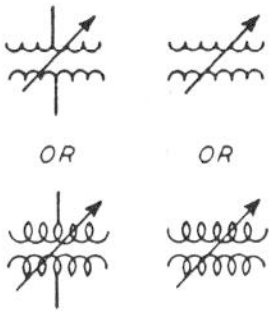

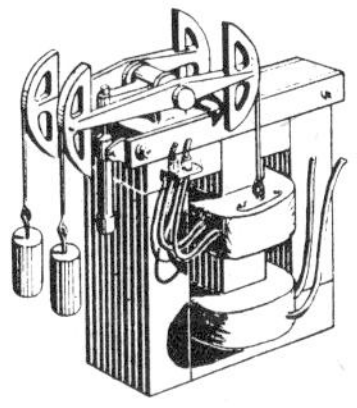

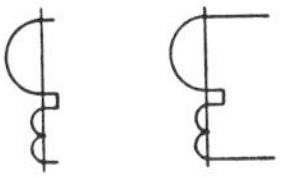

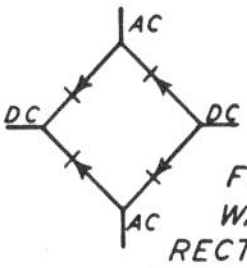

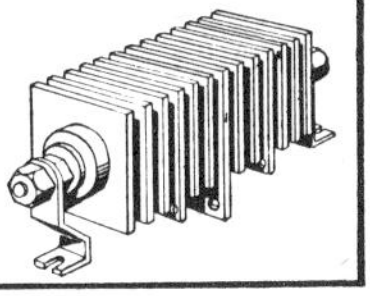

Transformer Symbols

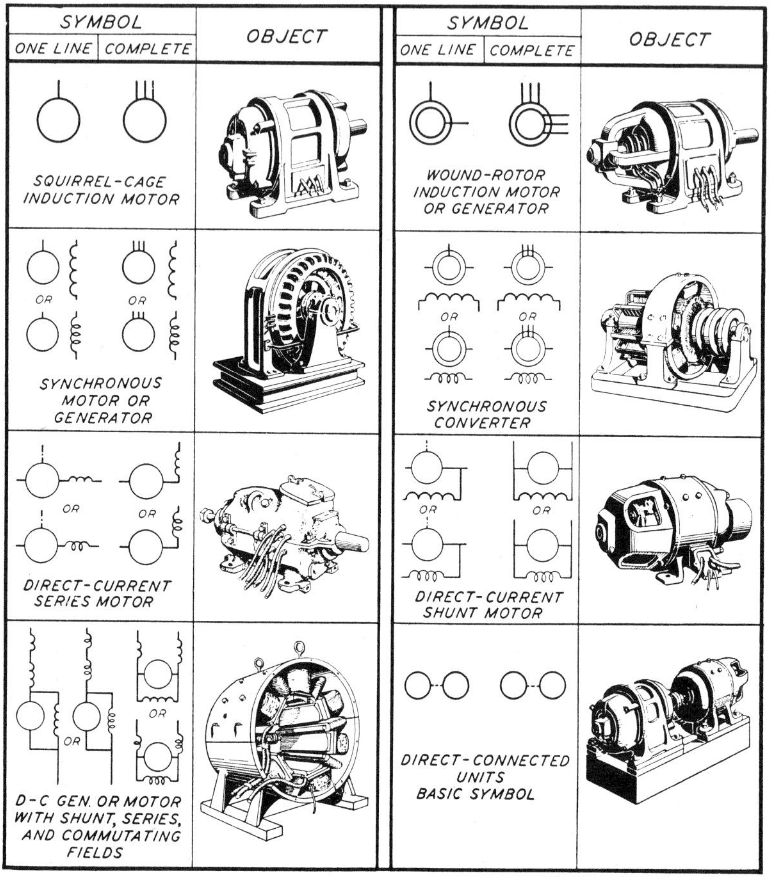

SYMBOL		OBJECT
ONE LINE	COMPLETE	
SQUIRREL-CAGE INDUCTION MOTOR		
SYNCHRONOUS MOTOR OR GENERATOR		
DIRECT-CURRENT SERIES MOTOR		
D-C GEN. OR MOTOR WITH SHUNT, SERIES, AND COMMUTATING FIELDS		

SYMBOL		OBJECT
ONE LINE	COMPLETE	
WOUND-ROTOR INDUCTION MOTOR OR GENERATOR		
SYNCHRONOUS CONVERTER		
DIRECT-CURRENT SHUNT MOTOR		
DIRECT-CONNECTED UNITS BASIC SYMBOL		

Motor and Generator Symbols

GRAPHICAL SYMBOLS

SYMBOL	OBJECT	SYMBOL	OBJECT
A OR AM AMMETER	 AMPERES	AH AMPERE-HOUR METER	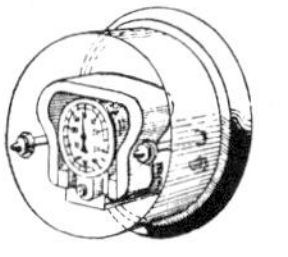
V OR VM VOLTMETER	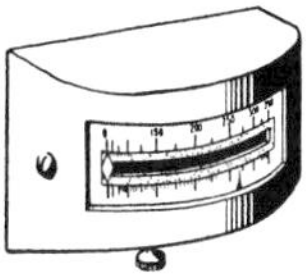	I INDICATING METER	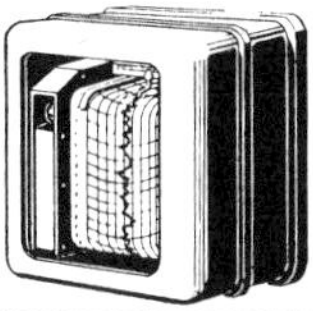
W WATTMETER	 500 1000 1500 WATTS	WH WATT-HOUR METER	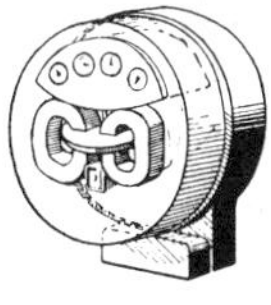
VAR VARMETER REACTIVE VOLT-AMPERE METER	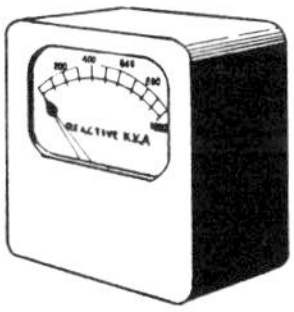 REACTIVE K.V.A	MD MAXIMUM DEMAND	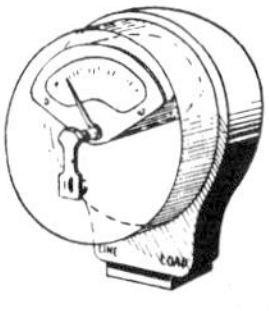 LINE LOAD
PF POWER FACTOR METER	 POWER FACTOR	F FREQUENCY METER	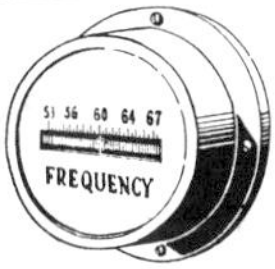 51 56 60 64 67 FREQUENCY
S SYNCHROSCOPE	 SLOW FAST	GD GROUND DETECTOR	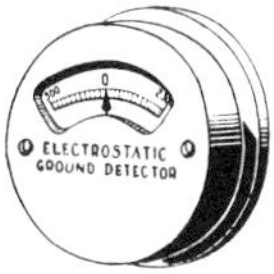 0 ELECTROSTATIC GROUND DETECTOR
REG GENERATOR VOLTAGE REGULATOR		CMV CONTACT MAKING VOLTMETER	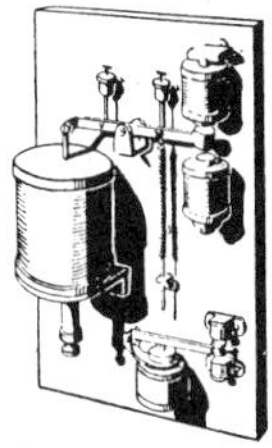

Instrument Symbols

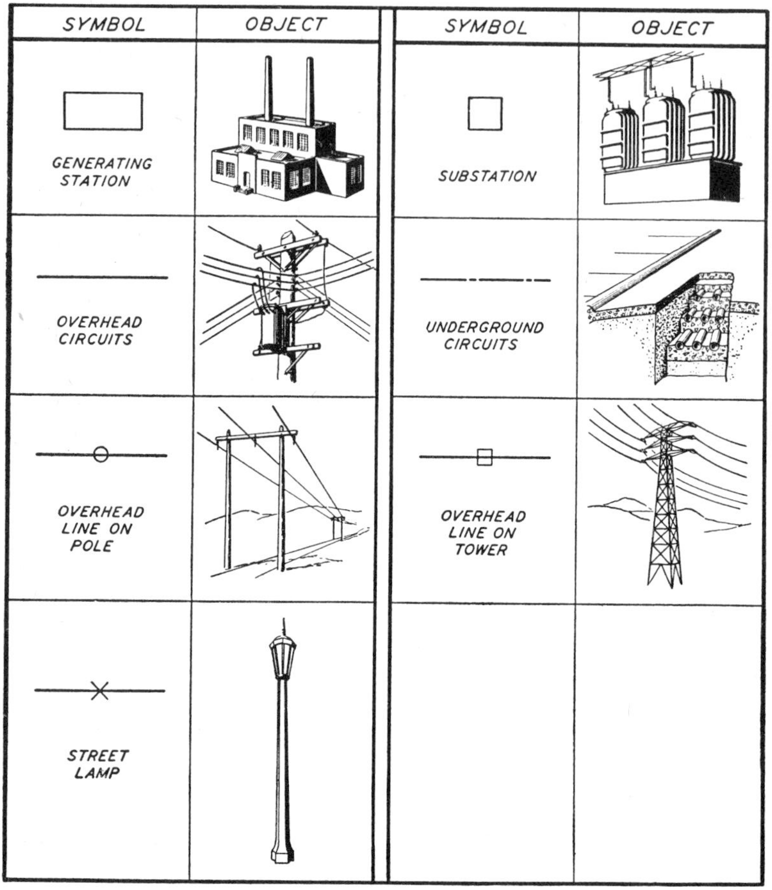

SYMBOL	OBJECT	SYMBOL	OBJECT
GENERATING STATION		SUBSTATION	
OVERHEAD CIRCUITS		UNDERGROUND CIRCUITS	
OVERHEAD LINE ON POLE		OVERHEAD LINE ON TOWER	
STREET LAMP			

Symbols Used on Transmission Line Map Drawings

Dictionary of Electrical Terms

A

A.C.: Abbreviation for alternating current.

abscissa: A distance measured horizontally to the right and left of a vertical line.

absolute units: A unit of measurement which has been determined from certain physical properties and upon which all other units are based.

accumulator: A storage battery.

acid proof paint: A paint made especially to resist the action of acid.

admittance: A unit used in alternating current circuits, which is the opposite to impedance, measured in ohms.

aerial: Wires supported above ground and used for receiving or sending electrical waves.

advance wire: An alloy of copper and nickel used for electric heating units.

air blast transformer: A transformer cooled by forcing a circulation of air around its windings.

air gap: Air space between magnetic poles. Space between stationary and rotating parts of an electric motor and generator.

algebraic: Taking into account the sign used in algebra.

alive: Carrying a voltage or current.

alkaline battery: A storage battery using an alkali instead of acid for electrolyte Edison Cells.

all-day-efficiency: The total output divided by the total input of energy for the entire day.

alloy: A metal composed of two or more different metals.

alphaduct: A flexible non-metal conduit.

alternating current: An electric current that reverses its direction of flow at regular intervals.

alternation: One vibration instead of a cycle. One-half a cycle of alternating current.

alternator: An electric generator producing alternating current.

aluminum: A white metal, light in weight but having a higher electrical resistance than copper.

aluminum cell arrester: A lightning arrester using a series of aluminum plates and an electrolyte which forms a thin insulating film on the plates at normal voltage, but becoming a conductor when a high voltage, like lightning, occurs. As soon as the high voltage is reduced to normal, the insulating film is formed again.

aluminum rectifier: A jar containing aluminum plates and iron or lead plates immersed in a solution of ammonium phosphate and which will allow current to flow, though only in one direction, from the iron or lead plates to the aluminum plate.

amalgam: An alloy of mercury or quicksilver with other metals.

amber: A yellowish resinous substance that can be used to produce static electricity by friction.

American wire gauge: The gauge is used for designating the sizes of solid copper wires used in United States. Formerly called Brown and Sharpe (Best gauge).

ammeter: The instrument that indicates the rate of flow of electricity through a circuit.

ammeter shunt: A special low resistance conductor connected to the terminals of an ammeter so as to carry nearly all the current, allowing only a very small current to flow through the instrument itself.

ampere: The practical unit that indicates the rate of flow of electricity through a circuit.

ampere-hour: The quantity of electricity delivered by a current of one ampere flowing for one hour. Used in rating storage batteries.

ampere-hour meter: An instrument that registers or records the number of ampere-hours of electrical energy that have passed througn a circuit.

ampere-turn: The amount of magnetism or magnetizing force produced by a current of one ampere flowing around a coil of one turn. The product of the current flowing through a coil by the number of turns or loops of wire on the coil.

amplifier: A device by which weak currents or sounds acting on another circuit are increased in strength.

anchor: A metal placed in the ground and to which a guy wire from a pole is attached.

angle of dip: The number of degrees that one end of a magnet dips or points downward.

angle of lag and lead: The distance expressed in degrees that an alternating current lags or leads the voltage wave. The cosine of this angle is called the power factor.

anion: The ion which moves toward the anode in an electrolytic cell.

anneal: To soften by heating and allowing to cool slowly.

annunciator: An electric signal equipment having a number of push buttons located at different places which are wired to an electromagnet in the annunciator box. Press any push button and it causes a signal to be displayed showing what button was operated.

annunciator wire: A soft copper wire that has two layers of cotton threads wound on it in opposite direction and covered with paraffin wax.

anode: The terminal or electrode through which current flows into the electrolyte.

antenna: Wires arranged to receive or send out electromagnetic (Radio) waves into the air.

anti: A prefix, meaning opposite, against, opposed to, etc., to the word that follows it.

apparent E.M.F.: The apparent voltage as measured by the drop in pressure due to current flowing through the resistance.

apparent efficiency: In alternating current apparatus it is the ratio of net power output to volt-amperes input.

apparent watts: The product of volts times amperes in an alternating current circuit.

arc: The flow of electric current across a gap in a circuit which causes a light or glow.

arc furnace: An electric furnace in which heat is produced by an arc between two electrodes.

arc lamp: A lamp producing light from an arc.

arc lamp carbon: A carbon rod between which the arc is produced in an arc lamp.

arc light generator: A generator producing a constant current for an arc light circuit. Nearly obsolete.

arc welding: Joining two pieces of metal together by use of an electric arc.

argon: An odorless, colorless, inert gas taken from the air. Used in some types of incandescent light bulbs.

armature: The rotating part of a direct current motor or generator. The part of the generator that delivers electrical energy or the part of the motor that receives electrical energy from the circuit. Also a piece of iron or steel joining the poles of an electromagnet.

armature air gap: The air space between the stationary and rotating parts of a motor or generator where the magnetic lines of force pass from one to the other.

armature back ampere turns: The magnetic field produced by current flowing in the armature winding that opposes and reduces the number of magnetic lines of force produced by the field magnets of a motor or generator.

armature band: A group of wires wound closely together, or a metal band placed on the coils of the armature to hold them in place.

armature bar: Copper bars used in place of wire winding the armatures of large generators and motors.

armature bore: The space between opposite pole pieces in which the armature revolves.

armature circuit: The path that the current takes in flowing through the windings from one brush to another.

armature coil: The loop or coil of copper wire placed on the armature core and which forms part of the winding.

armature core: The laminated iron part of the armature, formed from thin sheets or disks of steel, and on which the windings are placed.

armature current: The current flowing from the armature of a generator or to the armature of a motor. It does not include the current taken by the shunt field coils.

armature disks: Thin sheets of iron or steel used in building up the armature core.

armature demagnetization: The reduction in the effective magnetic lines of force produced by the armature current.

armature reaction: The effect that the magnetism produced by the current flowing in the armature has on the magnetism (magnetic lines of force) produced by the field coils.

armature resistance: The resistance of the wire used in the windings of the armature measured between rings or brushes, or from positive to negative terminal.

armature slot: The groove or slot in the armature core into which the coils or windings are placed.

armature stand: A device for supporting or holding an armature by the shaft when it is being wound or worked on.

armature tester: Any device or instrument used for locating faults or defects in the armature winding.

armature tooth: The metal between the slots in an armature core.

armature varnish: A liquid put on the field and armature windings to improve the insulation of the cotton coverings on the wires.

armature winding: All of the copper wire placed on the armature and through which current flows when the machine is operating.

armored cable: Rubber-covered wires that have been covered with an iron, steel, or other flexible metallic covering. Often called BX.

artificial magnet: A manufactured permanent magnet, as distinguished from natural magnets.

asbestos: A mineral fiber formed from a certain rock. It is a poor conductor of heat and can withstand high temperatures. Used to insulate wires exposed to a high temperature.

astatic system: An arrangement of two parallel magnets with the north end of one pointing the same way as the south end of the other, so that the two together make a very poor compass needle.

astatic galvanometer: A galvanometer in which the moving parts are arranged in an astatic system or manner.

astatic meter: A meter in which the moving part of element is arranged in an astatic system.

asynchronous: Not having the same frequency; not synchronous; not in step or phase.

asynchronous generator: An induction generator.

asynchronous motor: An induction motor. A motor whose speed is not synchronous with the frequency of the supply line.

atmosphere: The air surrounding the earth. A pressure of 1 atmosphere is 14.7 pounds to the square inch.

atmosphere electricity: Static electricity produced in the sky or between clouds.

atom: The smallest particle or unit of matter that can be chemically united.

atomic weight: The weight of one atom of a chemical element as compared to the weight of an atom of hydrogen.

atonic interrupter: A special interrupter that can be adjusted to operate at a large number of different frequencies.

attachment plugs: A plug that is screwed into a lamp socket, connecting the two wires from an electrical appliance to the circuit.

attenutation: The weakening of an alternating current that flows along a line that has resistance and capacity or leakage.

Aurora Borealis: A light or glow sometimes seen in the northern sky on certain nights.

auto call: A device that sounds a certain code of signals in various places; in a building or factory.

auto-transformer: A transformer in which one winding or coil serves both for the primary and the secondary circuit.

automatic: A device that is operated by certain changes or conditions in an electric circuit and which is not controlled by any person.

automatic telephone: A telephone system where the connection from one party to another is made by means of automatic switches, without the aid of an operator.

automatic time switch: A switch operated at certain times by means of a clock.

automotive: Self propelled vehicles, such as automobiles, trucks, tractors and motorcyles.

automobile battery: The storage battery used in an electric vehicle. The storage battery used for starting and lighting a gasoline automobile.

automobile fuse: A small fuse used to protect the generator and lighting circuits on an automobile.

auxiliary: Extra, or something added to the main one.

auxiliary bus: A second bus that may have a different voltage from the main bus and to which a few machines are connected.

auxiliary circuit: Another circuit besides the main circuit; often a control circuit.

auxiliary switch: A switch operated or controlled by the action of another circuit.

B

b: A symbol used for "susceptance" in an alternating current circuit.

B: A symbol for magnetic flux density.

B.B.: Abbreviation for Best Best iron telephone wire.

B-battery: The radio battery that keeps the plate of an electron tube positive in relation to the filament.

B.S.G.: British Standard Gauge.

B. board: One of the switchboards in a large telephone exchange where one subscriber is connected to another.

B.t.u.: British thermal unit; the heat required to raise the temperture of 1 pound of water 1 degree F.

B.W.G.: Birmingham wire gauge. The same as Stubs' Copper wire gauge.

BX: A term often used for flexible armored cable.

B. & S.: Brown & Sharpe wire gauge which is the same as American wire gauge.

babbitt metal: An alloy of lead, tin, copper, zinc, and antimony used for bearings of electrical machines.

back pitch: The distance between the two sides of an armature coil at the back side of the armature, usually expressed in number of slots.

back ampere turns: The ampere turns on the armature that produce magnetism that opposes that produced by the field coils.

bakelite: A moulded insulating material.

balanced load: Arranging the load equally on the two sides of a three-wire system.

balancer coil: An auto transformer used to provide a neutral wire on a 3-wire system.

balancer set: Two direct current generators or motors coupled together and used to keep the voltage the same on each side of a 3-wire system.

ballastic galvanometer: A type of galvanometer used for measuring the quantity of electricity suddenly discharged through it, from usually a condenser, expressed as the angle through which the movable part turns.

bank of lamps: A number of lamps, connected either in series or in parallel, used as a resistance.

bank of transformers: A number of transformers located at one place and connected to the same circuit.

bar magnet: A straight permanent magnet.

bar windings: Windings composed of copper bars or rods instead of wire.

barometer: An instrument for measuring the pressure of the atmosphere.

barrier: A partition, slab, or plate of insulating material placed between blades of switches, wires, or conductor in order to separate or insulate them.

battery: A number of similar units arranged to work together. A number of primary or storage cells connected either in series or in parallel.

battery acid: The liquid used in a storage battery. This is usually sulphuric acid.

battery box: The box holding the cells forming the battery.

battery capacity: The amount of energy that can be obtained from a storage battery—usually expressed in ampere-hours.

battery case: A battery box.

battery charger: A rectifier used for changing alternating current into direct current for charging a battery.

battery connector: A lead covered link or bar used to connect one terminal of a cell to the terminal of the next cell of a battery.

battery discharger: An adjustable resistance used to test the condition of the battery by discharging the battery.

battery hydrometer: A hydrometer used for testing the specific gravity or density of the electrolyte in a storage battery.

battery oven: An oven into which storage batteries are placed and heated in order to soften the compound that seals the cover to the battery cells.

battery paint: A paint, that will resist the action of acids, used to paint the battery boxes or battery rooms.

battery resistance: The internal resistance of a cell or number of cells. The resistance of the plates and electrolyte measured between the external terminals.

battery steamer: An apparatus used for producing steam inside a storage battery case in order to soften the sealing compound.

bayonet socket: A lamp socket that has two lengthwise slots in the sides of socket and at the bottom the slots make a right angle turn. The lamp base has two pins in it that slide in the slots in the socket. The lamp is held in the socket by being given a slight turn when the pins reach the bottom of the slots.

bearing: That part which holds or supports the shaft.

bearing bracket: That part of the machine extending outward from the frame of a machine and which supports or holds the bearings.

bearing loss: Loss of power due to the friction between the shaft and the bearing of a machine.

bearing metal: A special alloy that has the smallest amount of friction between itself and the rotating shaft. Often used as a lining in the bearing.

bell hanger's bit: A long slim wood bit used to drill through the frame of a building when installing door bells.

bell ringing transformer: A small transformer, slipping the voltage down from 110 volts to about 10 volts, used on a door bell.

B-H curve: A curve that shows the relation between the magnetizing force and the number of lines of force per square inch or centimeter produced in different metals.

Bi: A chemical symbol for bismuth.

bichromate cell: A primary cell consisting of carbon and zinc electrodes immersed in a solution of potassium bichromate and sulphuric acid.

binding posts: Terminals used on apparatus or circuits so that other circuits can be quickly attached.

bipolar: Having only two magnetic poles.

Birmingham wire gauge: Wire gauge used for measuring galvanized iron telephone and telegraph wires; also called Stubs' gauge.

block lead: A form of carbon called graphite.

blow-out coil. An electromagnet used for deflecting the arc between two contacts and thus blowing out the arc.

bond: A short high-grade conductor cable or wire used to connect the end of one rail to the next.

booster: A generator connected in series with a circuit in order to increase the voltage of that circuit.

booster converter: A machine that changes the current from alternating to direct or tne opposite, that has a booster built in as part of the machine.

booster transformer: A transformer used to raise the voltage of an alternating current feeder or circuit.

box connector: An attachment used for fastening the ends of cable to a box.

braided wire: A conductor composed of a number of small wires twisted or braided together.

brake shoe: A metallic casting that bears against the wheel in order to stop the wheel from turning.

brake horsepower: The actual power of a machine measured by use of a Prony brake or dynamometer.

branch circuit: That part of the wiring system between the final set of fuses protecting it and the place where the lighting fixtures or drop cords are attached.

branch cutout: The fuse holder for the branch circuit fuse.

brazing: Uniting two metals by a joint composed of a film of brass or alloy that has a higher melting point than solder.

bridge: A Wheatstone bridge.

bridge duplex: A duplex telegraph system dependent for its operation upon the use of a Wheatstone bridge connection in which the telegraph circuit and an artificial line similar to it are the two arms.

bridging set: A telephone set designed to be connected in parallel with other telephones to a telephone line.

British thermal unit: The amount of heat required to raise the temperature of one pound of water 1 degree F.

Brown and Sharpe gauge: The gauge used in United States for copper wires. Same as American wire gauge.

bronze: An alloy of copper and tin.

brush: A conductor that makes connection between the rotating and stationary parts of an electrical machine.

brush discharge: A faint glowing discharge at sharp points from a conductor carrying high voltages. It occurs at a voltage slightly less than that required to cause a spark or arc to jump across the gap.

brush holder: The device used to hold or guide the brushes against a commutator or slip ring.

brush holder cable: A stranded conductor composed of a large number of copper wires, smaller in size than those used on regular stranded cables.

brush holder spring: A spring used to press the brush against the commutator or slip ring.

brush holder stud: An insulated bolt or rod to which the brush holders are fastened.

brush lag: The distance that the brushes on a motor are shifted against rotation in order to overcome the effect of armature reaction.

brush lead: The distance that the brushes on a generator are shifted with rotation in order to overcome armature reaction.

brush pig-tail: A short braided wire fastened to the brush. It conducts the current from the brush holder to the brush.

brush rocker: A support for the brush holders and studs arranged so the location of the brushes can be shifted around the commutator.

brush yoke: Iron framework or support for the brush holders.

bucking: One electrical circuit or action opposing another one.

buckling: Warping or twisting of storage battery plates due to too high a rate of charge or discharge.

bulb: The glass inclosing part of an incandescent lamp that surrounds the filament.

Bunsen cell: A primary cell using zinc and graphite electrodes.

burn out: Damage to electric machine or conductors caused by a heavy flow of current due to short circuit or grounds.

burning rack: A frame for holding storage battery plates when connectors or straps are being fastened to them.

bus: A contraction for bus bar.

bus bar: The main circuit to which all the generators and feeders in a power station can be connected.

bushing: An insulating tube or sleeve protecting a conductor where it passes through a hole in building or apparatus.

butt joint: A splice or connection formed by putting the ends of two conductors together and joining them by welding, brazing, or soldering.

buzzer: A door bell with the hammer and gong removed.

B-X cable: Trade name for armored cable made by General Electric Co. commonly used to refer to armored cable.

C

C: When used with temperature, refers to centigrade thermometer.

C: Capacity of condenser, usually expressed in farads or microfarads.

Cd: Chemical symbol for cadmium.

C.C.W.: Counterclockwise rotation.

Ckt: Circuit.

C.G.S.: Abbreviation for centimeter gram second units—the centimeter being the unit of length, the gram the unit of weight, and the second the unit of time.

C.P.: An abbreviation for constant potential; also for candle-power of a light.

C.W.: Clockwise rotation.

cabinet: Iron box containing fuse, cutouts, and switches.

cable: A conductor composed of a number of wires twisted together.

cable box: A box which protects the connections or splices joining cables of one circuit to another.

cable clamp: A clamp used to fasten cables to their supports.

cable grip: A clamp that grips the cable when it is being pulled into place.

cable rack: A frame for supporting electric cables.

cadmium: A silvery white metal.

cadmium test: A test of the condition of the positive and negative plates of a storage battery.

calibrate: To compare the readings of one meter with those of a standard meter that is accurate.

calido: A nickel-chrome electrical resistance wire.

call-bell: An electric bell that tells a person or operator that he is wanted.

calorie: The amount of heat required to raise the temperature of 1 gram of water 1 degree centigrade.

calorizing: A process of coating a metal with a fine deposit of aluminum similar to galvanizing with zinc.

cambric tape: A cotton tape that has been treated with insulating varnish.

candelabra lamp: A small size lamp that has a smaller size screw base than the standard lamp base but larger than the miniature base.

candle: A unit of light intensity.

candle-power: The amount of light for a source as compared to a standard candle.

canopy: The exterior part of a lighting fixture that fits against the wall or ceilings, thus covering the outlet box.

canopy switch: A switch fastened to the canopy and used to turn on and off the light in the fixture.

caoutchouc: A crude rubber, known as india rubber.

capacity: Ability to hold or carry an electric charge. The unit of capacity is farad or microfarads.

capacity of a condenser:. The quantity of electricity that a condenser can receive or hold.

capacity reactance: The measure of the opposition to the passage of an alternating current through a condenser expressed in ohms.

capillary attraction: The course of the raising and lowering of the liquid in a tube above or below the surrounding liquid.

carbon: A non-metallic element or substance found in graphite, charcoal, coal, and coke.

carbon brush: A block of carbon used to carry the current from the stationary to the rotating part of a machine.

carbon contact: A contact made of carbon used where the circuit is opened frequently.

carbon disk: A piece of carbon used as a resistance in a rheostat.

carbon holder: A device for holding and feeding the carbon rods in an arc light.

carbon pile regulator: A number of pieces of carbon arranged as a rheostat to regulate the current to another circuit.

carbon resistance: A resistance formed by carbon plates or powder and arranged so that the pressure on the plates can be varied. The less the pressure, the greater will be the resistance.

carbonize: To turn some other material to carbon by fire.

carrier current: A very high frequency current used to provide the energy for transmitting a radio message.

carrying capacity: The amount of current a wire can carry without overheating.

cartridge fuse: A fuse inclosed in an insulating tube in order to confine the arc or vapor when the fuse blows.

case-hardening: The hardening of the outside of metals with heat.

cascade connection: An electrical connection in which the winding of one machine is connected to a different winding of the next machine.

cascade converter: A rotary converter that receives its energy from the rotor (secondary) of an induction motor connected to the same shaft.

cat whisker: A fine wire spring, one end of which makes contact with a crystal in a crystal radio set.

catenary curve: The curve or sag formed by the weight of a wire hanging freely between two points.

cathion: That part of the electrolyte that tends to be liberated at the terminal when the current leaves the electrolyte.

cathode: The electrode toward which the current flows in an electrolyte. The negative electrode or terminal.

cathode rays: Those rays coming from the cathode of a vacuum tube which produce X-Rays when they strike a solid substance in the tube.

cauterize: The searing or burning of flesh with an electrical heated wire.

C.C.: An abbreviation for cubic centimeter; also **Cu c.n.** is used.

cell: A jar or container holding the plates and electrolyte of one unit of a storage or primary battery.

cell vent: An opening in the cover of a cell which allows the gasses found in the cell to escape.

celluloid: An insulating material made from gun cotton and camphor; it ignites easily and burns up very quickly.

cement: A material used to bind substances together.

cementation: The forming of lead sulphate in small quantities on storage battery plates when they are drying after being made.

center of distribution: A point near the center of the area or section served by a feeder or circuit from a power station or substation. The feeder is usually run directly to this point, and then branches out in all directions from there.

centigrade: A thermometer whose scale is 0 at the freezing point and 100 at the boiling point of water.

centimeter: The one-hundredth part of a meter; 0.3937 inches, or longer than ⅜ of an inch.

central: A telephone office or exchange.

central station: A power plant supplying electric light and power to a number of users.

centrifugal cutout: A switch opened by centrifugal force of a rotating body and closed by a spring when the centrifugal force is reduced.

centrifugal force: The force that tends to throw a rotating body, or weight, outward and away from the center of rotation.

chain winding: A type of armature winding which resembles a chain.

characteristic: A curve that shows the ability of a machine to produce certain results under a certain given condition.

charge: That quantity of static electricity stored between the plates of a condenser.

charging: Sending electric current through a storage battery.

charging rate: The number of amperes of current flowing through a storage battery when it is being charged.

choke coil: A coil of a low ohmic resistance and a high inductance which will hold back unusual currents but allow regular steady currents to flow through easily; also reactors or reactance coils.

circuit: The path taken by an electrical current in flowing through a conductor from one terminal of the source of supply to the other.

circuit breaker: A device used to open a circuit automatically.

circular loom: A flexible non-metallic tubing slipped over rubber covered wires for additional insulation and protection.

circular mil: The area of a circle one-thousandth of an inch in diameter; area in circular mils = diameter, in mils, squared or multiplied by itself.

Clark cell: A primary cell that produces a constant voltage for several years and used as a standard source of voltage.

cleat: Piece of insulating material used for fastening wires to flat surfaces.

climber: A sharp steel spur or spike fastened to the shoe and legs of linemen to aid them in climbing poles.

lockwise rotation: Turning in the same direction as the hands of a clock; right-handed rotation.

closed circuit: A complete electric circuit through which current will flow when voltage is applied.

closed circuit battery: Primary cells that will deliver a steady current for a long time. A battery that can be used on a closed circuit system.

closed coil armature: The usual armature windings in which the connection of all coils forms a complete or closed circuit.

closed magnetic circuit: A complete magnetic path through iron or other metal without an air gap.

cluster: A lighting fixture having two or more lamps on it.

cobalt: A white metal similar to nickel.

code: A series of long and short sounds given in order to convey certain signals or information.

coefficient of expansion: The increase in length of a rod or body for each degree that the temperature is increased.

coherer: A device used in the early days of radio to detect radio signals.

coil box: A box containing ignition or induction coils.

coil pitch: The number of slots spanned by an armature coil.

collector ring: A metal ring fastened to the rotating part of a machine, and completing the circuit to the rotating part of the machine.

combination fixture: A fixture arranged for both gas and electric lights.

combination switch: A switch on automobiles used to control both lights and ignition.

commercial efficiency: The ratio of total output to input of power.

commutating machines: Generator, motors, and rotary converters that have commutators.

commutating pole: An interpole placed between the pole pieces of a dynamo in order to reduce sparking at the brushes.

commutating pole rectifier: A rotary converter fitted with interpoles.

commutation: Changing the alternating current produced in the armature windings into direct current by use of the commutator and brushes.

commutator: A device by which alternating current produced in a generator is changed into direct current. It consists of a ring made up of a number of copper bars or segments; each bar is insulated from the next one and connected to the end of the armature windings.

commutator bar: A small piece of copper used in building a commutator; a commutator segment.

commutator cement: An insulating substance used in repairing or replacing mica in a commutator.

commutator compound: A compound applied to the surface of a commutator to assist in obtaining a smooth polish.

compass: A small magnetized needle pivoted at the center and pointing in a north and south direction, which is in line with the earth's magnetism, unless influenced by stronger magnets.

compensated machine: A motor or generator with a series field winding placed in slots in the face of the pole piece.

compensated voltmeter: A voltmeter connected with the bus bars at a power station. It indicates the voltage in the feeders, showing the actual pressure furnished at the far end of the circuit.

compensated winding: A winding which is placed in slots cut in the face of the pole pieces parallel with the armature slots. The current in this winding flows in the opposite direction to that in the armature slots.

compensator: A name that is applied to any device which offsets or equalizes in its effect some undesired effect.

component: A part of any thing; used in reference to the analyzing of a current in a circuit by vectors.

composite line: A telephone or telegraph line composed partly of underground and partly of overhead open wires. A line that telegraph and telephone messages may be sent over at the same time.

compound field winding: A winding composed of shunt and series coils either acting together or against each other.

compound generator: A generator that has shunt and series field coils acting together to produce a steady voltage.

compound magnet: A permanent magnet built up from a number of thin magnets of the same shape.

compound motor: A motor that has shunt and series field coils or windings.

concentrated acid: Pure acid that must be diluted before it can be used.

concentric cable: A number of wires wound spirally around and insulated from a central conductor or cable.

condenser: Two conductors separated by an insulating material that is capable of holding an electrical charge.

condenser capacity: The amount of electrical charge that a condenser will hold, measured in microfarads.

condenser dielectric: Insulating material between condenser plates or conductors.

condenser plate: One of the conductors forming the condenser.

condensite: A kind of moulded insulation.

conductance: The ease with which a conductor carries an electric current; it is the opposite of resistance. The unit of conductance is the mho (word "ohm" spelled backward).

conductivity: The ability of a substance to carry an electric current.

conductor: A wire or path through which a current of elecricity flows; that which carries a current of electricity.

conduit: A pipe or tube, made of metal or other material, in which electrical conductors or wires are placed.

conduit box: An iron or steel box located between the ends of the conduit where the wires or cables are spliced.

conduit bushing: A short threaded sleeve fastened to the end of the conduit inside the outlet box. Inside of sleeve is rounded out on one end to prevent injury to the wires.

conduit coupling: A short metal tube threaded on the inside and used to fasten two pieces of conduit end to end.

conduit elbow: A short piece of conduit bent to an angle, usually to 45 or 90 degrees.

conduit rigid: A mild steel tubing used to inclose electric light and power wires.

conduit rod: A short rod which is coupled to other rods and pushed through the large conduit to remove obstructions and pull a cable into the conduit.

conduit wiring: Electric light wires placed inside conduit.

condulet: The trade name for a number of conduit fittings made by Crouse-Hinds Co.

connected load: The sum of the rating of all the lamps, motors, heating devices, etc., connected to that circuit.

connecting-up: The process in making splices and connections to complete an electric circuit.

connector: A device used to connect or join one circuit or terminal to another.

connector switch: A device in an automatic telephone exchange that makes connection with the desired line.

consequent pole: A magnetic pole produced by placing together or near each other two north or two south poles. The forming of a pole along a magnet as well as at the ends.

consonant: A condition in a transformer which produces resonance in the primary circuit due to a certain combination of capacity and reactance in the secondary circuit. A condition to be avoided except in radio work.

constant current: A current whose amperage is the same all the time.

constant-current circuit: A series circuit, such as a street lighting circuit.

constant-current generator. A generator in which the voltage is increased as the load increases while the current is kept constant.

constant-current motor: A motor designed to operate on a constant-current circuit.

constant - current transformer: A transformer whose secondary delivers a constant alternating current, usually to a series street lighting circuit. The primary is connected to a constant-potential circuit.

constant potential: A constant voltage or pressure in the usual power and light circuit.

constant-potential generator: A generator that produces a constant voltage even though the speed is varying or changing.

constant- potential transformer: A transformer used on a constant-potential circuit.

constant-speed motor: A motor that runs at the same speed when carrying a full load as when lightly loaded.

constant-voltage regulator: A regulator that causes a generator to produce a steady voltage at varying loads.

contact: A place where a circuit is completed by a metallic point being pressed against a conductor. When the pressure is removed, the circuit is opened and flow of current stopped.

contact drop: The voltage drop across the terminals of a contact.

contact resistance: The resistance in ohms across the contact points.

contact sparking: The spark or arc formed at the contact points when a circuit carrying current is opened.

contactor: A device used to open and close an electrical circuit rapidly and often.

continental code: A series of dot and dash signals generally used in radio work to send telegraph messages.

continuous current: A direct current that is free from pulsations.

continuous rating: The output at which a machine can operate continuously without overheating or exceeding a certain temperature.

contractor: One who agrees to do a certain job for a sum of money agreed upon before the work is started.

control switch: A small switch used to open and close a circuit which operates a motor or an electromagnet coil. This motor or electromagnet is used to operate or control some electric machine.

controller: A device that governs or controls the action of electrical machines connected to it.

controller resistance: The resistance used with a controller to start and vary the speed of the motor.

converter: A machine that changes electric current of one kind into current of another kind by the use of rotating parts.

conveyors: Mechanical devices used to carry material from one place to another.

Coolidge tube: An X-ray tube first developed by Wm. D. Coolidge.

copper: A metal used for electrical conductors because it has less resistance than any other metal except silver.

copper bath: An electrolyte composed of copper salts or crystals used for copper plating.

copper clad: Iron or steel wire covered with a layer of copper in order to increase the conductivity

copper loss: The I^2R loss in power due to the resistance of the copper conductors or wires.

copper plating: Depositing a layer of copper or other metals by the electroplating process.

copper ribbon: A thin bar or strip of copper.

copper strip: A long thin bar of copper, usually about 1/16 to 3/8 of an inch thick.

cord: Two insulated flexible wires or cables twisted or held together with a covering of rubber, tape, or braid.

core: The iron or steel in the center of a coil through which magnetic lines of force pass.

core iron: Iron sheets used for making cores of magnets, transformers, generators, and motors.

core loss: The power lost in a machine due to eddy currents and hysteresis losses.

core transformer: A transformer with the windings placed on the outside of the core.

corona: A violet light glow that occurs on high voltage conductors just before the voltage becomes high enough to cause a spark or arc.

corrosion: The rusting of iron and a similar action and deposit formed on other metals.

cotton-covered wire: A wire covered with a layer of thin cotton threads wound spirally around it.

cotton-enameled wire: An enameled insulated wire covered with a layer of cotton threads.

cotton sleeving: A woven cotton sleeve or tube slipped over wires to insulate them.

coulomb: The quantity of electricity passing through a circuit. It is equal to amperes times seconds. An ampere hour = 3600 coulombs.

counter-clockwise rotation: Turning left handed, which is in a direction opposite to that of the hands of a clock.

counter-electromotive force: The voltage or pressure that opposes the normal voltage tending to force a current through a circuit.

cowl lamp: A lamp placed on the dashboard of an automobile to light the instruments on it.

creeping of wattmeter: A slow turning of the wattmeter disk when there is no power passing through it.

Crookes' tubes: Tubes used for producing X-rays.

cross arm: An arm fastened at the top of the pole to support the wires.

cross magnetization: The magnetic lines of force produced in the armature that are at right angles to those produced by field coils.

cross over: A device that enables one wire to cross over another or a car to pass from one track to another parallel one.

cross-section area: The surface of the end of a wire, rod, or other object. It is measured in square inches, square centimeters, square mills, etc.

crow foot: A small fitting fastened in an outlet box to which fixtures are fastened.

crow-foot zinc: A zinc plate having extending arms, used in a gravity cell.

current: The flow of electricity through a circuit.

current coil: The coil or winding through which the current in a circuit flows.

current density: The number of amperes per square centimeter or square inch of cross sectional area of the conductor.

current regulator: A device that regulates or limits the flow of current through a circuit.

current strength: The flow of current in amperes.

current transformer: A transformer in which the flow of current in the secondary winding is in proportion to that flowing through the primary circuit, also called series transformer.

cut-in: A device operating in an electric circuit which connects two circuits together.

cut-out: A device that opens or disconnects one circuit from another.

cut-out box: The box in which fuse holder blocks, and fuses are located.

cycle: The flow of alternating current first in one direction and then in the opposite direction in one cycle. This occurs 60 times every second in a 60-cycle circuit.

D

D.C.: Used as an abbreviation for "direct current." Used as an abbreviation for "double contact."

D.C.C.: Used as an abbreviation for "double cotton-covered wire."

D.P.: Used as an abbreviation for "double pole."

D.P.S.: Used as an abbreviation for "double pole snap switch."

D.P.S.T.: Used as an abbreviation for "double pole single throw."

D.P.D.T.: Used as an abbreviation for "double pole double throw."

damper winding: As applied to copper pieces so placed in the pole faces of alternating-current machines as to reduce hunting.

damping: Causes the needle of an electric measuring instrument to come to rest quickly.

damping coil: Used to cause the needle of a galvanometer to quickly return to zero.

damping magnet: Any magnet used to check the motions of a moving object or magnet.

Daniel cell: A primary electric cell, using copper and zinc for electrodes, used on closed circuit work.

D'Arsonval meter: A voltmeter or ammeter whose pointer is attached to a moving coil of fine wire carried between the poles of a permanent magnet.

dashboard instruments: Ammeter, voltmeter, or current indicator, suitable for mounting on the dashboard or cowl board of an automobile.

dash pot: A cylindrical chamber containing oil, air, or other fluid in which moves a plunger attached to some part in which it is desired to avoid sudden changes of position.

dead beat: An instrument whose pointer comes immediately to its true reading without swinging back and forth.

dead coil: An armature coil which is not connected in the armature circuit of the windings but which is required in order that there may be the proper number of coil sides in each slot.

dead end: The end of a wire to which no electrical connection is made. The end used for supporting the wire. The part of a coil or winding that is not in use.

dead end eye: A metal eye threaded at one end to attach to a rod and holding a cable in the loop of the

dead ground: An accidental ground of low resistance through which most of the current can escape from a circuit.

dead man: A short pole with cross-arms to which the guy wire from another pole is fastened.

dead wire: A wire in which there is no electric current or voltage.

decade bridge: A Wheatstone bridge having ten separate coils of equal resistance value.

deci: Is a term meaning one-tenth.

deci-ampere: One-tenth of an ampere.

declination: The difference between the position of a compass needle and the true position of geographical north and south.

declinometer: An instrument for measuring the declination of a compass needle.

de-energize: To stop current from flowing in a circuit or an electrical part.

deflection: The movement of the indicating pointer of an electric measuring instrument.

deflection of compass needle: The movement of a needle from a point of repose either in the earth's magnetic field or in that of another magnet and produced by the influence of the flux of an electric current or of a magnet.

deka: A prefix meaning ten times.

deka ampere: Ten amperes.

delivered power: The power delivered at one end of a line, in a system of electrical transmission in contradistinction to the power delivered into the line at the other end.

delta connection: Series hookup of three circuits of an alternator, the end of one circuit being connected to the beginning of the next, etc. The wiring diagram of this arrangement resembles a triangle or the letter Delta of the Greek alphabet.

demagnetization: Process of removing the magnetism from a magnetized substance. This may be done either by heating to a red heat, by violent jarring, or by holding the magnetized substance in and then gradually removing it from the magnetic field of a solenoid operated on an alternating current.

demagnetizing armature turns: Inductors of an armature, which, while moving in the field of the poles, set up a counter-magnetic field that tends to demagnetize the poles.

demand: Amount of electric current needed from a circuit or generator.

demand factor: Ratio of the maximum amount of current consumed in one sub-circuit to the total load or current draw on the whole circuit.

demand meter: Device which registers the maximum ampere consumption of appreciable duration in a circuit.

density: The ratio of a quantity of a substance to the space it occupies; i.e., the ratio of mass to volume.

density of current: Amount of current flowing through a conductor of given cross-sectional area.

density of field: Amount of magnetic flux, or lines of force, contained in a given cross-sectional area.

density of electrolyte: The proportion of chemical in the water with which it is mixed to make an electrolyte. See "specific gravity."

depolarize: (a) To eliminate or retard the gas which tends to collect on the electrodes of an electric cell when it is being charged or discharged. (b) Synonym for demagnetize.

depolarizer: A chemical, electrochemical, or mechanical agent introduced into the cell to prevent or retard the formation of gas which polarizes the electrodes.

derived circuit: Shunt or parallel circuit, the current for which is obtained from another circuit.

deviation factor: Difference between an alternating-current wave of a generator and a true sine wave.

diamagnetic substance: One that is repelled by a magnet, as bismuth and phosphorus.

diaphragm: A disk or sheet of metal or other substance having enough flexibility to vibrate, as a telephone-receiver diaphragm.

dielectric: Insulation between conductors of opposite polarity; term generally used only when induction may take place through it.

dielectric constant: A number representing the dielectric quality of a given substance as compared to that of air.

dielectric current: Leakage of current through a dielectric.

dielectric hysteresis: Consumption of energy caused by molecular friction in a dielectric under changes of electrostatic pressure.

dielectric resistance: Resistance of a dielectric to electrical pressure.

dielectric strain: Strain to which a dielectric is subjected while it is under electrical pressure.

dielectric strength: Ability of a dielectric to withstand electrical pressure before breaking down. This is measured in volts necessary to puncture the dielectric.

dies (pipe): Tools for cutting and threading metal conduit.

difference of potential: Difference in voltage between two conductors or two points along one conductor carrying an electric current.

differential booster: Generator in a battery-charging arrangement to maintain a constant voltage.

differential electromagnet: An electromagnet having part of its winding reversed to oppose the other part to permit adjustment of the pull.

differential field winding: Field winding in which the shunt and series windings of a compound-wound motor or generator oppose each other.

differential galvanometer: Galvanometer having two coils wound to counteract each other.

differential generator: Generator in which the shunt and series field windings counteract each other to limit the maximum amperage.

differential motor: A direct-current motor having its shunt and series field windings opposing each other, to obtain a constant speed.

differential relay: A relay consisting of a differential electromagnet.

differential winding: Coil which is wound opposite to another to counteract it.

diffusion of magnetic flux: Deviation of the magnetic lines of force from a straight path between the poles.

dimmer: A resistance coil connected in series with a lamp to reduce the amount of current flowing through it, and consequently to dim or reduce the light.

dinkey: Small, two-wheeled cart used for hauling poles in line construction.

dip: Angle which a magnetic needle, pivoted in a vertical plane, makes with the horizontal.

dipping needle: Magnetized needle pivoted freely at its center of gravity in a vertical plane so that, when set in a magnetic meridian, it dips until it lies parallel to the magnetic lines of force of the earth.

diphase generator: Generator producing two alternating currents a quarter of a cycle apart.

diplex telegraphy: Transmission of two telegraphic messages over the same wire, at the same time, and in the same direction.

direct-connected: Two electrical machines, such as a motor and a generator, connected together mechanically and in line, by having their shafts coupled together or by both being mounted on the same shaft.

direct current: Electric current flowing over a conductor in one direction only. Abbreviation d.c.

direct-current convertor: Device for changing a direct current of one potential to a direct current of another potential.

direct-current generator: Generator that delivers direct current.

direct-current instrument: Device operated on direct current.

direct-current magnet: Electromagnet operated on direct current.

direct-reading galvanometer: A galvanometer provided with a scale so calibrated that the current flow may be read directly, without the necessity of calculating it from the proportions of the coil and the magnetic moment of the needle.

disc armature: Armature of a generator consisting of a flat disc on which the coils are mounted.

discharge: Removal of electricity from its source through a circuit.

discharge recorder: Device which detects and records discharges through a lightning arrestor.

discharge resistance: Resistance coil which is connected across a circuit breaker to prevent arcing when the contacts separate.

discharger: Resistance device which is connected across the terminals of a storage battery to discharge it slowly without damaging it.

disconnect: To remove an electrical device from a circuit, or to unfasten a wire, making part or all of the circuit inoperative. The word is particularly applied to the act of severing a telephone connection to permit repairs.

disconnector: Switch for cutting out circuits having high voltages, done only under a minimum load.

displacement current: Small current of electricity in a dielectric which is under strain of a high potential.

disruptive discharge: Violent discharge of electricity accompanied by a spark.

dissonance: Lack of consonance or agreement; as of alternating currents of opposite phase.

dissociation: Separation of the component elements of a chemical mixture or compound, without the aid of any other chemical agency.

distortion of field: A condition causing magnetic flux between the poles of a magnet to assume an arched or curved path instead of a straight one from pole to pole.

distribution box: Small metal box in a conduit installation, giving accessibility for connecting branch circuits.

distributing frame: Structure where connections are made between the inside and outside wires of a telephone exchange.

distribution: Division of current between the branches of an electrical circuit.

distribution lines: The main feed line of a circuit to which branch circuits are connected.

distribution center: Point along the main feed lines which is approximately in the center of the branch lines.

distribution panel: Insulated board from which connections are made between the main feed lines and branch lines.

distribution system: The whole circuit and all of its branches which supply electricity to consumers.

distributive: Tending or serving to distribute.

divided circuits: Approximate division of a distribution system to balance both sides of the lines. A divided magnetic circuit is one having more than one path through which the flux passes.

dome lamp: Small lamp attached to the underside of the top of an automobile.

door lamp: Small lamp for lighting the doorway and running board of an automobile.

door lantern: Lamp hung so as to illuminate the entrance of a house.

door opener: Motor-driven device for opening and closing garage doors.

door switch: Switch which is operated by opening and closing the door to which it is connected.

double armature: An armature which has two separate windings on one core.

double-break switch: Switch which connects and disconnects two contacts at the same time.

double-contact lamp: Lamp with a base having two terminals to which electrical contact is made when it is inserted in a socket.

double-cotton-covered: Wire covered with two layers of cotton insulation. Abbreviation d.c.c.

double-current generator: A generator delivering both direct and alternating current.

double deck: Arrangement of two electrical machines, one mounted above the other.

double delta connection: Connection of three transformers by which a 3-phase system is connected to a 6-phase system.

double-filament lamp: Lamp having two separate filaments of different resistances to provide low and high brilliancy.

double-pole: A term designating two contacts or connections on a device, for instance, a double-pole knife switch. Abbreviation d.p.

double reduction: Speed reduction in a machine obtained by using two sets of gears or pulleys.

double-silk-covered. Wire covered with two layers of silk insulation. Abbreviation d.s.c.

double-throw switch: Switch which can be operated by making contact with two circuits. Abbreviation d.t.

double trolley: Street-railway system using two overhead trolleys instead of one, carrying the positive and negative current. This arrangement eliminates electrolysis caused by grounding one conductor, but it increases trolley troubles, and for this reason is seldom used.

double re-entrant winding: Armature winding, half the conductors of which make a closed circuit.

draft: Air drawn or forced up into the fire-box to accelerate fuel combustion.

draft tube: Tube or passage through which the discharge from a hydraulic turbine flows into the tailrace.

draw bar: Bar on a locomotive which is used to connect it to a train.

draw-bar pull: Force available at the draw bar of a locomotive to pull a train, as distinguished from the actual power of the engine or motor.

drive shaft: Shaft employed to drive a number of machines. Line shaft.

driven pulley: A pulley to which movement is imparted by means of a belt from another pulley.

driving pulley: Pulley that drives another through the medium of a belt.

drop: Usual term for drop of potential.

drop annunciator: Annunciator having one or more electromagnets, each of which, when operated, releases a catch holding a small plate or shutter, and allows it to drop, exposing a number or letter.

drop of potential or voltage: Decrease of voltage at points along a circuit, caused by resistance.

drop wire: Wire which is connected to a feed wire outside of a building, and brings the supply inside.

drum: The laminated iron cylinder or core of an armature for a generator or motor.

dry battery: A number of dry cells connected together in series or parallel to obtain more voltage or amperage, respectively.

dry cell: A primary source of electric current consisting of three elements; a zinc cylinder, a paste electrolyte and a carbon rod or electrode. The zinc cylinder is filled with the electrolyte and the carbon electrode is placed in the center but not touching the zinc; the top of the cell is sealed with a wax compound. The chemical action of the electrolyte on the zinc sets up an electric current when the cell is connected to a current-consuming device, as a bell. The carbon electrode is the positive and the zinc is the negative.

dry storage: Method of keeping a storage battery, when not in use, by removing the electrolyte.

dual ignition: Ignition system for an internal combustion engine which may obtain current from either a battery or a magneto as desired.

dual magneto: Ignition magneto which has its armature wound so that it can deliver both its own current and that of a battery to the distributor.

duct: (a) A space in an underground conduit to hold a cable or conductor. (b) A ventilating passage for cooling an electrical machine.

duct-foot: Unit expressing the total length of all the cableways in one lineal foot of an underground conduit. Thus, a 6-duct conduit, one foot long, contains 6 duct feet.

duo-lateral coils: Form of honeycomb inductance coils used in radio, which are designed to reduce the distributed capacity.

duplex cable: Cable consisting of two wires insulated from each other and having a common insulation covering both.

duplex ignition: Ignition system capable of sending both the battery and the magneto current into the induction coil at the same time.

duplex telegraphy: Telegraph circuit permitting the transmission of two messages in opposite directions at the same time over a single wire.

duplex winding: Two separate windings on the same armature or coil.

duplex wire: Same as duplex cable.

dynamic braking: Method of stopping a motor quickly without the aid of a mechanical brake. On d.c., a resistor connected across the armature changes the electrical energy produced by the motor, which acts as a generator when the line circuit is broken, into heat. On polyphase a.c. motors this method of braking is obtained by energizing one phase winding with direct current.

dynamic electricity: Electricity in motion as distinguished from static electricity.

dynamo: A synonym for generator; formerly applied to both motor and generator, although modern use tends to confine its meaning to d.c. generators.

dynamometer: Mechanical or electrical device for measuring the torque of a machine in order to determine its power output.

dynamotor: Electrical machine which acts as both motor and generator, running on and producing either direct or alternating current. It has one field and two separate armatures or a double-wound armature.

dyne: Unit of force. Power or force required to cause an acceleration of one centimeter per second to a mass of one gram.

E

E: Symbol for volts.

EBB: Abbreviation for "extra best best" iron wire used for telephone and telegraphic purposes.

E.C.&M.: Trade name for electric-control equipment, lifting magnets, etc.

E.H.P.: Abbreviation for electrical horsepower.

E.M.F.: Abbreviation for electromotive force.

E.P.C.: Abbreviation for Electric Power Club.

ear: Device for supporting a trolley line; a bronze casting grooved to receive the trolley and having lips which are clinched around it. The ear is supported on a trolley hanger.

earth: Synonym of "ground," meaning the grounded side of an electrical circuit or machine.

earth current: Current passing through the ground.

ebonite: Substance consisting of black hard rubber and sulphur. It is hard and brittle, has high insulating qualities, and possesses inductive qualities to a high degree.

economizer: Device used on boilers to absorb the heat that has passed the flues and would be wasted out of the stack; used to preheat boiler feed water.

eddy-current loss: Loss of energy of an electrical machine which is caused by eddy currents.

eddy currents: Currents in armatures, pole pieces, and magnetic cores, induced by changing electromotive force. It is wasted energy and creates heat.

Edison battery: Storage battery having plates made of nickel peroxide and iron, and using potassium hydrate and water for an electrolyte.

Edison distributing box: Box used in three-way distribution systems.

Edison-Lalande cell: Primary electric cell having electrodes made of copper oxide and zinc and using a caustic soda solution as an electrolyte.

"Ediswan" or bayonet socket: Lamp socket having a bayonet base, which is popular on automobile-lighting systems, and is used for house lighting in England.

"Ediswan" connector: Plug connector having a base similar to that of an "Ediswan" socket.

effective current: Value of a current as shown on a steady-reading ammeter.

effective electromotive force: Difference between the impressed and the counter e.m.f.

effective resistance: All electrical and inductive losses of a current.

efficiency: The ratio of the amount of power or work obtained from a machine and the amount of power used to operate it.

elastance: Inability or opposition to retaining an electrostatic charge. Opposite to capacity.

elastivity: Specific elastance of a substance.

elbow: Hollow fixture for connecting two lengths of conduit at an angle, usually fitted with a removable cap to facilitate drawing the wires through one conduit and then inserting them in the other one.

Electragist: Term used by the National Association of Electrical Contractors and Dealers, now the Association of Electragists, to denote a person conducting an electrical-contracting business.

electric or electrical: Pertaining to electricity.

electric circuit: Path through which an electric current flows.

electric breeze or wind: Emission of negative electricity from a sharp point of a conductor carrying a high potential.

electric candle: Small electric arc lamp.

electric charge: Quantity of electricity on a conductor.

electric eel: An eel found in South American waters which is capable of giving off painful and dangerous shocks of high potential, estimated equal to the combined charge of 15 Leyden jars, each having 1 2/3 square feet of tinfoil coating.

electric energy: Power of electricity to perform work, mechanically or in the production of heat and light.

electric furnace: Furnace using electricity to produce heat.

electric glow: electrostatic discharge causing a violet light around conductors carrying high potentials, occurring just before the emission of a spark or a steady brush discharge.

electric heater: Heater consisting of resistance wire which becomes hot as the current flows through it.

electric horsepower: The equivalent of one horsepower in electrical energy, which is 746 watts.

electric potential: Pressure or voltage of electricity.

electric power plant: Installation consisting of a prime mover driving a generator to produce electricity.

electric spectrum: The component colors of an electric arc separated by means of a glass prism.

electric units: Standards of measurement of electrical properties; for instance, ampere, volt, ohm, farad, henry, etc.

electric wave: Theoretical form of movement of an electric current transmitted through air.

electric welding: Process of welding with the use of an electric arc or with heat generated by current flowing through the resistance of the work to be welded.

electrical codes: Rules and regulations for the installation and operation of electrical devices and currents.

electrical series: A list of substances which, when two are rubbed together, will produce an electrostatic charge, as silk and hard rubber.

electrical sheet: Steel or iron sheets from which laminations for electrical machines are punched.

Electrician: Person working or experimenting with electrical devices.

electricity: Invisible energy capable of moving 186,000 miles per second. Electricity is really not capable of being defined exactly, with present knowledge.

electrification: (a) Providing means to operate devices with electricity. (b) To impose a static charge.

Electrochemical: Pertaining to the interaction of certain chemicals and electricity, the production of electricity by chemical changes, the effect of electricity upon chemicals, etc.

electrochemistry: Science of electrochemical interaction.

electrodynamic: Pertaining to electricity in action.

electrodynamometer: Device for measuring the strength of an electric current by its attraction or repulsion to conductors carrying current.

electrocute: (a) To execute a criminal by electricity. (b) Persons accidentally killed by electricity are said to be electrocuted.

electrode: Either terminal of an electric source, particularly an electric cell. Also applied to the terminals of electrical apparatus applied to the human body in the treatment of disease.

electrokinetic: Pertaining to electricity in action.

electrolier: Hanging electric fixture holding lamps which can be lighted separately or all at once.

electrolier switch: Switch which controls the lamps of an electrolier.

electrolysis: Chemical decomposition caused by an electric current.

electrolyte: Chemical solution used in an electrical device which passes an electric current.

electrolytic: Pertaining to electrolysis.

electrolytic condenser: Condenser using an electrolyte as a dielectric.

electrolytic decomposition: Separation of the elements in an electrolyte.

electrolytic generator: Generator for charging storage batteries.

electrolytic interrupter: Device for rapidly interrupting or breaking up a direct current into pulsations, consisting of a cathode, generally a lead plate, immersed in a dilute solution of sulphuric acid, and an anode, which is a small platinum wire projecting into the electrolyte from a porcelain tube. Often called a Wehnelt interrupter after the inventor.

electrolytic lightning arrestor: Lightning arrestor consisting of an electrolyte, which covers two electrodes immersed in it with a film. This breaks down under a lightning discharge.

electrolytic rectifier: Device for changing an alternating current to a direct current by passing it through an electrolyte in which electrodes are immersed. The device acts as a "valve" to allow current to pass in one direction only.

electromagnet: Soft iron core having a coil wound around it through which an electric current is passed. The core is magnetized while the current flows, but is demagnetized when the current stops.

electromagnetic attraction: Attraction between opposite poles of an electromagnet.

electromagnetic brake: Brake used on car wheels and operated by electromagnets.

electromagnetic field: Space around a conductor or instrument, traversed by the electromagnetic waves set up by current in the conductor.

electromagnetic induction: Electric current set up in a conductor cutting the field of flux of an electromagnet.

electromagnetic repulsion: Repulsion between like poles of an electromagnet.

electromagnetic unit: Unit or standard of measurement of electromagnetic effects.

electromagnetic vibrator: Mechanical interrupter operated by an electromagnet.

electromagnetic wave: Form of electromagnetic energy radiated from a conductor and theoretically assuming the form of a wave. The rate of travel of these waves is approximately 186,000 miles per second.

electromagnetism: Science dealing with electricity and magnetism and their interaction.

electrometallurgy: Branch of metallurgy dealing with the use of electric currents either for electrolytic separation and deposition of metals from solutions, or with the utilization of electricity for smelting, refining, welding, annealing, etc.

electrometer: Device for measuring small voltages.

electromotive force: Electrical pressure or voltage which forces an electric current through a circuit.

electron: Electrical particle, of negative polarity.

electron theory: Theory that all matter consists of atoms which in turn comprise a positive nucleus and a number of negative electrons, which may be detached from the atom under certain conditions, leaving it positively charged.

electro-negative: Having a negative polarity.

electropathy: Science dealing with the use of electricity for medical purposes.

electrophorous: Device consisting of a disc of ebonite or similar substance, a metal plate and an insulator, used to produce an electric charge by induction.

electropism: Science dealing with the stimulation of vegetable growth by means of electricity.

electroplating: Process of covering a metal article with a metal deposit taken from an electrode and conveyed by an electrolyte in which the article is submerged.

electro-positive: Having a positive electrical polarity.

electro-receptive device: Device that receives electricity for its operation.

electroscope: Device that indicates the presence of a very small charge of electricity. It consists of a glass bottle having an electrode, which holds two strips of light foil. These attract or repel each other, depending upon the nature of the charge.

electrostatic: Pertaining to static electricity, or electricity at rest.

electrostatic capacity: Capacity to hold an electric charge, which is measured in farads and microfarads.

electrostatic field: Range around conductors, electrical machines and instruments where electrostatic effects take place.

electrostatic galvanometer: Galvanometer operated by the effect of two electric charges on each other.

electrostatic machine: Device which produces high-potential charges of static electricity by means of friction.

electrotherapeutics: Science dealing with the use of electric currents for curing diseases.

electrothermal: Pertaining to the heating effect of electric currents, and to electric currents produced by heat, as in thermo-couple.

electrotype: Metal plate used for printing. It is made by depositing metal on a form by means of electroplating.

element: (a) One of the parts to which all matter can be reduced. (b) One of the parts constituting a device, as a radio-tube element. (c) The resistor of an electrical heating device.

elevator cable: Flexible cable conveying electricity to an elevator. Also one of the cables supporting an elevator.

"Elexit": Trade name for certain standardized interchangeable fixture receptacles and plugs.

emissivity: Rate at which particles of electricity or heat are radiated from an object.

empire cloth: Cotton or linen cloth coated with linseed oil, and used as an insulator.

enameled wire: Wire having a coating or enamel baked on, which serves as insulation.

enclosed fuse: Fuse inside of a glass tube to prevent ignition of gas or dust.

end cell: One of a number of cells at the end of a storage battery, which can be cut in or out of the circuit to regulate the voltage.

end play: Distance of movement of a shaft in line with its length.

end thrust: Thrust exerted in line with the length of a shaft.

Endosmosis: The flow of a thin liquid to a denser liquid through a permeable partition.

energize: To put energy into; e.g., magnetizing an iron core of an electromagnet by passing a current through the coil.

energy: Capacity for performing work.

entrance switch: Switch to which the wires entering a building are connected.

equalizer: Connection between generators in parallel to equalize their voltage and current.

equalizing charge: Slight overcharge on a storage battery to raise the reading of the cells having the lowest specific gravity.

equator of magnet: Position halfway between the opposite poles of a magnet.

equipotential: Having the same potential.

equilibrium: State of rest or balance between two opposite forces, produced by their counter-action.

ether: Hypothetical element filling space to permit the passage of heat, light, electricity, gravity, etc., between solar bodies.

Evaporator: Heating device for evaporating water.

excite: To send a current through the field windings of a generator to set up a magnetic flux.

exciter: Small battery of generator furnishing current for the field windings of a large generator.

exciting current: Current which passes through the field windings of a generator.

extension: Length of cable or lamp-cord fitted with a plug and a socket to extend a lamp or other electric device further than the original point.

exploring coil: Device used for the detection of faults in underground cables. It consists of a coil and telephone receiver or head set, a current being induced in the coil at the point of leakage and causing a noise in the receiver. (b) Coil used to locate underground metals.

"Extra Best Best" iron wire: Trade name for the highest grade iron telegraph and telephone wire. Abbreviation EBB.

external circuit: A circuit entirely outside of the source of supply.

F

F: Abbreviation for frequency.

Fabrikoid: Trade name for a substitute for leather.

factor: Any one of the elements that contribute to produce a result.

factor of safety: Multiplier used in machine and structure design, designating the overload or safety capacity. E.g., a pressure vessel designed to withstand a pressure of 10 pounds per square inch may actually withstand 50 pounds per square inch, and the factor of safety is 5.

fading: Temporary diminution of signal strength in radio reception, due to atmospheric conditions.

Fahrenheit: A thermometer scale so graduated that the freezing point of water is 32° and its boiling point is 212°.

fall of potential: Drop in voltage between two points of an electric circuit.

false resistance: Resistance of counter e.m.f.

fan motor: Motor operating a fan.

farad: Unit for measuring electrical capacity. It is the capacity of a condenser which will give a pressure of one volt when a one-ampere current flows into it for one second.

farm-lighting generator: Small, gasoline-driven generator, producing current for farm light and power; usually a 32-volt and 2 or 3 kilowatt unit.

fathom: Nautical measure of length, equal to 6 feet. This unit is used to measure cables.

fault: Trouble in an electrical circuit.

fault finder: A resistance bridge for locating faults in telephone and telegraph circuits.

fault resistance: Resistance caused by a fault.

Fauré plate: Storage-battery plate consisting of a lead grid filled with paste.

feeder: Line supplying all the branch circuits with the main supply of current.

feeder box: Box into which the feeder is run for connection to a branch circuit.

fender: Device attached to street cars and other vehicles to pick up or brush aside obstacles.

ferro-manganese: Containing iron and manganese.

ferro-nickel: Containing iron and nickel.

fibre: A hard, tough insulating substance.

fibre cleats: Cleats made of fibre, used for holding conductors on flat surfaces.

fibre conduit: Insulating tubing made of moulded fibre.

field: Space occupied by the flux of a magnet.

field coil: Coil or winding around the field magnets of a generator or motor.

field discharge resistance: A resistance coil connected across the field winding of a generator permitting the winding to be discharged without a dangerous rise in voltage when the field circuit is opened by a switch. It is usually connected to a special d.p.d.t. knife switch having an auxilliary blade which connects the resistance just before the current to the winding is cut off.

field distortion: Variation of magnetic flux from the straight path between opposite poles in a generator, which is caused by armature reaction.

field flux: Space occupied by the lines of force of a generator field.

field intensity: Density of the field flux of a generator.

field magnet: The iron parts of a generator frame through which the flux of the coils concentrates.

field rheostat: A variable resistance device connected in the field circuit to control the voltage of a generator and the speed of a motor.

field winding. Coil on a field pole of a generator.

filament: Small wire in a lamp, which becomes white hot when electric current is passed through it.

film cutout: Insulating film between the two opposite wires inside of a lamp. The film burns out when the filament breaks and this permits the two wires to make contact, which provides a path for the current so that it can flow to other lamps, connected in series. These will not light unless the current passes through the defective lamp.

filters: Devices having inductance and capacity, and designed to suppress certain electrical frequencies.

fire-alarm systems: Apparatus which gives alarm in case of fire. Some of these systems consist of electrical circuits which, when closed automatically or otherwise, sound the alarm.

fire extinguisher: Devices using a liquid or powder to extinguish fire. They are used in power houses where there is danger of burning insulation on cables. Fire extinguishers used for this purpose must contain non-conducting liquids such as carbon tetrachlorid.

fish paper: Strong paper used for insulation.

fish wire: Flat, narrow, flexible, steel wire which is used to pull conductors through lengths of conduit.

fixed resistance: Non-Adjustable resistance.

fixture: Device for holding electric lamps, which is wired inside and is securely attached to the wall or ceiling.

fixture wire: Insulated, stranded wire used for wiring fixtures.

flaming arc: Arc which gives different colors due to impregnating the carbons with various salts and minerals.

flaming of arc: A flame bridging the gap between two carbons, instead of a steady arc, caused by the carbons being too far apart.

flasher: Automatic or motor-driven switch or series of switches for lighting electric signs intermittently.

flashing over: Passage of sparks from commutator segments traveling away from the brush, to the edge of the brush, which is then touching a segment adjacent to the one from which the spark originates.

flashlight: (a) Small, portable, electric light operated on one or more dry cells. (b) Trade name for an electric alarm clock.

flat-compound generator: Compound-wound generator having windings which give a constant voltage under different loads and speeds.

Fleming's rules: Rules for finding the direction of a conductor's motion through a magnetic field, the direction of the lines of force, and the direction of current flow through a conductor, applicable to direct current. Rule for Generators: Hold the thumb, the index finger, and the middle finger of the right hand so that they are at right angles to each other. The thumb will then point in the direction of the motion of the conductor, the index finger will point in the direction of the lines of force, and the middle finger will point in the direction of the current through the conductor. Rule for Motors: Hold the thumb, the index finger, and the middle finger of the left hand at right angles to each other. The thumb will then point in the direction of the motion of the conductor, the index finger will point in the direction of the lines of force, and the middle finger will point in the direction of current through the conductor.

flexible cable: Cable consisting of insulated, stranded or woven conductors.

flexible conduit: Non-rigid conduit made of fabric or metal strip wound spirally.

flexible cord: Insulated conductor consisting of stranded wire.

floating battery: Storage battery connected in parallel with a generator and the load, so that the battery will consume the surplus current from the generator if the load is small, and will supply additional current if the load exceeds the output of the generator.

flood lights: Battery of lamps of high brilliancy, equipped with reflectors to supply a strong light.

flow: Passage of a current through a conductor.

fluctuating current: Current which changes in voltage and amperage at irregular intervals.

flush receptacle. Type of lamp socket, the top of which is flush with the wall into which the socket is recessed.

flush switch: Push-button or key switch, the top of which is flush with the wall into which it is recessed.

flux: Magnetic lines of force existing between two opposite magnetic poles.

flux density: Number of lines of force in a given cross-sectional area, which is measured in gausses.

focus: The point where rays of light, heat, sound, etc., meet after being reflected or refracted.

foot candle: See "candle foot."

foot-pound: Unit for measuring work. It is the energy required to raise a weight of one pound through a distance of one foot.

force: Energy exerted between two or more bodies which tends to change their relative shape or position.

form factor: Ratio of effective value of one half of a cycle of an alternating current to the average value of similar half cycles.

formers: Forms used for producing a number of windings of the same shape.

form-wound coils: Coils or windings built up on formers before they are placed in their proper position on armatures, field poles, etc.

forming battery plates: Passing an electric current through a storage battery to deposit peroxide of lead and spongy lead on the plates which makes them active.

Foucault currents: Same as Eddy currents.

four-pole: (a) Having four poles, as in a generator. (b) Having four contacts, as in a four-pole switch.

four-way switch: Switch that controls the current in four conductors by making or breaking four separate contacts.

four-wire, three-phase system: Distribution system having a 3-phase star connection, one lead being taken from the end of each winding and the fourth from the point where they are all connected together.

fractional pitch: Term used when the number of slots between the sides of an armature coil is not equal to the number of slots of each pole.

franchise: Permit from municipal, state, or national government to use public property, such as streets, for special purposes, as the installation of street-car lines.

frequency: Number of cycles or vibrations per second.

frequency changer: Motor-generator driven by an alternating current of one frequency and delivering current of another frequency.

frequency convertor: Same as "frequency changer."

frequency indicator: Device showing when two alternating currents are in phase or have the same frequency.

frequency meter: Device showing the frequency of an alternating current.

friction tape: Tape coated with black adhesive compound, used as insulation on wire joints, etc.

frog: Fixture for street-car tracks or trolleys where one track or trolley branches off, permitting the car to be run from one track onto another.

full pitch: Term used when the number of slots between the sides of an armature coil is equal to the number of slots of each pole.

fuller cell: Primary electric cell having two electrolytes: sulphuric acid and water, and a bichromate solution. These are separated by a porous cup. A cone-shaped zinc electrode is immersed in the cup, which also contains the sulphuric-acid solution and an ounce of mercury, and a carbon electrode is immersed in the bichromate solution.

fundamental units: Basic standards of measurement.

fuse: Safety device to prevent overloading a current. It consists of a short length of conducting metal which melts at a certain heat and thereby breaks the circuit.

fuse block: Insulated block designed to hold fuses.

fuse clip: Spring holder for a cartridge-type fuse.

fuse cutout: Fuse which, when melted, cuts out the circuit.

fuse link: An open fuse, or a length of fuse wire for refilling fuses.

fuse plug: Fuse mounted in a screw plug, which is screwed in the fuse block like a lamp in a socket.

fuse strip: A length of ribbon fuse as distinguished from wire fuse.

fuse wire: Wire made of an alloy which melts at a comparatively low temperature.

G

G: (a) Abbreviation for gram. (b) Symbol for mho, the unit of conductivity.

gage: Device for measuring.

galvanized: (a) Affected by galvanic action. (b) Metal coated with zinc.

galvanometer: Device for measuring small currents and voltages.

gang switch: Two or more switches installed in one box or one holder.

gas-filled: Filled with a gas as, for instance, an ordinary electric lamp.

gasoline-electric: Pertaining to a machine consisting of a gasoline engine, a generator driven by the engine, and one or more motors to produce electric power.

gauge: Same as "gage."

Gauss: Unit of flux density equal to one maxwell per square centimeter.

gauze brush: Generator or motor brush made of copper gauze.

Geissler tube: Gas-filled tubes, with or without fluorescent liquids, solids, or both, which emit light of various colors when a high-frequency current is passed through them.

gelatine battery: Battery having a jelly-like electrolyte.

generator: Machine that produces electricity.

generator busbar: Conductors on power switchboards to which a generator is connected.

generator loss: Difference between power required to drive a generator and the power it delivers, which is always less than the power input.

generator output: Power delivered by a generator, measured in watts or kilowatts.

geographical equator: Imaginary line around the earth halfway between the poles.

german silver: Alloy containing copper, nickel, and zinc, which is used for making resistance wire.

gilbert: Unit for measuring magnetic force. One gilbert is the magnetic force which sends one maxwell of flux through a magnetic circuit having a reluctance of one oersted.

glaze: Smooth finish applied to porcelain insulators to close the pores in order to prevent the absorption of moisture.

gramme armature: A ring type of armature.

graphite: A form of soft carbon.

gravity cell: Primary electric cell having two electrolytes, copper sulphate, and sulphuric-acid solutions, which are separated by gravity. The electrodes are zinc and copper.

gravity drop: A shutter or plate of an annunciator which, when released from a catch, drops by gravity.

Greenfield conductor: Flexible cable having a spirally wound metal covering.

Grenet cell: Primary electric cell of which the electrolyte is a solution of bichromate of potash in a mixture of sulphuric acid and water, and the electrodes are zinc and carbon. The zinc electrode is lifted out of the electrolyte when the cell is not in use.

grid: (a) Frame of a storage-battery plate having spaces in which the paste is pressed. (b) An element of a vacuum tube which controls the rate of electron emission from the filament to the grid.

grid condenser: Small fixed condenser inserted in the line connecting with the grid of a vacuum tube used as a detector.

grid leak: Resistance shunted across a grid condenser in a radio circuit to allow dissipation of an excessive charge on the grid.

ground: See "earth."

ground circuit: Part of an electric circuit in which the ground serves as a path for the current.

ground clamp: Clamp on a pipe or other metal conductor connected to the ground for attaching a conductor of an electrical circuit.

ground detector: Device used in a power station to indicate whether part of the circuit is accidentally grounded.

ground indicator: Same as "ground detector."

ground plate: Metal plate buried in moist earth to make a good ground contact for an electrical circuit.

ground return: Ground used as one conductor of an electrical circuit.

ground wire: Conductor connecting an electrical device or circuit to the ground.

grounded neutral wire: The neutral wire of a 3-way distribution system which is connected to the ground.

grounded primary: Primary circuit of an induction coil or transformer connected to the ground.

grounding brush: Brush for making a ground connection to a moving part.

Grove cell: Primary electric cell which is similar to a Bunsen cell but has a platinum electrode instead of a carbon electrode.

growler: Coil around an iron core which is placed in contact with the core of an armature. When an alternating current or a pulsating direct current is passed through the growler coil, it magnetizes the core, which in turn induces a current in the armature winding. The purpose is to show whether a short circuit exists in the armature coil.

gutta percha: Hardened sap of a tropical tree which has high insulating quality and great resistance to destructive agencies such as water.

guy: A wire, rope, chain, or similar support for a structure such as a telephone pole, radio mast, etc.

H

H.: An abbreviation or symbol for intensity of magnetism.

h.p.: Horsepower.

hand advance: A device for controlling the advance and retard of the sparks in the ignition system.

hand regulation: Controlling the current or voltage by means of a hand operated device.

hard drawn copper: A method of producing high-grade copper of good mechanical strength.

hard fiber: A material made from a number of sheets of paper compressed tightly together. A good insulator.

hard rubber: An electrical insulation made by vulcanizing rubber.

harmonic currents: A series of currents which have frequencies that are multiple of the main current.

heat coil: A small coil placed on a telephone circuit to protect it from stray currents.

heat loss: The energy lost in a conductor due to its resistance.

heat run: A test made on a generator or motor to determine the amount of heating that takes place.

heating unit: That part of a heating appliance through which the current passes and produces heat.

head guy: A cable or wire fastened near the top of a pole to hold it in place.

head light: A light placed on the front end of a moving vehicle.

helix: A coil of wire; a solenoid.

henry: The electrical unit of inductance.

Hertzian wave: A radio wave.

high frequency: An alternating current that has many thousand cycles or alternations per second.

high potential: A high pressure or voltage, usually about six hundred volts.

high tension: A term used to refer to high voltage.

high tension magneto: A magneto used for ignition work in which the high-voltage current is produced in the magneto generator without the use of a separate induction coil.

holding magnet: An electromagnet used to hold metal objects while work is being done on them.

Holtz machine: A static electricity machine.

holophane: An electrical lighting globe with special surface for diffusing light.

homopolor generator: A generator having poles of one magnetic polarity only, instead of having alternate north and south pole.

hook-switch: A switch and hook on a telephone which is operated by placing or removing the receiver from that hook.

horizontal candle-power: The amount of light given off by a lamp measured in a horizontal direction from the light.

horn gap: A gap which is narrow at the bottom and widens out towards the top.

horsepower: The unit of power or work. An electrical horsepower is equal to 746 watts.

horsepower hour: The amount of power performed by 746 watts per one hour.

horseshoe magnet: A magnet bent in the shape of the letter U, or horseshoe.

hot conductor: A term used to refer to a conductor or wire which is carrying a current or voltage.

hot-wire meter: A meter which obtains a reading by the expansion of the length of wire or metal through which current flows.

howler: A device used in a telephone exchange to cause a noise in the receiver to indicate to the customer that the receiver has been left off the hook.

humming: A noise caused by the rapid magnetizing and demagnetizing of the iron core of a transformer, motor, or generator.

hunting: A condition in an electrical circuit where one machine tends to oscillate or run faster than another, and then run slower.

hydraulic: Pertaining to water or fluids in motion.

hydroelectric: The production of electricity by water-power.

hydrometer: An instrument or device which shows the specific gravity of a liquid as compared to water.

hysteresis: The tendency of magnetism to lag behind the current that produces it.

hysteresis curve: A curve that shows the relation between the magnetizing current and the amount of magnetism produced by it.

hysteresis loss: The heat produced by repeatedly magnetizing and demagnetizing the iron core of a machine.

I

I: An abbreviation for amperes of current.

I.E.S.: Illuminating Engineering Society.

i.h.p.: Indicated horsepower.

I-beam: A steel beam made in the form of a capital I.

idle coil: A coil which does not produce any voltage or through which no current flows.

ignition: The igniting of a combustible charge in the cylinder of a gas engine.

ignition battery: A battery used to furnish the ignition current for an automobile engine.

ignition coil: An induction coil that produces a high-voltage current which jumps the gap in a spark-plug and ignites the charge in an automobile engine.

ignition distributor: A device that connects the proper spark-plug to the high-tension current at the right time in an automobile engine.

ignition generator: A generator used to produce the ignition current for an automobile engine.

ignition spark: The spark that passes between the gaps of the spark-plug, inside an automobile cylinder.

ignition switch: A switch that is used for turning on and off the primary ignition coil.

ignition timer: A device that closes and opens the primary circuit of an induction coil at the proper instant, to produce a spark in a cylinder of an automobile engine.

illumination: The directing of light from its source to where it can be used to the best advantage.

impedance: The apparent resistance of a circuit to alternating current. It is composed of resistance and reactance.

impedance coil: A reactance or choke coil, used to limit the flow of current.

impregnated cloth: A cotton cloth that has been saturated with insulating varnish and dried.

impressed voltage: The voltage or pressure acting upon any device.

impulse: A sudden change, such as an increase or decrease in voltage or current.

incandescent lamp: A lamp in which light is produced by the heating of a small filament inside of a glass bulb.

inclined coil instrument: A voltmeter or ammeter in which the coil or moving vane are inclined in relation to the pointer.

incomplete circuit: An open circuit.

india rubber: A soft rubber used to insulate or cover electrical conductors and wires.

indicated horsepower: The horsepower determined by calculation taken from an indicator diagram.

indicating switch: A switch that shows whether it is turned "ON" or "OFF."

indirect lighting: Light that is thrown against a ceiling having a light colored surface and reflected and diffused in the room being lighted.

induced current: Current that is produced by inductance from another circuit.

induced e.m.f.: A voltage that is produced by induction from another circuit.

induced magnetism: Magnetism that is produced by electric current or by the action of other magnetism.

induced voltage: A voltage or pressure produced by induction.

inductance: The ability of an electric circuit to produce induction within itself.

inductance coil: A coil connected in an electric circuit in order to increase the resistance of that circuit to alternating current.

induction: The influence exerted by a magnet or magnetic field upon conductors.

induction coil: A coil used to produce a high-voltage. It consists of two windings placed on an iron core. The voltage is produced by stopping quickly the flow of current in the coil.

induction furnace: An electric furnace in which the metal forms a secondary circuit of the transformer and is heated by current flowing through the metal.

induction generator: An induction motor, operated about synchronous speed, which produces an electric current.

induction meter: A meter used on alternating current in which rotation of a disk is caused by the magnetic lines of force produced by a current and a voltage coil passing through the disk.

induction motor: An alternating-current motor which is operated by induced magnetism from the winding placed on the stator. It does not operate at synchronous speed.

induction regulator: A transformer in which the voltage produced in a secondary winding is varied by the changing of position of the primary winding.

inductive load: The load connected to an alternating-current system which causes the current to lag behind the voltage.

inductive reactance: The reactance produced by self-inductance.

inductive resistance: The apparent resistance that is caused by self-induction in a circuit.

inductor: That part of an armature winding which lies entirely on one side of the armature coil, and in which a voltage is produced.

industrial controller: A device or rheostat for controlling the speed of electric motors.

inertia: The tendency of a body to remain at rest or in motion at the same speed.

initial voltage: The pressure at the start, as the voltage at the terminal of a storage battery when it is placed on change; that voltage which causes the appearance of corona around an electric conductor.

input: All of the power delivered to an electric device or motor.

inside wiring: The wiring inside of a residence or building.

installation: All of the electrical equipment or apparatus used in a building including the wiring.

instrument transformer: A transformer used to change the voltage or current supplied to meters.

insulate: To place insulation around conductors or conducting parts of a device or object.

insulating: The placing of insulation around electrical conductors.

insulating compound: An insulating wax which is melted and poured around electrical conductors in order to insulate them from other objects.

insulating joint: A thread or coupling in which the two parts are insulated from each other.

insulation resistance: The resistance offered by an insulating material to the flow of electric current through it.

insulating varnish: A special prepared varnish which has good insulating property and is used to cover the coils and windings on electric machines and improve the insulation.

insulator: A device used to insulate electric conductors.

intake: A place where air or water enters a machine, tunnel, or pipe.

integrating meter: A meter that keeps the record of the total amount of power, current, etc., that passes through it in a given time.

intensity: The intensity of the current is the number of amperes that flows through a conductor in a given time.

intercommunicating telephone: A telephone system that connects up to the several offices in the same building or plant without the use of a central operator.

interior wiring: Wiring placed on the inside of buildings.

intermittent current: A current, that starts and stops its flow at regular intervals.

intermittent rating: When a machine is operated for a short time only and allows a long period of rest, it has an intermittent rating.

internal circuit: The circuit formed inside a device or machine.

internal resistance: The resistance of the winding of an electrical machine, or between terminals of a primary cell or a storage battery.

internal short-circuit: A short-circuit occurring between the positive and negative plates in a storage battery due to a defective separator.

internal wiring: The wiring inside of a device or a machine.

interpoles: Magnetic poles placed between the main poles of a motor or generator.

interrupter: A device that opens or closes a circuit many times per second.

interrupter contact: The contact where a circuit is broken by an interrupter.

interrupter gap: The greatest amount of distance or space between the contacts of an interrupter.

invar: A resistance wire composed of nickel and steel.

inverse ratio: A ratio where one value increases and the other value decreases.

inverted converter: A rotary or synchronous converter which changes direct current into alternating current.

ion: The two minute parts into which a molecule is divided when it is separated into its elements.

I^2R loss: The power loss due to the current flowing through the conductor which has resistance. This loss is converted into heat.

iron loss: The hysteresis and eddy current losses in iron cores of electric machinery.

ironclad armature: An armature in which the windings are placed in slots cut in the armature core.

ironclad magnet: A magnet which has an iron core extending around the outside of the coil and through which the magnetism flows.

isolated plant: An electric light plant used to furnish power for a small community or a few firms, and the power of the plant is not sold to the public.

J

J: Abbreviation for joule.

jack: The terminal of two telephone lines on a switchboard of a telephone exchange.

joint: The uniting of two conductors by means of solder.

joint resistance: The combined or total resistance of two or more resistances connected in series or parallel.

joule: A unit of electrical work. A current of one ampere flowing through a resistance of one ohm for one second.

journal: That part of a shaft that turns or revolves in the bearings.

jump spark: A spark that passes between two terminals or across a gap. It is produced by high voltage.

jumper: A temporary connection made around part of a circuit.

junction box: A box in a street distribution system where one main is connected to another main; also a box where a circuit is connected to a main.

K

K.: Abbreviation or symbol for dielectric constant.

k.w.: Abbreviation for kilowatt.

kaolin: A kind of clay used in making porcelain insulators.

keeper of magnet: A bar of soft-iron placed across the poles of a magnet when it is not being used.

Key: A device for opening and closing a circuit by moving a lever. It is used in telephone and telegraph apparatus.

key switch: A switch for turning on and off electric circuits which are operated by means of a special key.

key socket: A socket with a device that opens and closes the circuit, thus turning the lamp off or on.

keyless socket: A socket which does not have a key or device for turning on or off the lamp.

kicking coil: A reactance or choke coil.

kilo: A prefix when placed before a word means 1000 times that indicated by the word.

kiloampere: One thousand amperes.

kilovolt: One thousand volts.

kilowatt: One thousand watts.

kilowatt-hour: One thousand watt-hours.

knife switch: A switch that has a thin blade that makes contact between two flat surfaces or short blades to complete the circuit.

knob insulator: A porcelain knob to which electric wires may be fastened.

L

L.: An abbreviation for length.

lag: To drop behind.

lag of brushes: The distance the brushes are shifted on a motor or generator in order to prevent sparking.

lagging coil: A small coil used in alternating watt-hour meter to compensate for the lagging current in the voltage coil.

lagging current: The lagging of the current behind the voltage wave in an inductive alternating-current system.

laminated: Built up out of thin sheets or plates which are fastened together.

laminated core: A core built up of thin soft iron sheets placed side by side and fastened together.

laminations: One of the plates used in building a laminated core.

lamp: A device used to produce light.

lamp bank: A number of incandescent lamps connected in series or in parallel and used as resistances.

lamp base: The metal part of an incandescent lamp which makes contact with the socket.

lamp bulb: A term used in referring to an incandescent electric lamp.

lamp circuit: A branch circuit supplying current to lamps only, and not to motors.

lamp cord: Two flexible stranded insulated wires twisted together and used to carry the current from the outlet box to the lamp socket.

lamp dimmer: An adjustable resistance connected in a lamp circuit in order to reduce the voltage and the brightness of the lamps.

lamp socket: A receptacle into which the base of the lamp is inserted, and which makes connection from the lamp to the circuit.

lap winding: An armature winding in which the leads from the coil to the commutator lap over each other.

lap-wound armature: An armature that has a lap winding.

lateral: A conduit that branches off to the side from the main conduit.

lava: A kind of stone that has insulating properties.

lead (pronounced lĕd): An acid resisting metal that is used in making parts for storage batteries.

lead battery: A storage battery in which the plates are made from lead.

lead burning: The process of uniting two pieces of lead together by melting the edges.

leads (pronounced leeds): Short lengths of insulated wires that conduct current to and from a device.

lead of brushes: The distance that the brushes are moved on the commutator of a generator or motor to prevent sparking.

leading current: When the current of an alternating-current system reaches its maximum value before the voltage does, it is called a leading current.

leading-in wires: Wires used to carry current from the outside of buildings to the inside of buildings.

leak: A loss of charge in a storage battery where current can flow through a circuit, or to ground, due to defective insulation.

leakage flux: Lines of force or magnetism that do not flow through the path intended for them but take another path and do not do any useful work.

Leclanche cell: A primary cell which uses carbon and zinc rods or plates for electrodes.

left-hand rotation: A shaft or motor that revolves in a counter clockwise direction; that is, opposite to that of the hands of a clock.

Leyden jar: A glass jar covered inside and out with a thin metal covering, and used as a condenser.

lifting magnet: An electromagnet used to lift iron and steel objects.

light load: A load that is less than the usual or normal load on the circuit.

lighting fixture: An ornamental device that is fastened to the outlet box in the ceiling and which has sockets for holding the lamps.

lighting transformer: A transformer that is used to supply a distribution circuit that does not have motors connected to it.

lightning arrester: A device that allows the lightning to pass to the ground thus protecting electrical machines.

lightning rod: A rod that is run from the ground up above the highest point of a building.

limit switch: A switch that opens the circuit when a device has reached the end of its travel.

line of force: An imaginary line which represents the direction of magnetism around a conductor or from the end of a magnet.

line drop: The loss in voltage in the conductors of a circuit due to their resistance.

line insulator: An insulator for use on an overhead transmission line.

line reactance: The reactance in the transmission line or conductor outside of the supply station.

line resistance: The resistance of the conductor forming the transmission line.

lineman: A man who erects or works on an electric transmission line.

link fuse: A fuse that is not protected by an outside covering.

litharge: A compound made from lead used in the active material of storage battery plates.

live: A circuit carrying a current or having a voltage on it.

load: The work required to be done by a machine. The current flowing through a circuit.

load control: Changing the output of a generator as the changes of load occur on a circuit.

load dispatcher: A person who supervises or controls the amount of load carried by the generating station on a system.

load factor: The average power consumed divided by the maximum power in a given time.

loading coils: Small coils placed in series with telephone lines in order to improve the transmission of speech.

local action: A discharge between different parts of a plate in a storage battery or primary cell caused by impurities in the parts used.

local current: An Eddy current.

locked torque: The twisting or turning power exerted by a motor when the rotating part is held stationary and normal current supplied to the winding.

lodestone: Magnetic iron ore.

log: A record of events taken down as they occur.

long shunt: Connecting the shunt across the series field and armature, instead of across the armature terminals.

loop circuit: A parallel or multiple circuit.

loop test: A test using the Wheatstone bridge, and a good line to locate an accidental ground on a line.

loose contact: A poor connection that does not make proper contact.

loud speaker: An electrical device that reproduces sound loud enough to be heard across a room.

low frequency: A current having a small number of cycles per second.

low potential: A system where the voltage between wires is usually less than 600 volts.

low tension: Low pressure or voltage.

low tension winding: The winding on a transformer which produces or has the lowest voltage.

low voltage release: A device that opens the circuit when the voltage drops down to a certain value, for which it is adjusted.

lugs: Terminals placed on the end of conductors to enable the wire to be attached or detached quickly.

lumen: The unit of electric lighting.

luminarre: An ornamental electric lighting fixture.

luminosity: In electric lighting work it is the brightness of a color compared with light.

luminous flux: In lighting work it is the amount of light directed down toward the point where it can be used.

M

M: A symbol of mutual induction the unit for which is a henry.

M.C.B.: Master Car Builder.

M.D.F.: Main distributing frame in a telephone exchange.

m.f.d.: Microfarad.

M-G: An abbreviation for motor-generator sets.

m.p.h.: Miles per hour.

machine rating: The amount of load or power a machine can deliver without overheating.

machine switching: A telephone exchange where the connections from one party to another are made by a machine instead of by an operator.

magnet: A body that will attract iron or steel.

magnet charger: A large electromagnet used to magnetize permanent magnets.

magnetic coil: The winding of an electromagnet.

magnet core: The iron in the center of the electromagnet.

magnet winding: The wire wound on a spool, forming an electromagnet.

magnet wire: A small single conductor copper wire insulated with enamel, cotton, or silk, used in winding armatures, field coils, induction coils, and electromagnets.

magnetic attraction: The pull or force exerted between two magnets or between magnets and an iron or steel body.

magnetic blow-out: A magnet arranged so that the arc between contacts is quickly lengthened and extinguished.

magnetic brake: A friction brake which is applied or operated by an electromagnet.

magnetic bridge: An instrument that measures the permeability and reluctance of magnetic material.

magnetic circuit: The paths taken by lines of force in going from one end of the magnet to the other.

magnetic compass: A small magnetized needle which indicates north and south directions.

magnetic contactor: A device, operated by an electromagnet, which opens and closes a circuit.

magnetic density: The amount of magnetism or magnetic lines of force per square inch or centimeter.

magnetic dip: The angles that a balanced needle makes with the earth when it is magnetized.

magnetic equator: An imaginary line joining the points about the earth where the compass needle does not have any dip.

magnetic field: The magnetic lines of force that pass in the space around a magnet.

magnetic flux: Magnetism or the number of lines of force in a magnetic circuit.

magnetic force: The attraction between magnetic poles or magnets, producing magnetism in a magnetic body by bringing it near a magnetic field.

magnetic lag: The tendency for magnetism to lag behind the current or force producing magnetism.

magnetic leakage: Lines of force that do not do useful work by passing through a path that is not in a working field.

magnetic lines of force: Magnetism about a conductor or flowing from magnet.

magnetic material: Materials which conduct lines of force easily—iron and steel.

magnetic needle: A small magnet that points in the direction of the magnetic lines of force about the earth.

magnetic pole: The ends of the magnet where the magnetism enters or leaves the magnet.

magnetic potential: Magnetic pressure which produces a flow of magnetic lines of force.

magnetic pulley: A pulley with an electromagnet inside of it, and used to separate iron and steel from other materials passed over it.

magnetic saturation: The greatest number of magnetic lines of force or magnetism that a body or substance can carry.

magnetic screen: A soft iron body around which magnetism is conducted instead of going through the center of that object.

magnetic shunt: A definite path for magnetic lines of force to pass through instead of the main path.

magnetic switch: A switch that is operated or controlled by an electromagnet.

magnetism: That invisible force that causes a magnet to attract iron and steel bodies.

magnetite: Magnetic iron ore.

magnetization curve: A curve that shows the amount of magnetism, expressed in lines of force, produced by a certain magnetizing force.

magnetize: To cause a substance to become a magnet.

magnetizing force: That force which produces magnetism. It is measured in ampere-turns.

magneto: A small generator that has a permanent field magnet.

magneto ignition: Igniting the charge in a combustion engine from a magneto generator.

magnetomotive force: That force which produces magnetism; it is expressed in ampere-turns.

main: The circuit from which all other smaller circuits are taken.

main feeder: A feeder supplying power from the generating station to the main.

make-and-break ignition: Igniting the charge in an internal combustion engine by the spark produced when contacts carrying current are opened.

maintenance: Repairing and keeping in working order.

manhole in conduit: An opening or chamber placed in a conduit run large enough to admit a man to splice or join cables together.

manganese steel: An alloy of steel having a large percent of the metal called manganese.

manual: Operated by hand.

mariner's compass: A compass used by sailors for directing the course of a ship.

master switch: A switch that controls the operation of other switches or contact switches.

maximum demand: The greatest load on a system occurring during a certain interval of time.

maximum demand meter: A meter that registers or indicates the greatest amount of current or power passing through a circuit within a given time.

maxwell: A unit of magnetic flux or lines of force.

mazda lamp: A certain trade name for an incandescent lamp using a tungsten filament.

mean horizontal candle-power: The average candle-power measured on a horizontal plane in all directions from the lamp filament.

mean spherical candle-power: The average candle-power of a lamp measured in all directions from the center of the lamp.

meg or mega: A prefix that means one million times.

megger: An instrument that measures the resistance in megohms.

megohms : A resistance of one million ohms.

mercury: A silvery white metal liquid; often called quicksilver.

mercury-arc rectifier: A rectifier in which alternating current is changed to direct current by the action of mercury vapor on electrodes.

mercury vapor lamps: The lamps or lights in which light is produced by passing a current through mercury vapor.

mesh connection: A closed circuit connection in armature winding.

messenger wire: A wire used to support a trolley, feeders, or cable.

metal conduit: Iron or steel pipe in which electric wires and cables are installed.

metal moulding: A metal tube or pipe, installed on the ceiling or walls of a building, in which electric wires are installed.

metallic circuit: A circuit that uses wires to return the current to the starting point instead of returning it through the ground.

metallic filament: An incandescent lamp filament made from a metal such as tantalum or tungsten.

meter: A device that records and indicates a certain value of electricity.

meter loops: Short pieces of insulated wire used to connect a watt-hour meter to the circuit.

metric system: A system of weights and measures based upon a meter (39.37 inches) for length and a gram ($\frac{1}{28}$ ounce) for weight.

Mho: The reciprocal of the resistance of a circuit which is called conductivity.

mica: A transparent mineral substance used for insulating commutators.

mica undercutter: A tool used to cut the mica below the surface of the commutator segment.

micanite: A trade name for small pieces of flake mica cemented together with an insulating compound.

micro: A prefix meaning one-millionth part.

micro-ampere: The one-millionth part of an ampere. $\frac{1}{1,000,000}$ or .000001 amperes.

microfarad: One-millionth of a farad.

microhm: One-millionth of an ohm.

microphone: A telephone transmitter in which the resistance is varied by a slight change in pressure on it.

microvolt: One-millionth of a volt.

mil: One-thousandth part of an inch; $\frac{1}{1000}$ or .001 inch.

mile-ohm: A conductor that is one mile long and has a resistance of one ohm.

mil-foot: A wire that is one-thousandth of an inch in diameter and one foot long.

milli: Prefix to a unit of measurement, denoting one-thousandth part of it.

milli-ammeter: An instrument that reads the current in thousandths of an ampere.

milli-ampere: $\frac{1}{1000}$ or .001 amperes. One-thousandth of an ampere.

milli-henry: One-thousandth of a henry.

milli-volt: One thousandth of a volt.

milli-voltmeter: A voltmeter that reads the pressure in one-thousandth of a volt.

mineralac: A trade name of an insulating compound or wax.

miniature lamp: The smallest size of incandescent lamp that uses a screw threaded base.

mirror galvanometer: A very sensitive galvanometer with a mirror attached to the moving element which reflects a spot of light over a scale.

moment: That which produces motion.

monel metal: An alloy of nickel and copper that is not eaten away by acids.

momentum: The tendency of a moving body to remain in motion at the same speed.

molecule: The smallest existing particle of a compound substance.

moonlight schedule: A list showing the time to turn the street lights out one hour after the moon rises, and turn them on one hour before the moon sets.

Morse code: A series of dots and dashes as signals transmitted by telegraph used to transmit messages.

motor: A machine that changes electrical energy into mechanical power.

motor converter: A form of rotary or cascade converter.

motor circuit: A circuit supplying current to an electric motor.

motor-generator: An electric motor driving a generator changing alternating to direct current or the reverse.

moulded insulation: A form of insulating material that can be placed in a mold and pressed into shape.

moulding: A wooden or metal strip provided with grooves to receive rubber covered electric wires.

moving coil meter: An electrical instrument of the d'Arsonval type which has a coil of fine wire moving between permanent magnets.

multiple: Connected in parallel with other circuits.

multiple circuit: A circuit in which the devices are connected in parallel with each other.

multiple series: A parallel connection of two or more series circuits.

multiple winding: A winding where there are several circuits in parallel.

multiple unit control: Controlling the operation of motors on several cars of an electric train from one point.

multiplex telegraphy: Sending one or more messages in both directions in the same circuit at the same time.

multiplex wave winding: A wave-wound armature that has more than two circuits in parallel.

multiplier: An accurately calibrated resistance connected in series with a voltmeter to enable it to be used on higher voltage circuits.

multipolar: Having more than two pole-pieces and field coils.

multi-speed: An electric motor that can be operated at several definite speeds.

mush coil: An armature coil that is not wound in regular layers.

N

N: A symbol used for revolutions per second or minute; often used to denote the North pole of a magnet.

N.E.C.: Abbreviation for National Electric Code; often called Underwriter's Code.

N.E.L.A.: Abbreviation for National Electric Light Association.

N.F.P.A.: Abbreviation for National Fire Prevention Association.

n.h.p.: Abbreviation for nominal horsepower.

name plate: A small plate placed on electrical machines which gives the rating of the machine and the manufacturer's name.

natural magnet: Magnetic ore or lodestone.

needle: A magnetized piece of steel which can be swung from the center and will point in the direction in which the magnetic lines of force are flowing.

needle point: The sharp point on a spark gap.

negative: The point towards which current flows in an external electrical circuit; opposite to positive.

negative brush: The brush of a generator out of which current enters the armature. In a motor the brush at which current leaves the armature.

negative charge: Having a charge of negative electricity.

negative conductor: The conductor that returns the current to the source after it has passed through a device and has been used.

negative electrode: The electrode by which the current leaves an electrolyte and returns to its source.

negative feeder: A feeder connected to the negative terminal on a generator to aid the current returning to the generator.

negative plate: The sponge lead plate of a lead acid-battery. In a primary cell the terminals to which the current returns from the external circuit.

negative pole: The S-pole of a magnet. The pole that the lines of force enter the magnet.

negative side: That part of the circuit from where the current leaves the consuming device to where it re-enters the generator.

negative terminal: That terminal to which the current returns from the external circuit.

neon: An inert gas used in electric lamps.

nernst lamp: A lamp in which light is produced by passing the current or electricity through rare oxide contained in a tube.

network: A number of electrical circuits or distribution lines joined together.

neutral: Not positive or negative although it may act as positive to one circuit and negative to another.

neutral conductor: A middle conductor of a three-wire direct-current or single-phase circuit.

neutral induction: The variation of current in one circuit which causes a voltage to be produced in another circuit.

neutral position: That point on the commutator where the armature conductors do not produce any voltage, because they are not cutting lines of force at that point.

neutral terminal: A terminal which may be positive to one circuit and negative to another circuit.

neutral wire: That wire in a three-wire distribution circuit which is positive to one circuit and negative to the other.

nichrome: An alloy of nickel and chromium which forms a resistance wire that can be used at a high temperature.

nickel: A silver white metal.

nickel silver: An alloy of copper, zinc, and nickel.

nickel steel: An alloy steel containing a small per cent of nickel.

nitrogen lamp: An incandescent lamp containing nitrogen or other inert gas instead of a vacuum.

non-conductor: That material which does not easily conduct electric current; an insulator.

non-inductive: Having very little self-induction.

non-inductive load: A load connected to a circuit that does not have self-induction. With alternating-current circuit, the current is in phase with the voltage.

non-inductive winding: A winding arranged so that it does not have any self-induction.

non-magnetic: Materials that are not attracted by a magnet are called non-magnetic.

normal: The general or usual conditions for that particular device or machine.

North pole: The end of the magnet at which the lines of force leave it. The end of a freely suspended magnet that will point towards the North.

numerator: In fractions the word or number written above the horizontal line.

O

O.K.: An abbreviation which means all right.

oersted: The unit of magnetic reluctance which is the resistance of metal to the flow of magnetism through them.

ohm: The unit used to express the resistance of a conductor to the flow of electric current through it.

Ohm's law: A rule that gives the relation between current, voltage, and resistance of an electric circuit. The voltage (**E**) is equal to the current (**I**) in amperes times resistance (**R**) in ohms. The current (**I**) equals the voltage (**E**) divided by the resistance (**R**) of the circuit. The resistance (**R**) is equal to the voltage (**E**) divided by the current (**I**).

ohm-mile: A conductor a mile long and has a resistance of one ohm.

ohmic resistance: The resistance of a conductor due to its size, length, and material.

oil circuit breaker: A device that opens an alternating-current circuit in a tank of oil which extinguishes the arc.

oil switch: A switch whose contacts are opened in a tank of oil.

oiled paper: A paper treated with an insulating oil or varnish.

open circuit: A break in a circuit. Not having a complete path or circuit.

open circuit battery: A primary cell that can only be used for a short time, and requires a period of rest in order to overcome polarization.

open coil armature: An armature winding in which the ends of each coil are connected to separate commutator bars.

open delta connection. A transformer connection in which two single-phase transformers are used to form two sides of a delta connection.

open wiring: Electric wires fastened to surfaces by the use of porcelain knobs. Wiring that is not concealed.

ordinate: The vertical lines drawn at various points along the horizontal base line to indicate values on that base line.

oscillating discharge: A number of discharges obtained one after another from a condenser; each one is less than the one before.

oscillograph: A very sensitive and rapid galvanometer which shows changes occurring in electrical circuits.

outboard bearing: A bearing placed on the outside of a pulley of a machine.

outlet: A place where electrical wires are exposed so that one can be joined to the other.

outlet box: An iron box placed at the end of conduit where electric wires are joined to one another and to the fixtures.

output: The amount of current in amperes or watts produced by a generator or a battery.

overcompound: When the series field coils of a generator are designed so that the voltage will increase with an increase in load, the generator is said to be overcompounded.

overdischarge: Discharge from a storage battery after the voltage has dropped to the lowest normal discharge value.

overhead: Electric light wires carried out doors on poles.

overload: Carrying a greater load than the machine or device is designed to carry.

overload capacity: The amount of load beyond a rated load that a machine will carry for a short time without dangerously overheating.

overvoltage: A voltage higher than the normal or usual voltage.

ozone: A form of oxygen produced by electrical discharge through air.

P

P: Abbreviation for power.

P.B.X.: Private branch telephone exchange.

P.D.: Potential difference.

panel box: The box in which switches and fuses for branch circuits are located.

parabolic reflector: A reflector built in the form of a parabolic curve in order to reflect the light in a narrow beam.

paraffin: A wax used for insulating bell wire.

parallax: The difference caused by reading the scale and pointer of an instrument at an angle instead of straight in front of it.

parallel: Two lines extending in the same direction which are equally distant at all points Connecting machines or devices so that the current flows through each one separately from one line wire to another line wire. Also called multiple.

parallel circuit: A multiple circuit. A connection where the current divides and part flows through each device connected to it.

parallel series: A multiple series. A number of devices connected in series with each other, forming a group; and the groups are connected in parallel with each other.

parallel winding: A lap armature winding.

paramagnetic: Material that can be attracted by a magnet.

para rubber: The best grade of india rubber.

pasted plate: A storage battery plate in which the active material is prepared as a paste and forced into openings in the grid.

peak load: The highest load on a system, or generator, occurring during a particular period of time.

peak voltage: The highest voltage occurring in a circuit during a certain time.

pendant switch: A small push button switch, hanging from the ceiling by a drop cord, used to control the flow of current to a ceiling light.

permanent magnet: A magnet that holds its magnetism for a long time.

permeability: The ease with which a substance conducts or carries magnetic lines of force.

permeability curve: A curve that shows the relation of the magnetizing force (ampere-turns) and number of lines of force produced through a certain material.

permeameter: An instrument used to test the permeability of iron and steel.

permittivity: The dielectric constant.

peroxide of lead: A lead compound used in making storage battery plates.

petticoat insulator: An insulator the bottom part of which is in the shape of a cone with the inside hollow for some distance.

phantom line: An artificial line over which messages can be sent the same as over an ordinary line.

phase: The fraction of a period of cycle that has passed since an alternating voltage or current has passed through zero value in the positive direction.

phase advancer: A machine used to improve the power factor of a system by overcoming the logging current.

phase angle: The difference in time between two alternating-current waves expressed in degrees. A complete cycle of 360 degrees.

phase converter: A machine that changes the number of phases in an alternating-current circuit without changing the frequency.

phase failure: The blowing of a fuse or an opening of one wire or line in a two- or three-phase circuit.

phase indicator: A device that shows whether two electric machines are "in step" or in synchronism.

phase rotation: The order in which the voltage waves of a three-phase circuit reach their maximum value, as ABC or ACB.

phase shifters: Devices by which power-factor can be varied on a circuit when testing meters.

phase splitter: A device that causes an alternating current to be divided into a number of currents that differ in phase from the original.

phase winding: One of the individual armature windings on a polyphase motor or generator.

phosphor bronze: Bronze to which phosphor has been added in order to increase its strength.

photometer: An instrument used to measure the intensity of light.

pig tail: Five braided copper wires used to connect the carbon brush to its holder.

pike pole: A small pole with a sharp spike in one end. It is used by wiremen in raising and setting wood poles.

pilot brush: A small brush used to measure the voltage between adjacent commutator bars.

pilot cell: A cell in a storage battery used as a standard in taking voltage and specific gravity readings.

pilot lamp: A small lamp used on switchboards to indicate when a circuit switch or device has operated.

pitch: The number of slots between the sides of an armature coil. The distance from a certain point on one to a like point on the next.

pith balls: Small balls made from the light soft spongy substance in the center part of some plants and corn cobs.

pivots of meters: The shaft to which the moving part of the meter is fastened and which turns on a bearing.

Planté plates: A storage battery plate in which the active material is formed by charging and discharging the battery many times.

plate condenser: A condenser formed by a number of plates with insulating material between them.

plating dynamo: A generator that produces a low voltage direct current for use in electroplating work.

platinum: A gray-white metal that is not easily oxidized and which makes good contact points.

platinum-iridium: An alloy of platinum and iridium, which is a harder metal than platinum.

plug: A screw thread device that screws into an electric light socket and completes the connection from the socket to the wires fastened to the plug.

pocket meter: A small voltmeter or ammeter mounted in a case that can be carried in the coat pocket.

polar relay: A relay that operates when the direction of the flow of current changes.

polarity: Being positive or negative in voltage, current flow, or magnetism.

polarity indicator: An instrument that indicates the positive or negative wires of a circuit.

polarity wiring: Using a white or marked wire for the ground side of a branch circuit.

polarization: The forming of gas bubbles on the plates of a primary cell which reduces the current produced by the cell.

polarized: Having a definite magnetic polarity.

polarized armature: The armature of a magnet that has a polarity of its own and which is attracted only when the direction of the flow of current in the windings produces a pole of opposite polarity.

pole: The positive and negative terminal of an electric circuit. The ends of a magnet.

pole changer: A device that changes direct current into alternating current.

pole piece: The end of the field magnet or electromagnet that forms a magnetic pole.

pole pitch: The number of armature slots divided by the number of poles.

pole shoe: A piece of metal having the same curve as the armature that is fastened to the field magnet of a generator or motor.

pole strength: The number of magnetic lines of force produced by a magnet.

pole tips: The edges of the field magnets toward and away from which the armature rotates.

polyphase: Having more than one phase.

polyphase circuit: A two- or three-phase circuit.

polyphase transformer: A transformer in which the windings of all the phases are located inside the same case or cover.

porcelain: A hard insulating material made from sand and clay which is molded into shape and baked.

porous cell: A porous jar used with primary cells that use two different electrolytes that must be kept separate.

portable instrument: A meter so designed that it can be moved from one place to another.

positive: The point in a circuit from which the current flows; opposite to negative.

positive brush: The brush of a generator from which the current leaves the commutator; the brush of the motor through which current passes to the commutator.

positive electricity: The kind of electricity produced by rubbing a glass rod with silk.

positive electrode: The electrode or terminal that carries the current into the electrolyte.

positive feeder: A wire or cable acting as a feeder that is connected to the positive terminal of a generator.

positive plate: The peroxide of lead plate in a lead-acid storage battery.

positive terminal: The terminal of a battery or generator from which the current flows to the external circuit.

potential: The pressure, voltage, or electromotive force that forces the current through a circuit.

potential coil: The voltage or pressure coil of a meter that is connected across the circuit and is affected by changes in voltage.

potential regulator: A device for controlling or regulating the voltage of a generator or circuit.

potential transformer: A transformer used to step the voltage down for voltmeters and other instruments.

potentiometer: An instrument used to compare a known or standard voltage with another voltage.

pothead: A flared out pot or bell attached to the end of a lead covered cable and filled with insulating compound.

poundal: The unit of force which, acting for one second, will give a body that has mass of one pound a velocity of one foot per second.

power: The rate of doing work. In direct current circuits it is equal to **E** $\times$ **I.** The electrical unit is the watt.

power circuit: Wires that carry current to electric motors and other devices using electric current.

power factor: The ratio of the true power (watts) to the apparent power (volts $\times$ amperes). Cosine of the angle of lag between the alternating current and voltage waves.

power factor meter: A meter that indicates the power factor of the circuit to which it is connected.

power loss: The energy lost in a circuit due to the resistance of the conductors; often called I^2R loss.

power plant: The generators, machines, and buildings where electrical power or energy is produced.

practical units: The electrical units used in everyday practical work —the ohm, volt, ampere, watt, etc.

precision instrument or meter: A very accurate meter or instrument used in testing or comparing other meters.

press board: A hard smooth paper or cardboard used for insulation in generators and transformers.

pressure: The voltage which forces a current through a circuit; also called potential difference.

pressure wires: Wires going from the end of a feeder to a voltmeter in the power station.

primary: That which is attached to a source of power, as distinguished from the secondary.

primary cell: A cell producing electricity by chemical action, usually in acid acting on two different metallic plates.

primary circuit: The coil or circuit to which electric power is given and which transfers it to the secondary by induction.

primary winding: The winding which receives power from the outside circuit.

prime mover: An engine, turbine, or water wheel that drives or operates an electric generator.

prony brake: A friction brake or a pulley used as a dynamometer to measure the torque turning power of a shaft.

proportional: A change in one thing which causes a relative change in another thing.

protective reactor: A reactance coil used in a circuit to keep the current within a safe value when a short circuit occurs.

pull boxes: An iron box placed in a long conduit, or where a number of conduits make a sharp bend.

pull-offs: A hanger used to keep the trolley wire in proper place on a curve.

pulsating current: A current that flows in the same direction all the time, but rises and falls at regular intervals.

puncture: The breaking through insulation by a high voltage.

push button: A small contact device having a button which, when pressed, closes a circuit and causes a signal bell to ring.

push-button switch: A switch that opens and closes a circuit when a button is pushed.

push - pull transformer: A transformer used in radio work with a tap brought out at the center of the coil windings.

pyrometer: An instrument that indicates or measures temperatures higher than a thermometer will handle.

Q

Q: Abbreviation for "quantity" of electricity. The unit is coulomb or ampere-hours.

Q.S.T.: A radio code call—"Have you received the general call"?

quad: An abbreviation for quadruple telegraph; means Four.

quaded cable: A telephone or telegraph cable in which every two pairs (4 wires) are twisted together.

quadrature: Angle of 90 electrical degrees or quarter cycle difference between two alternating-current waves.

quarter phase: Same as two phase. The voltage waves are one-fourth of a cycle apart.

quick-break switch: A knife switch arranged so it will break the circuit quicker than when pulled open by hand.

R

R: Abbreviation for resistance, the unit of which is the ohm.

R.L.M.: Abbreviation for a dome type of lighting reflector.

r.p.m.: Abbreviation for revolutions per minute.

R.S.A : Railway Signal Association.

racing of motor: A rapid change or excessive speed of a motor.

raceways: Metal molding or conduit that has a thinner wall than standard rigid conduit used in exposed wiring.

racks and hooks: Supports for lead covered cables placed in underground manholes.

radial: In a straight line from the center outward.

radian: The angle at the center of a circle where the arc of circumstance is equal to the radius of the circle. It is 57.3 degrees.

radiation: The process of giving off or sending out light or heat waves.

radio: Referring to methods, materials, and equipment for communicating from one place to another without the use of wires between them.

radioactive: Giving off positive and negative charged particles.

rail bond: A short piece of wire or cable connecting the end of one rail to the next.

rating: The capacity or limit of load of an electrical machine expressed in horsepower, watts, volts, amperes, etc.

ratio: The relation of one number or value to another.

ratio arms: The two arms of a Wheatstone bridge whose resistances are known and form the ratio of the bridge.

ratio of a transformer: The relation of the number of turns in the primary winding to the secondary winding.

reactance: The influence or action of one turn of a coil or conductor upon another conductor which chokes or holds back an alternating current but allows a steady direct current to flow without any opposition.

reactance coil: A choke coil. It is used to hold back lightning and other high frequency currents in a circuit.

reactive current: That part of the current that does not do any useful work because it lags behind the voltage.

reactive load: A load, such as magnets, coils, or induction motors, where there is reactance which causes the current to lag behind the voltage.

reactor: Choke coils or condensers used in a circuit for protection or for changing the power factor.

reamer: A cone shaped tool used with a hand brace to remove the burr on the inner edge of conduit.

receiver: The part of the telephone that changes the talking current into sound that can be heard by the ear.

receiving sets: Devices used to receive radio messages and especially radio broadcast programs.

receptacle: A device placed in an outlet box to which the wires in the conduit are fastened, enabling quick electrical connection to be made by pushing an attachment plug into it.

receptacle plug: A device that enables quick electrical connection to be made between an appliance and a receptacle.

reciprocal: One divided by the number whose reciprocal is being obtained. The reciprocal of 2 is ½; of 3 is ⅓, etc.

recorder: A device that makes a record on paper of changing conditions in a circuit, apparatus, or equipment.

rectifier: A device that changes alternating current into continuous or direct current.

rectigon: Trade name for a battery charging rectifier.

red lead: Minimum, or peroxide of lead, used in making pasted battery plates.

re-entrant: Armature windings which return to a starting point, thus forming a closed circuit.

reflector: A device used to direct light to the proper place.

regenerative braking: Using electric motors on a car or locomotive as generators to slow down the train.

regulation: A change in one condition which causes a change in another condition or factor.

regulator: A device for controlling the current or voltage, or both, from a generator or through a circuit. Devices for controlling other machines.

relay: A device by which contacts in one circuit are operated by a change in conditions in the same or another circuit.

reluctance: The resistance to flow of magnetism through materials.

reluctivity: The reciprocal of permeability. The resistance to being magnetized.

remagnetizer: A large direct-current electromagnet used to magnetize the permanent magnets that have lost their magnetism.

remote control: Operating switches, motors, and devices located some distance from the control point by electrical circuits, relays, electromagnets, etc.

renewable fuse: An inclosed fuse so constructed that the fusing material can be replaced easily.

repeater: A device that reproduces the signals from one circuit to another.

repeating coil: An induction coil or transformer used in telephone work that has the same number of turns on each winding.

repulsion: The pushing of two magnets away from each other.

repulsion induction motor: An alternating current which operates as a repulsion motor during the starting period and as an induction motor at normal speed.

residual magnetism: The magnetism retained by the iron core of an electromagnet. Often the flow of current is stopped.

resistance: That property of a substance which causes it to oppose the flow of electricity through it.

resistance bridge: A Wheatstone bridge.

resistance furnace: A furnace where heat is obtained by electric current flowing through resistance coils.

resistor: Several resistances used for the operation control or protection of a circuit.

resonance: A condition in a circuit when the choke coil reactance is exactly balanced or equalized by a condenser.

resultant: The sum of two forces acting on a body.

retarding coil: A choke coil.

retentivity: Holding or retaining magnetism.

retreiver: Device that pulls down the trolley pole of a car when the trolley wheel leaves the wire.

return circuit: The path the current takes in going from the apparatus back to the generator.

return feeders: Copper cables connected at different points of the rail to carry the current back to the generators.

reverse: Going in the opposite direction.

reverse current relay: A relay that operates when the current flows in the opposite direction to what it should.

reverse phase: A change in the phase of the current due to changing the generator or circuit wiring.

reverse power: Sending electric energy in the opposite direction in a circuit to the usual direction.

reversing switches: Switches used to change the direction of rotation of a motor.

rheostat: A resistance having means for adjusting its value.

ribbon conductor: A conductor made from a thin flat piece of metal.

right-hand rule: A rule used to determine the direction of flow of current in a dynamo.

ring armature: An armature with a core in the shape of a ring.

ring oiling: A system of oiling where a ring on the shaft carries oil to the top of the bearing.

ring system: Where two transmission lines from a station are joined together at a substation, thus forming a loop or ring.

risers: Wires or cables that are run vertically from one floor to another and supply electric current on these floors.

rocker arms: The arms to which the brush holders of a motor are fastened or supported.

rodding: Pushing short rods which are joined together through a conduit in order to pull a cable into it.

Roentgen rays: Similar to X-rays.

rosettes: A device to permit a drop cord to be attached to a ceiling outlet or fixture.

rotary converter: A direct-current motor with collector rings connected to the armature windings which changes alternating to direct current or the reverse; a synchronous converter.

rotary switch: A switch where the circuit is opened and closed by turning a knob or handle.

rotor: The part of an electrical machine that turns or rotates.

rotor slots: Openings punched in the disk of the rotor and in which the winding is placed.

r.p.m.: Abbreviation for revolutions per minute.

r.p.s.: Abbreviation for revolutions per second.

rubber-covered wire: Wires covered with an insulation of rubber.

rubber gloves: Insulated gloves worn by linemen when working on "Live" lines.

rubber tape: An adhesive elastic tape made from a rubber compound.

runner: The revolving part of a water turbine.

running torque: The turning power of a motor when it is running at rated speed.

runoff: The quantity of water flowing in a stream at any time.

S

s.: Abbreviation for second of time.

S.A.E.: Society of Automotive Engineers.

s.c.: Abbreviation for single contact.

s.c.c.: Abbreviation for single cotton-covered wire.

S.E.D.: Society for Electrical Development.

s.c.e.: Abbreviation for cotton enameled wire.

s.p.: Abbreviation for single pole.

S.S.: Abbreviation for steamship when placed before the name of the vessel.

s.s.c.: Abbreviation for single silk-covered wire.

S.K.F.: The trade name for a ball bearing.

safe carrying capacity: The maximum current a conductor will carry without overheating.

safety catch or fuse: A device that opens the circuit when it becomes too hot; often placed in base of appliances for heating liquids.

safety switch: A knife switch inclosed in a metal box and opened and closed by a handle on the outside.

salammoniac: Common name for ammonium chloride, NH_4Cl, used as electrolyte in primary cells.

salient poles: The ordinary poles formed at the end of a magnet as distinguished from consequent poles.

saturation curve: A curve showing the relation between the voltage produced by a generator and the ampere turns on the field coils.

Scott connection: A transformer connection for changing alternating current from two- to three-phase or the reverse.

seal: A piece of lead or metal used to close meter to prevent tempering.

second: $\frac{1}{60}$ part of a minute.

secondary: The circuit that receives power from another circuit, called the primary.

secondary battery: A storage battery.

secondary circuit: The wiring connected to the secondary terminals of a transformer, induction coil, etc.

secondary currents: Currents produced by induction due to changes in current values in another circuit.

section: An insulated length of line or circuit fed by a separate feeder.

sediment: Loose material that drops off storage battery plates and separators into bottom of cell.

segment: One of the parts into which an object is divided; often used to refer to commutator bars.

selector switch: A switch used in an automatic telephone system to locate an idle line.

selenium: A rare metal, the resistance of which changes when under action of light.

self-cooled transformer: A transformer in which the windings are cooled by contact with air or oil and without additional means for radiation.

self-discharge: The discharge of a cell due to leakage or short circuit inside of it.

self-excited: A generator in which the current in the field coils is produced by the generator itself.

self-induced current: An extra current produced in a circuit by change of the current flowing in that circuit.

self-inductance: The magnetic property of a circuit that tends to oppose a change of the current flowing through that circuit.

separators: Wood or rubber plates placed between the plates of a storage battery.

semaphore: A post or stand supporting a railroad signal.

separately-excited: A generator in which the current for the field coils is obtained from another generator or battery.

series: Connected one after another so the same current will flow through each one.

series arc lamp: An arc lamp in which the same current flows through all the lamps connected to the circuit.

series circuit: A circuit in which the same current flows through all the devices.

series generator: A constant-current generator used for operating a street lighting circuit where all lamps are connected in series.

series motor: A motor where all the current flows through the field coils and armature, because they are connected in series.

series-multiple: Same as series parallel.

series - parallel: An arrangement where several devices are connected into series groups and these groups are connected in parallel with each other.

series transformer: A current transformer. A transformer where the primary is connected in series with the circuit.

series winding: A wave-wound armature. A field coil winding through which the armature current flows.

service connections: The wiring from the distributing mains to a building.

service switch: The main switch which connects all the lamps or motors in a building to the service wires.

service entrance: The place where the service wires are run into a building.

service wires: The wires that connect the wiring in a building to the outside supply wires.

sheath: The outside covering which protects a wire or cable from injury.

shell transformer: A transformer with the iron core built around the coils.

shellac: A gum dissolved in alcohol, which forms a good insulating liquid.

sherardizing: Coating iron or steel with zinc to prevent rusting.

short: A contraction for short circuit.

short circuit: An accidental connection of low resistance joining two sides of a circuit, through which nearly all the current will flow.

short shunt: Connecting the shunt fields directly to the armature of a compound generator or motor instead of having them in parallel with armature and series fields.

short time rating: A device that can only operate for a short time without being allowed to cool.

shunt: A parallel circuit. A bypass circuit.

shunt coil: A coil connected in parallel with other devices and through which part of the current flows.

shunt field: A field winding connected in parallel with the armature.

shunt ratio: The ratio of current flowing through the shunt circuit to the total current.

shunt winding: A winding connected in parallel with the main winding.

shuttle armature: An H-type armature.

silicon bronze: A bronze or brass containing silicon and sodium which give it strength and toughness.

silicon steel: An alloy steel having low hysteresis and eddy current loss, used in transformer cores.

silk - covered wire: Small copper wires insulated by a covering of silk threads.

simplex circuit: A telegraph which sends in only one direction at a time.

simplex winding: A type of armature winding with two parallel paths from one brush to another.

sin: Abbreviation for sine of an angle; as sin 30°.

sine of an angle: In a right angle triangle it is the length of the side opposite the angle divided by the hypotenuse.

sine wave: The most perfect wave form. An alternating-current wave form.

single contact lamp: An automobile lamp which has one contact in end at base which makes contact with the socket; the side of the base and socket completes the circuit.

single phase: A generator or circuit in which only one alternating-current voltage is produced.

single-phase circuit: A 2- or 3-wire circuit carrying a single-phase current.

single-phase motor: An alternating-current motor designed to operate from a single-phase circuit.

single-pole switch: A switch that opens and closes only one side of a circuit.

single-stroke bell: A bell that strikes only once when the circuit is opened or closed.

single-throw switch: A knife switch that can be closed to one set of contacts only instead of two, as with a double-throw switch.

single-wire circuit: A circuit using one wire for one side and ground for the other side or return conductor.

single re-entrant: An armature winding in which the circuit is traced through every conductor before it closes upon itself.

sinusoid: A sine curve.

six phase: A circuit or machine where the voltage waves are $\frac{1}{6}$ of a cycle behind each other.

skin effect: The action of alternating current that causes more of a current to flow near the outside than in the center of a wire.

slate: A rock that is cut into slabs and used for switchboards. It is a fair insulator.

sleet cutter: A device placed on the trolley wheel to cut or scrape sleet from the trolley wire of a railway system.

sleeve joint: Joining the ends of two wires or cables together by forcing the ends into a hollow sleeve and soldering them.

sleeving: A small woven cotton tube slipped over the ends of armature leads to give additional insulation.

slide wire bridge: A Wheatstone bridge in which the balance is obtained by moving a contact over a wire.

slip: The difference in speed between the speed of a rotating magnetic field and the rotor of an induction motor.

slip ring: A ring placed on a rotor, which conducts the current from the rotor to the external circuit. Collector ring.

slot: The groove in the armature core where the armature coils are placed.

slot insulation: Material placed in armature slot to insulate the coils for the core.

slow-burning insulation: An insulation that chars or burns without a flame or blaze.

smooth core: An armature where the conductors are bound on the surface instead of being placed in slots or grooves.

snap switch: A rotary switch where the contacts are operated quickly by a knob winding up a spring.

sneak current: A weak current that enters a telephone circuit by accident. It will not blow a fuse, but it will do damage if allowed to continue.

soaking charge: A low rate charge given to a storage battery for a long time to remove excess sulphate from the plates.

soapstone: A soft oily stone sometimes used for insulating barriers. The powder is used when pulling wires into conduit.

socket: A receptacle or device into which a lamp bulb is placed.

sodium chloride: Common ordinary salt.

soft-drawn wire: Wire that has been annealed and made soft; often being drawn to size.

soldering flux: A compound that dissolves the oxide from the surfaces being soldered.

soldering paste: A soldering flux prepared in the form of a paste.

solenoid: A coil of insulating wire wound in the form of a spring or on a spool.

solenoid core: The soft iron plunger or body placed inside a solenoid.

solid wire: A conductor of one piece instead of being composed of a number of smaller wires.

sounder: A telegraph relay that delivers a sound at the receiving end which the operator can understand.

south pole: The end of a magnet at which the lines of force enter.

space factor: The actual cross-sectional area of copper in a winding divided by the total space occupied by the insulation and winding.

spaghetti insulation: A closely woven cotton tube impregnated with an elastic varnish that is slipped over ends of bare wires to insulate them.

spark coil: An induction coil used to produce a high voltage which causes a spark to jump a gap.

spark gap: A device which allows a high voltage current to jump a gap.

spark plug: A threaded metal shell having a center insulated conductor, which is screwed into the cylinder of an automobile engine.

spark voltage: The lowest voltage that will force a spark between two conductors insulated from each other.

sparking at brushes: Small arcs or flashes occurring between the commutator and brush, due to poor contact or incorrect brush position.

sparkless commutation: Operation of a direct-current generator or motor without any sparking at the brushes.

specific gravity: The weight of any volume of liquid or solid divided by the weight of an equal volume of water; or of any gas divided by an equal volume of air.

specific resistance: The resistance of a cube of any material which is one centimeter long on each edge.

speed counter: An instrument that records the number of revolutions made by a shaft.

speed regulation: The per cent of full load speed that the speed of a motor changes, when the load is suddenly removed.

sphere gap: A spark gap formed between two spheres fastened to conductors.

spherical candle-power: The average candle-power from a light measured in all directions.

spider: A cast-iron frame with radially projecting arms on which the rotating part of an electrical machine is built.

splice: The joining of the ends of two wires or cables together.

splice box: An iron box in which cable connections and splices are made.

split knobs: Porcelain knobs made into two pieces to receive a wire or cable and held together by a screw.

split phase: Obtaining currents of different phases from a single-phase circuit by use of reactances of different value in parallel circuits.

split-phase motor: A three-phase motor that is operated by split-phase current obtained from a single-phase circuit.

split-pole converter: A synchronous converter with divided or additional field poles for regulating the voltage.

sponge lead: Porous lead used in the active material of the negative plate of an acid storage battery.

spot welding: Uniting two metals together by electric welding them at several spots.

square mil: The actual area of a wire or conductor expressed in mils. The $\frac{1}{1,000,000}$ part of a square inch.

squirrel cage: The arrangement of copper rods in cylindrical form and fastened to copper rings at each end of the rotor core of an induction motor.

squirted filament: The old method of forcing a soft material for a lamp filament through small holes.

staggering of brushes: Arranging the brushes on a commutator so they will not all bear or rub on the same place.

stalling torque: The twisting or turning power of a motor, just before the armature stops turning, due to heavy load being applied.

standard candle: A standard of lighting power.

standard cell: A primary cell that gives the legal standard of voltage.

standard ohm: The unit of resistance.

standard resistance: An accurate resistance that is used for comparison with unknown resistances.

stand-by battery: A storage battery connected to the distribution system to carry the load should the generators fail.

static machines: Generators that produce static electricity.

star connection: Connecting one end of each phase of a three-phase circuit or machine together, thus forming a common point called the neutral. A Y-connection.

starter: A device that enables a safe current to be supplied to a motor when starting.

starting battery: A storage battery designed to deliver current to a motor used for starting an automobile engine.

starting box: A rheostat used for a short time when starting a motor.

starting current: The current taken by a motor when starting.

starting motor: A motor used for cranking an automobile engine.

starting rheostat: A starting box.

starting torque: The turning power produced by a motor when the rotor begins to turn on that power required to start a machine at rest.

static charge: A quantity of electricity existing on the plates of a condenser.

static electricity: Electricity at rest as distinguished from electric current, which is electricity in motion.

static generator: A machine producing static electricity.

static transformer: An ordinary transformer in which all parts are stationary as distinguished from the earlier constant-current transformer with a moving coil.

stator: The stationary part of an induction motor on which the field windings are placed.

steady current: A direct current whose voltage does not change or vary.

step-down: Reducing from a higher to a lower value.

step-up: Increasing, or changing from a low to a higher value.

stop charge device: A device that disconnects a storage battery from the charging circuit when it is completely charged.

storage battery: A number of storage cells connected together to give the desired current and voltage and placed in one case.

storage cell: Two metal plates or sets of plates immersed in an electrolyte in which electric current can be passed into the cell and changed again into chemical energy and then afterwards changed again into electrical energy.

strain insulator: An insulator placed in a guy wire to insulate it from the current-carrying wire.

stranded wires: Wires or cables composed of a number of smaller wires twisted or braided together.

stray current: Current induced in a conductor or core and which flows in these parts. The return current of an electric railway system that flows through adjacent pipes and wires instead of the regular return circuit.

stray field: Magnetic lines of force that do not pass through the regular path and therefore do not do any useful work.

stray flux: The lines of force of a stray magnetic field.

stray power: The power losses of an electrical machine due to heating effects, as friction, hysteresis, and eddy currents.

strength of current: The number of amperes flowing through the circuit.

strength of magnetism: The number of magnetic lines of force per unit of area.

strip fuse: A fuse made from a flat piece of metal.

Stubs' wire gauge: An iron wire gauge, often called Birmingham wire gauge.

sub-station: The building or place where one form of electrical energy is changed into another, as alternating current into direct current, high voltage to low, or the reverse.

sulphating: The forming of a hard white substance on the plates of a storage battery.

sulphuric acid: The kind of acid that is diluted and put in a lead storage battery.

superposed circuit: An additional circuit obtained from a circuit used for another purpose without interfering with the first circuit.

surface leakage: The leaking of current over the surface of an insulator from one metal terminal to another.

surges: An oscillating high voltage and current waves that travel over a transmission line after a disturbance.

surging discharge: A high voltage oscillating discharge.

susceptance: One of the components in an alternating circuit; the power component is called conductance and the wattless component is called susceptance.

susceptibility: The ratio of the amount of magnetism produced in a body to the magnetzing force.

suspension insulator: An insulator hung from a support and with the conductor fastened to the bottom of the insulator.

swinging cross: The blowing together of the wires of a transmission line, causing a short-circuit.

switch: A device for closing, opening, or changing the connections of a circuit.

switch blade: The movable part of a switch.

switchboard: The panel or supports upon which are placed the switches, rheostats, meters, etc., for the control of electrical machines and systems.

switchboard instruments: Meters mounted on a switchboard.

switch house or room: The part of the building in a power plant where the high voltage switches are located.

switch plate: A small plate placed on the plastered wall to cover a push button or tumbler switch.

switch tongue: The movable part of an electric railway track switch.

symbol: A letter, abbreviation, or sign that stands for a certain unit or thing.

synchronism: Alternating-current voltage waves that have the same frequency and reach their maximum value at the same instant.

synchronize: To bring to the same frequency and in phase.

synchronizer: A device for indicating when two machines are in synchronism.

synchronoscope: An instrument which shows when two machines are in synchronism and which machine is leading the other in phase.

synchronous condenser: A synchronous motor operated without load and strong field current in order to improve the power factor.

synchronous converter: A direct-current motor fitted with collector rings and used to change alternating to direct current.

synchronous motor: An alternating-current motor whose speed is in proportion to the frequency of the supply current and the number of poles in the machine.

synchronous phase advancer: A synchronous motor operated as a condenser to improve the power factor.

T

T: Abbreviation for temperature.

t: Abbreviation for time in seconds.

Ta: Chemical symbol for tantalum

T-connector: A connector joining a wire to two branch circuits.

T-splice: A connection joining the end of one wire to the middle of another one.

tachometer: An instrument that shows the number of revolutions per minute made by a shaft.

talc: Powdered soapstone.

tan: An abbreviation for tangent of an angle.

tangent: A straight line that just touches the circumference of a circle.

tangent galvanometer: A galvanometer operated by current passing through a coil overcoming the earth's magnetism.

tap: A wire connected some distance from the end of the main wire or conductor.

tape: A narrow strip of treated cloth.

tapering charge: Charging a storage battery at constant voltage. The rate of current flow will decrease as the battery becomes charged.

taping: Wrapping layers of tape around a wire, coil, or conductor.

teaser winding: An extra winding on the poles of a series wound dynamo.

teeth of armature: The projections between the slots in an armature.

telegraph: A system of sending messages by dot and dash signals

telegraph relay: A relay used in a telegraph circuit.

telegraph code: The dot and dash signals used for letters or words.

telephone: A device that transmits speech and sound from one place to another by electric currents.

telephone cable: A number of small insulated copper wires bound together and covered with paper, cotton, braid, or lead covering.

telephone condenser: A condenser used in a telephone circuit, made by rolling strips of tin foil between sheets of paraffin paper.

telephone cord: Several very flexible wires covered with a cotton braid. Used to connect one part to another.

telephone exchange: The place where all telephone lines end and connections are made from one line to another.

telephone jack: A receptacle into which a plug is placed when connecting one telephone line to another.

telephone receiver: A device that changes electric current in the telephone circuit into sound.

telephone repeating coil: A transformer used to reproduce the signals from one circuit to another.

telephone set: All the parts, such as transmitter, ringer, receiver, etc., installed for the subscriber's use on his premises.

temperature: Condition in regard to heat and cold.

temperature coefficient: The rate of change in resistance per degree change in temperature.

temperature correction: The amount that must be added to a reading taken at one temperature in order to make it comparable with the same reading taken at a standard temperature.

temperature rise: The difference in temperature between a certain part of a machine and the surrounding air.

tension: The degree of stretching; also sometimes used to refer to voltage, difference of potential, or dielectric stress.

terminal: A connecting device placed at the end of a wire, appliance, machine, etc., to enable a connection to be made to it.

terminal lug: A lug soldered to the end of a cable so it can be bolted to another terminal.

terminal pressure: The voltage at the generator or source of supply.

Tesla coil: An induction coil on a transformer without an iron core, used to produce high frequency currents.

test clip: A spring clip fastened to the end of a wire used to make connections quickly when testing circuits or devices.

test lamp: An incandescent lamp bulb and socket connected in a circuit temporarily when making tests.

test point: The metallic end of an insulated conductor used in making tests.

test set: Electrical instruments and devices used for testing, mounted for convenient use.

testing transformer: A transformer designed to deliver a number of different voltages, and used in testing for defects.

theater dimmers: Variable rheostats connected in series with a lighting circuit to control the voltage to the lamps and amount of light produced by them.

thermal: Pertaining to heat.

thermocouple: Two different metals welded together and used for the purpose of producing thermo-electricity.

thermo-electricity: Electricity produced by the heating of metals.

thermo-galvanometer: A galvanometer operated by the heating effect of a current acting on a thermocouple.

thermometers: Instruments for indicating relative temperatures.

thermostat: A device that opens and closes a circuit when the temperature changes.

third-brush generator: A small generator placed on an automobile to charge a storage battery.

third-brush regulation: A generator whose voltage is regulated by armature reaction and the shunt field current obtained from a third brush bearing on the commutator.

third rail: An insulated rail, placed along side of the rails on an electric railway, which supplies the power to the cars.

three-phase: A generator or circuit delivering three voltages that are $\frac{1}{3}$ of a cycle apart in reaching their maximum value.

three-phase circuit: A circuit delivering three-phase current.

three-phase motor: An alternating-current motor that is operated from three-phase circuit.

three-pole: A switch that opens and closes three conductors or circuits at one time.

three-way switches: A switch with three terminals by which a circuit can be completed through any one of two paths.

three-wire circuit: A circuit using a neutral wire in which the voltage between outside wires is twice that between neutral and each side.

three-wire generator: A direct-current generator with a balancer coil connected to the armature windings and the middle point of the balancer coil connected to the neutral.

tie wire: A short length of wire used to fasten the overhead wires to a pin insulator.

time switch: A switch controlled by a clock that opens and closes a circuit at the desired time.

timer: A device that opens the primary circuit of an induction coil at the right time to produce a spark to fire the charge in an internal combustion engine.

tinfoil: Sheets of tin rolled out thinner than paper.

tinned wire: Wire covered with a coating of tin or solder.

torque: The twisting or turning effort.

torsion dynamometer: An instrument that measures the torque of a machine by twisting a calibrated spring.

track circuit: The circuit through the rails and bonds.

track return: The return circuit formed by the rails and bonds of a track.

train lighting battery: A storage battery used to furnish electricity for lighting railroad cars.

transformer: A device used to change alternating current from one voltage to another. It consists of two electrical circuits joined together by a magnetic circuit formed in an iron core.

transformer coil: A part or one of the windings of a transformer.

transformer efficiency: The power delivered by a transformer divided by the power input to it.

transformer loss. The difference between the power input and output.

transformer oil: Oil used in a transformer to insulate the windings and carry away the heat.

transformer ratio: The ratio of the primary to the secondary voltages.

transformer substation: A substation where the alternating-current voltage is stepped up or down by use of transformers.

transite: A kind of asbestos lumber used for insulating barriers in dry places.

transmission line: High voltage conductors used to carry electrical power from one place to another.

transmitter: The telephone device that receives the speech and changes it into electric current.

transposition: Changing the relation of telephone and electric light wires to each other in order to equalize the inductance and prevent cross talk.

trickle charge: A low rate of charge given a storage battery.

triphase: Same as three-phase.

triple-pole switch: Same as a three-pole switch.

trolley wire: A wire supported over the tracks of an electric railway which carries the power for operating the cars.

true resistance: Actual resistance measured in ohms as compared to counter-electromotive force.

trunk: The wires or circuits between switchboards or telephone exchanges.

tube insulator: Insulating material made in the form of a tube and used to carry conductors through walls and partitions.

tumbler switch: A switch similar to a flush push button, but operated by pushing up or down on a short lever.

tungar rectifier: A rectifier using a tungar bulb made or licensed by the General Electric Company.

tungsten: A very hard metal with a high melting point that resists the effects of arcing.

tungsten filament: A filament made from tungsten and used in a lamp bulb.

tungsten steel: An alloy of steel and tungsten which produces a hard tempered steel which retains this property when heated a dull red.

twin cable: Two insulated wires running side by side without being twisted and covered with a braid.

twisted pair: Two rubber-covered telephone wires twisted together and used to connect subscriber's set to overhead wires or cable.

two-phase circuit: A circuit in which there are two voltages differing by one quarter of a cycle.

two-phase motor: A motor made to be operated from a two-phase circuit.

two-phase generator: A generator producing two-phase current.

two-pole: A switch that opens or closes both sides of a circuit or two circuits at one time.

two-wire circuit: A circuit using two wires.

U

ultra violet rays: Light rays that are beyond the violet color and not visible.

unbalanced load: A distribution system where there is a greater load on one phase or side than on the other.

undamped waves: Radio waves whose maximum rise and frequency is constant.

under-charged battery: A storage battery that has not been sufficiently charged.

under-compounded: A compound-wound generator in which the voltage drops as the load increases.

under-cut mica: Cutting the mica between commutator segments below the surface so it will clear the brush.

underground cable: A cable insulated to withstand water and electrolysis and placed in underground conduit.

underload circuit breaker: A conduit breaker that opens when the load drops below a certain value.

underload relay: A relay that operates another circuit when the load drops below a certain value.

Underwriters' Code: The National Electric Code.

unidirectional current: Current that flows in one direction.

uniphase: A single-phase alternating current.

unipolar: Having one pole.

unit price: Cost of one piece, foot, pound, or whatever number is taken as a unit for that particular material.

unloader: A device that removes the load from a machine, such as a compresser, when a motor is starting it.

V

V: Abbreviation for volts or potential difference.

V.T.: Abbreviation for vacuum tube or electron tube.

vacuum cleaner: A machine that sucks dust and dirt out of rugs, drapes, upholstery, etc.

vacuum impregnated: Filling the spaces between electric parts with an insulating compound while they are placed in a vacuum.

vacuum tube: Any kind of a bulb or tube from which the air has been removed.

vapor: A gas from a substance that is ordinarily a liquid or solid.

vapor rectifier: A mercury arc rectifier.

variable condenser: A condenser whose capacity can be varied.

variable resistance: A resistance that can be changed or adjusted to different values.

variable-speed generator: A generator operated at different speeds with a method of regulation which causes it to deliver a constant voltage.

variable-speed motor: A motor whose speed depends upon the load.

Varley loop: A method of locating a cross, short-circuit, or ground on telephone or telegraph lines.

varnished cambric or cloth: Cotton cloth treated with an insulating varnish.

vector: A line whose length and direction represents a certain physical quantity.

vector diagram: A diagram that shows relations by use of vectors.

verdigris: A substance called copper sulphate that forms on copper by the action of sulphuric acid.

vibrating rectifier: A device that changes alternating current into direct current by means of a vibrating contact that closes the circuit for one-half of the cycle and opens it when the flow of alternating current is in the opposite direction.

vibrator coil: An induction coil used as an ignition coil.

volt: A unit of electrical pressure or electromotive force.

voltage coil: A coil connected across the line so that the current flowing through it changes as the voltage changes.

voltage drop: The difference in pressure between two points in a circuit caused by the resistance opposing the flow of current.

voltage loss: The voltage drop.

voltage regulator: A device for keeping a constant voltage at a certain point.

voltaic battery: A number of primary cells connected in series or parallel.

voltammeter: A voltmeter and ammeter combined in one case and using the same movement, but having separate terminals.

volt-ampere: The unit of apparent power; it is the product of the pressure times the current.

voltmeter: An instrument that shows the pressure or voltage of a circuit

vulcabeston: An asbestos and rubber composition used to make moulded parts.

vulcanite: A kind of hard rubber.

vulcanized fiber: An insulating material made of paper and cellulose under heavy pressure.

W

W: Abbreviation for watt.

W.A.E.I.: Western Association of Electrical Inspectors.

wall box: A metal box for switches, fuses, etc., placed in the wall.

wall insulator: An insulating tube used to protect a conductor passing through a wall.

wall socket: An electric outlet placed in the wall so that conductors can be connected to it by means of a plug.

water-cooled transformer: A large transformer having coiled pipes inside it through which water passes.

water rheostat: A rheostat that has its terminals placed in water through which the current flows.

watt: The unit of electric power.

watt-hour: The use of a watt of power for an hour.

watt-hour meter: An instrument that records the power used in watt-hours.

watt meter: An instrument used to indicate the power being used in a circuit.

watt minute: A power of one watt being used for one minute. $\frac{1}{60}$ of a watt-hour.

wattless: Not having any power or doing any useful work.

wave meter: An instrument used to determine the wave length or frequency of a radio broadcasting station.

wave winding: An armature winding with the end of the coils connected to commutator bars that are nearly opposite each other in a 4-pole machine.

weatherproof: Constructed so it will resist the action of rain, sun, etc.

welding transformer: A transformer built to deliver a large current used to heat metals to a welding temperature.

welding flux: A material, usually borax, used to remove scale from the joints being welded.

Western Union splice: A method of uniting two wires together by wrapping each one about the other.

Weston cell: A primary cell that has a constant voltage and used as a standard source of electrical pressure.

wet storage: A method of keeping a storage battery when it is not being used without removing the acid or plates.

Wheatstone bridge: An electrical balance used to measure resistance by comparing a known resistance with an unknown.

windage: The resistance of air against the rotating part of a machine.

wiping contact: A contact that rubs between two other contacts.

wire: A slender rod of drawn metal.

wire gauge: A method of expressing the diameter of different wires.

wired radio: Transmitting radio messages along telephone, electric light, and power lines instead of directly through the air.

wiring connector: A device for joining wire to another.

wiring symbols: Small signs placed on a wiring diagram to indicate different devices and connections.

wood separator: A thin sheet of wood placed between the plates of a storage.

wrought iron: A kind of iron that can be easily magnetized.

X

x: A symbol used to represent an unknown quantity.

x: A symbol for reactance, expressed in ohms.

X-ray: A kind of ray that passes through most materials as if they were transparent.

Y

Y: A symbol for admittance; the unit of which is mho.

Y-connection: A star connection; the joining together of one end of each phase of a 3-phase machine.

yoke: The iron frame of a generator or motor to which the magnetic pole pieces are fastened.

Z

Z: Symbol for impedance.

zero potential: Not having any voltage or pressure.

zinc battery: A primary cell in which the electric current is produced by zinc plates immersed in an electrolyte.

INDEX

INDEX

INDEX

INDEX

INDEX